Contents

Preface

The contents of this book were originally published in the author's three-volume work entitled *Building Services and Equipment*.

The chapters dealing with the various aspects of plumbing have been reproduced in this single volume reference book to meet the needs of plumbers.

The book should also assist students studying for the City and Guilds of London Institute examinations in plumbing.

This second edition includes recent Building Regulations and Codes of Practices applicable to heat losses, drainage, soil and waste systems, sanitary conveniences and water supply systems.

The principles of design and installation of unvented hot water storage systems has also been added.

F. Hall

Acknowledgements

We are grateful to the following for permission to reproduce copyright material:

British Gas Corporation for our Figs 6.29, 7.24—6 and 7.32—4; Extracts from British Standards are reproduced by permission of the British Standards Institution. Complete copies of the document can be obtained from BSI at Linford Wood, Milton Keynes, MK14 6LE; the Controller of Her Majesty's Stationery Office for extracts from *Building Research Establishment Digest Soil and Waste Systems for Offices*; Marley drainage for our Figs 8.30—2; Mather & Platt Ltd. for our Figs 11.7—8; Twyfords Ltd. for our Figs 10.2—3 and 10.5

Chapter 1

Cold-water supply

Water supply

A plentiful supply of wholesome water is essential for the occupants of the buildings intended for human habitation. Most buildings can obtain their supply from the Water Authorities' main, but in rural areas it is sometimes necessary to obtain water from private sources, such as streams, rivers, lakes, wells, springs or by catchment areas from roofs and paved surfaces. The water used must be colourless, free from small suspended matter and harmful bacteria, pleasant to taste and for health reasons moderately 'hard'. The River Pollution Commissioners classify water from the various sources as follows:

Wholesome	1. Spring water 2. Deep well water	Very palatable
	3. Uplands surface water	Moderately palatable
Suspicious	4. Stored rainwater	
	5. Surface water from cultivated lands	Palatable
Dangerous	6. River water to which sewage gains access 7. Shallow well water	

Figures 1.1 and 1.2 show various sources of water supply.

Hardness of water

Generally, surface waters are 'soft' and subterranean waters 'hard'; a great deal however depends upon the type of earth strata with which the water comes into contact.

1

Note: The term 'hardness' means it is difficult to obtain a lather with soap. Water is an excellent solvent and the presence of dissolved carbon dioxide increases this solvent power.

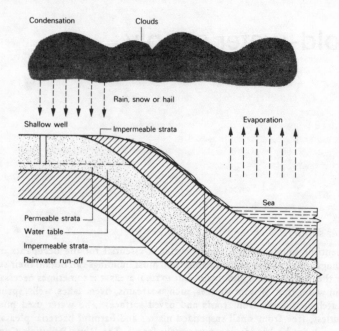

Fig. 1.1   The rain cycle

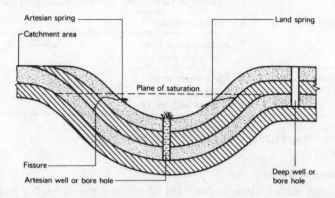

Fig. 1.2   Wells and springs

Two types of hardness

1. *Temporary:* If the water passes through strata containing a carbonate of calcium, or magnesium, a certain amount of these salts will be taken into the solution, depending upon the amount of carbon dioxide present in the water. Upon being dissolved the carbonate becomes bicarbonate due to the presence of carbon dioxide. This type of hardness can be removed by boiling the water, hence the term 'temporary'. It causes scaling or furring of hot-water pipes and boilers unless an indirect system is used (see Chapter 2, Hot-water supply).

2. *Permanent:* If the water passes through the strata containing calcium sulphate, calcium chloride or magnesium chloride, the salts are readily dissolved in the water without the presence of carbon dioxide. This type of hardness cannot be removed by boiling the water and hence the term 'permanent'. It will not cause scaling or furring, unless the water is brought up to high temperatures and pressures, but it may cause corrosion. Most waters contain both temporary and permanent hardness, usually more temporary; for example, Guildford in Surrey uses water containing 200 and 50 parts per million (p.p.m.) of temporary and permanent hardness respectively. The generally accepted classification of hardness is given in Table 1.1.

Table 1.1

Type	Hardness — p.p.m.
Soft	0—50
Moderately soft	50—100
Slightly hard	100—150
Moderately hard	150—200
Hard	200—300
Very hard	over 300

Removal of temporary hardness

Temporary hardness, as already stated, can be removed by boiling which drives off the carbon dioxide, allowing the carbonate of calcium or magnesium to precipitate. Whilst small quantities of water may be softened in this way it is, however, impractical for large-scale treatment.

Clark's process: This consists of adding small quantities of lime water or cream of lime to the supply and this takes up the carbon dioxide from the bicarbonate present, resulting in the precipitation of the insoluble carbonate and the removal of most of the temporary hardness. The precipitated carbonate is either allowed to settle out in a tank or is arrested in fine screens.

Removal of permanent hardness

The term 'permanent' is a misnomer, and has been used because this type of hardness cannot be removed by boiling the water. The hardness, however, may be removed by the addition of washing soda (sodium carbonate). The sodium carbonate becomes sodium sulphate which remains in solution in the water and is not harmful.

Base exchange process (Fig. 1.3)

This process removes both temporary and permanent hardness very efficiently by passing the water through zeolites contained in a steel cylinder. Zeolites have the property of exchanging their sodium base for the magnesium or calcium base, hence the term 'base exchange'.

The process is as follows:

Sodium Zeolite + Calcium Sulphate or carbonate
    (in softener)   (in water)

becomes

Calcium Zeolite + Sodium Sulphate or carbonate
  (held in softener)   (in solution with the water,
                       but harmless)

After a period of use, the sodium zeolite is converted into calcium and magnesium zeolite, thus losing its softening power. It is then regenerated by the addition of a strong solution of common salt (sodium chloride). The salt is kept in contact with the calcium zeolite for about half an hour, in which time the calcium zeolite is converted back into sodium zeolite.

The process is as follows:

Calcium Zeolite + Sodium Chloride
  (exhausted   (common salt)
  sodium)

becomes

Sodium Zeolite + Calcium Chloride
  (regenerated)   (flushed to drain)

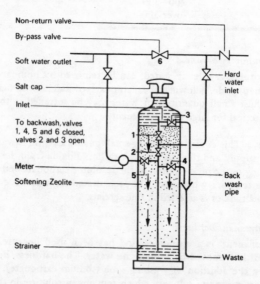

Fig. 1.3 Base-exchange water softener

Lime soda process

For industrial use, water which contains both temporary and permanent hardness may be softened by the addition of lime and soda in the correct proportions and the precipitated salts again settled out.

Scale reducers

In order to reduce scale formation and corrosion in hot-water systems, low concentration of metaphosphates may be used. Technically, the water remains hard and therefore these methods of water treatment should not be regarded as water softeners. A special dispenser may be connected to the cold-water main or suspended in the cold-water cistern.

Soft water

Although soft water readily lathers it is not as palatable for drinking as is water containing some degree of hardness. Soft water may cause corrosion of iron, steel, zinc, copper and lead. Copper is a safe metal to use because a small amount is non-poisonous. If lead, however, is taken into solution (Plumbo solvency) lead poisoning would result. The corrosion of metals is accelerated if the water passes through organic soils and it should be neutralised by passing it through limestone or chalk.

Filtration

Slow sand filters (Fig. 1.4)

These consist of rectangular tanks constructed of brickwork, or concrete, with porous slabs or perforated tiles over collecting channels at its base. The filter bed consists of a layer of fine sand about 1 m in depth, the top of which is kept flooded with water to a depth of about 1.2 m. When the filter is first put into operation it only removes suspended matter by straining. Clean fine sand will not keep back bacteria, but the surface of the sand soon becomes covered with a thin layer of colloidal matter, deposited from the water. This gelatinous film constitutes the actual filter and is a barrier to the passage of bacteria. The production of this film is sometimes done artificially, by the use of a chemical coagulant, such as aluminium sulphate.

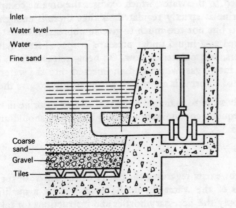

Fig. 1.4 Slow sand filter

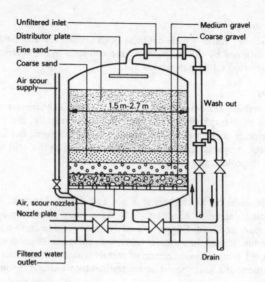

Labels on figure:
Unfiltered inlet
Distributor plate
Fine sand
Coarse sand
Air scour supply
Medium gravel
Coarse gravel
1.5 m–2.7 m
Wash out
Air, scour nozzles
Nozzle plate
Filtered water outlet
Drain

Fig. 1.5 Pressure filter

Pressure filters (Fig. 1.5)

These are now much used instead of the slow sand filter because they take less space for their installation and it is easier to clean the sand. The principle of operation is the same, but filtration is much quicker. purification of the water takes place in closed steel cylinders working under pressure. The efficiency of the filter is increased by adding a small dose of aluminium sulphate to the inlet water which forms a gelatinous film on the top of the sand, as described for the slow sand filter. This film is known as the 'vital layer'.

Sterilisation (Fig. 1.6)

All the water used for human consumption must be free from harmful bacteria. Chlorine is added to the water, which oxidises the organic compounds in it. The dosage of chlorine is strictly regulated so that there is enough to destroy any bacteria present, but not too much to give an unpleasant taste to the water. The chlorine is stored as a liquid under pressure in special steel cylinders similar to oxygen cylinders, but painted yellow. On being released from the cylinder the liquid converts into a gas, which is then injected into the water main or storage tank. The flow of chlorine is controlled automatically to give the correct dosage.

Note: It is advisable to maintain a residual of free chlorine in the water to deal with any subsequent contamination and chlorination should always follow the filtration process.

Sampling

Where any doubt exists regarding the purity of the water, or for a new source of supply, samples of the water should be examined by a qualified analyst. The analyst will supply the necessary bottles and instructions for taking the samples, which are both chemical and biological.

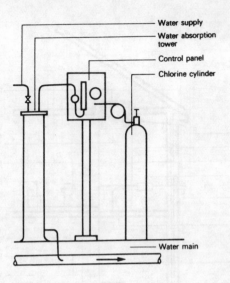

Fig. 1.6   Chlorinating plant

Chemical symbols

In order to make the descriptions easier to follow, the chemical symbols have been omitted from the text. For those students wishing to know the symbols, the following list should be useful:

Aluminium sulphate	$Al_2(SO_4)_3$	Magnesia	MgO
Calcium bicarbonate	$Ca(HCO_3)_2$	Magnesium carbonate	$MgCO_3$
Calcium carbonate	$CaCO_3$	Magnesium bicarbonate	$Mg(HCO_3)_2$
Calcium sulphate	$CaSO_4$	Magnesium sulphate	$MgSO_4$
Calcium zeolite	CaZ	Sodium carbonate	Na_2CO_3
Calcium chloride	$CaCl_2$	Sodium sulphate	Na_2SO_4
Hydrated lime	$Ca(OH)_2$	Sodium zeolite	Na_2Z
		Sodium chloride	$NaCl$

Cold-water system

Before designing a cold-water system for a building it is essential to know the local Water Authority requirements. There are two distinct systems, namely: direct and indirect, but some Water Authorities will allow some modifications to these systems.

Direct (Fig. 1.7)

This is a system used extensively in northern districts, where large high-level reservoirs provide a good mains supply and pressure. It is however permitted by several Water Authorities in other districts. In it all sanitary fittings are supplied with cold water direct from the main, and a cold-water feed cistern is required

7

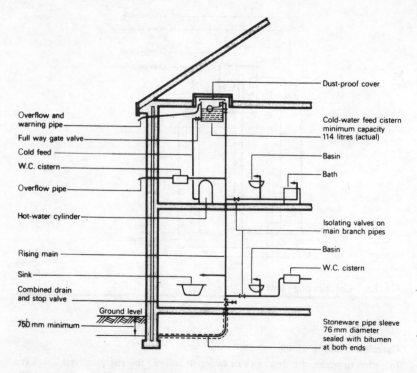

Overflow and warning pipe

Full way gate valve

Cold feed

W.C. cistern

Overflow pipe

Hot-water cylinder

Rising main

Sink

Combined drain and stop valve

750 mm minimum

Ground level

Dust-proof cover

Cold-water feed cistern minimum capacity 114 litres (actual)

Basin

Bath

Isolating valves on main branch pipes

Basin

W.C. cistern

Stoneware pipe sleeve 76 mm diameter sealed with bitumen at both ends

Fig. 1.7   Direct system of cold water supply

only to 'feed' the hot-water storage cylinder. The capacity in litres of the feed cistern is required to be at least equal to the capacity in litres of the hot-water cylinder. The Water Regulations require a cistern of 114 litres (minimum) capacity and is therefore small enough to be accommodated in the top of an airing cupboard, thus saving lagging of the cistern and pipework.

Indirect (Fig. 1.8)

In this system all the sanitary fittings, except drinking water draw-offs at sinks and fountains, are supplied indirectly from a cold-water storage cistern. Since the cistern supplies cold water to baths, basins, showers, etc., and also feeds the hot-water cylinder, its capacity in litres will be approximately double that required for the direct system. The Water Regulations require a cistern of 227 litres minimum capacity, and therefore it will have to be accommodated in the roof space and will require lagging (see Fig. 1.9). For larger buildings, the capacity of the storage cistern will have to be estimated and Table 1.2 gives the storage requirements for various types of buildings.

It is not always possible at the early design stage to know the exact number of people that will occupy the building but the number and type of sanitary fittings are known. Table 1.3 may be used as a guide to finding the storage of cold water, by estimating the possible maximum use of the fittings per day.

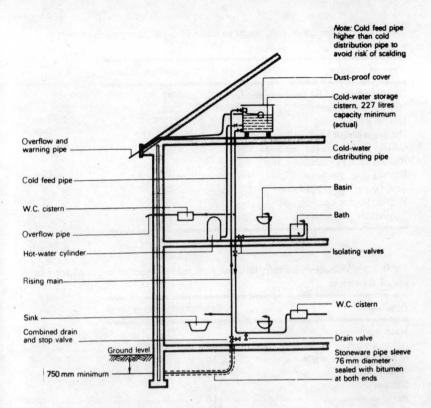

Note: Cold feed pipe higher than cold distribution pipe to avoid risk of scalding

Dust-proof cover

Cold-water storage cistern, 227 litres capacity minimum (actual)

Overflow and warning pipe

Cold-water distributing pipe

Cold feed pipe

Basin

W.C. cistern

Bath

Overflow pipe

Hot-water cylinder

Isolating valves

Rising main

W.C. cistern

Sink

Combined drain and stop valve

Drain valve

Ground level

750 mm minimum

Stoneware pipe sleeve 76 mm diameter sealed with bitumen at both ends

Fig. 1.8 Indirect system of cold water supply

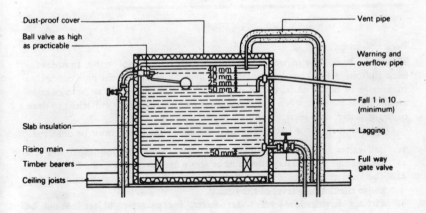

Dust-proof cover

Vent pipe

Ball valve as high as practicable

Warning and overflow pipe

40 mm
40 mm
19 mm
50 mm

Fall 1 in 10 (minimum)

Slab insulation

Lagging

Rising main

50 mm

Timber bearers

Full way gate valve

Ceiling joists

Fig. 1.9 Detail of cold water cistern

Table 1.2 Provision of cold water to cover 24-hour interruption of supply

Type of building	Storage in litres
Dwelling houses and flats *per resident*	91
Hostels *per resident*	91
Hotels *per resident*	136
Offices without canteens *per head*	37
Offices with canteens *per head*	45
Restaurants *per head/per meal*	7
Day schools *per head*	27
Boarding schools *per head*	91
Nurses' homes and medical quarters *per resident*	114

Table 1.3 Volumes of water, hot and cold, added together required for single use of appliances

Appliance	Volume required in litres
Wash basin	
hand wash	5
hand and face wash	10
hair wash	20
Shower	40
Bath	110
W.C.	10
Washing machine	150
Sink	
wash up	15
cleaning	10

Back siphonage

This is the back flow of water into the drinking water supply main. In order for back siphonage to occur a partial vacuum must be created in the pipe connected to a valve or tap, with its outlet submerged in water, which may be contaminated. This is possible when the demand on the water main is sufficient to draw back the water, thus leaving behind a partial vacuum.

In order to prevent back siphonage, the following points must be observed.

1. Ball valves in cisterns should be fitted above the overflow pipe, and if a silencer pipe is fitted its outlet must be above the valve (see Fig. 1.30).
2. The outlets of taps connected to sinks, baths and basins should be well above the flooding level of the fitting.
3. Fittings having low-level water inlets, for example, bidets, should be supplied with cold water from a storage cistern and never direct from the water main.

Advantages of direct and indirect systems

Direct

1. Less pipework and smaller storage cistern, making it cheaper to install.
2. Drinking water available at wash basins.
3. Smaller cold-water cistern which may be sited below the ceiling.

Indirect

1. Large capacity storage cistern, provides a reserve of water during the failure of the mains supply.
2. The water pressure on the taps supplied from the cistern is reduced, which minimises noise and wear on the taps.
3. Fittings supplied with water from the cistern are prevented from causing contamination of the drinking water by back siphonage.

Foreign practice

The USA and most European countries do not permit the use of a cold-water storage cistern; it is also claimed that this arrangement is more hygienic because water in a cistern has the risk of becoming contaminated. Many of these countries however are concerned with the possible contamination of the drinking water by back siphonage.

Connection to water main (Figs 1.10 and 1.11)

The local Water Authority requires at least 7 days' notice in writing for a new connection to the water main. The mains are usually tapped under pressure by means of a special apparatus. The Water Authority then connect a screw-down cock into the crown of the main and run a communication pipe up to the boundary of the building, where a stop valve is fitted. The authority provide the pipe, stop valve and protection chamber, but the cost is charged to the building owner.

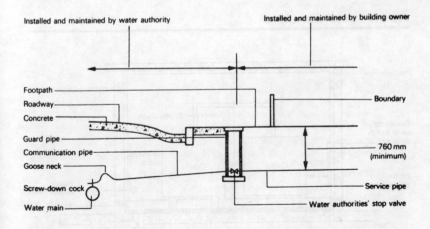

Fig. 1.10 Connection to water main

11

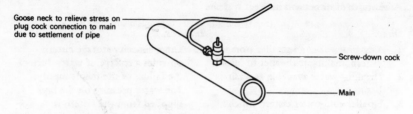

Goose neck to relieve stress on plug cock connection to main due to settlement of pipe

Screw-down cock

Main

Fig. 1.11 Connection to water main

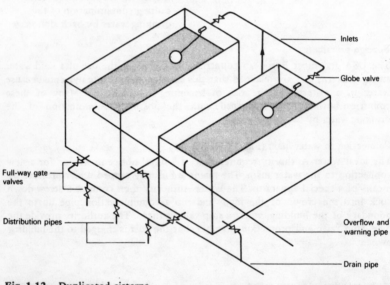

Inlets

Globe valve

Full-way gate valves

Distribution pipes

Overflow and warning pipe

Drain pipe

Fig. 1.12 Duplicated cisterns

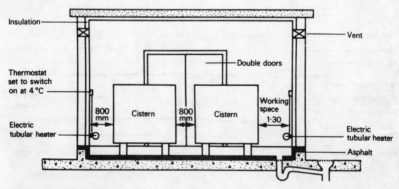

Insulation

Vent

Thermostat set to switch on at 4 °C

Double doors

Electric tubular heater

800 mm

Cistern

800 mm

Cistern

Working space 1·30

Electric tubular heater

Asphalt

Fig. 1.13 Cistern room

Duplicated storage cisterns (Fig. 1.12)

It is usually recommended that if the storage required is more than 4500 litres it is an advantage to provide two or more cisterns interconnected, so that each cistern can be isolated for cleaning and inspection without interfering with the supply of water to the building.

Cistern rooms (Fig. 1.13)

In large buildings the cisterns are housed in a special room on the roof, which should be well insulated and ventilated. The water in the cistern is prevented from freezing during winter by the use of thermostatically controlled electric tubular heaters or hot-water pipes. Sufficient room must be allowed around the cisterns for ease of maintenance and provision made for replacement of the cisterns.

Sterilisation of the systems

When the installation is complete all mains and services used for water for domestic purposes should be efficiently sterilised before use, and after being repaired the pipework and cisterns should be thoroughly flushed out and chlorine added gradually whilst the cistern is refilling. The dose should be 50 parts of chlorine to 1 million parts of water. When the cistern is full all taps on the distributing pipes should be opened successively, working progressively away from the cistern. Each tap should be closed when the water discharged begins to smell of chlorine and the cistern should then be refilled and more chlorine added as before. The cistern and pipes should then remain charged for at least 3 hours and then tested for residual chlorine; if none is found sterilisation will have to be carried out again. Finally, the cistern and pipes should be thoroughly flushed out.
out.

Water supplies for buildings where the mains pressure is insufficient

Principles

For high-rise buildings or for buildings constructed on high ground where the pressure is low, it is necessary to pump the water from inside the building. Before designing the water system it is necessary to ascertain the pressure on the water main during the peak demand period. If for example the water mains pressure during the peak demand is 300 kPa this pressure will supply water inside the building up to a height of approximately 30 m. In order to give a good supply of water, a residual head is required above the highest fittings and it is therefore usual to deduct 6 m from the mains pressure head. Therefore, in this example, the water main would supply water up to 24 m without pumping.

Direct pumping from the main (Fig. 1.14)

Where the water authority will allow this method of boosting, the pressure of water required to be developed by the pump will be reduced by the amount equal to the pressure of water on the main. The disadvantage of this method is that if the building is large the amount of water pumped from the main may cause a serious drop in pressure in other buildings supplied from the same main. The method does however save the cost of a break cistern, space inside the building and costs.

13

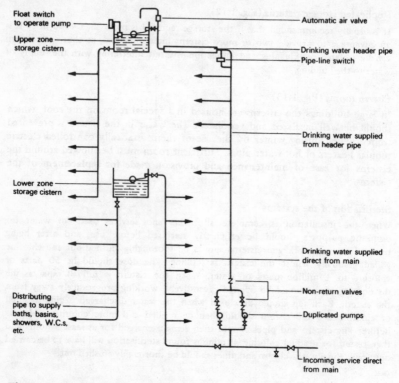

Fig. 1.14 Direct pumping from main

Labels (Fig. 1.14):
- Float switch to operate pump
- Upper zone storage cistern
- Automatic air valve
- Drinking water header pipe
- Pipe-line switch
- Drinking water supplied from header pipe
- Lower zone storage cistern
- Drinking water supplied direct from main
- Distributing pipe to supply baths, basins, showers, W.C.s, etc.
- Non-return valves
- Duplicated pumps
- Incoming service direct from main

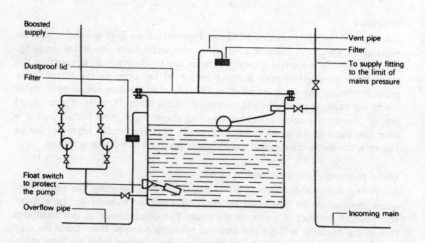

Fig. 1.15 Indirect pumping from main

Labels (Fig. 1.15):
- Boosted supply
- Dustproof lid
- Filter
- Vent pipe
- Filter
- To supply fitting to the limit of mains pressure
- Float switch to protect the pump
- Overflow pipe
- Incoming main

14

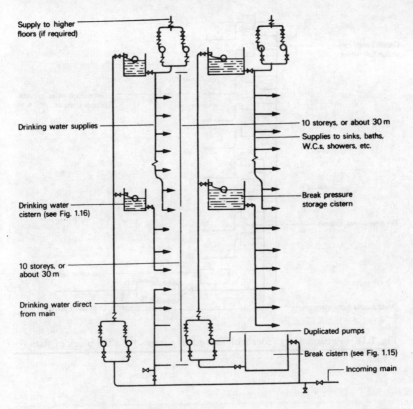

Fig. 1.16 System for 20 storeys and over

Labels (Fig. 1.16):
- Supply to higher floors (if required)
- Drinking water supplies
- Drinking water cistern (see Fig. 1.16)
- 10 storeys, or about 30 m
- Drinking water direct from main
- 10 storeys, or about 30 m
- Supplies to sinks, baths, W.C.s, showers, etc.
- Break pressure storage cistern
- Duplicated pumps
- Break cistern (see Fig. 1.15)
- Incoming main

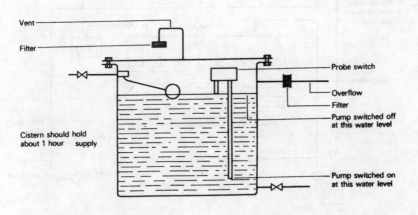

Fig. 1.17 Drinking water break cistern

Labels (Fig. 1.17):
- Vent
- Filter
- Cistern should hold about 1 hour supply
- Probe switch
- Overflow
- Filter
- Pump switched off at this water level
- Pump switched on at this water level

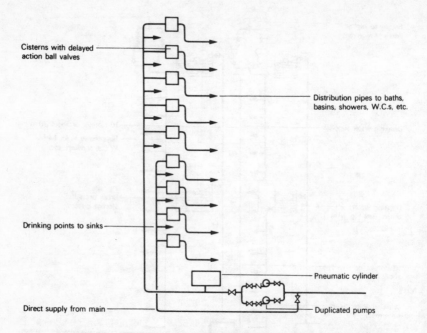

Fig. 1.18 Pneumatic cylinder with individual cisterns for a tall block of flats

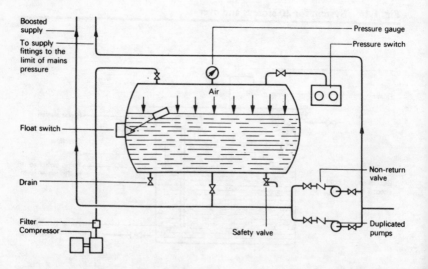

Fig. 1.19 Automatic pneumatic cylinder

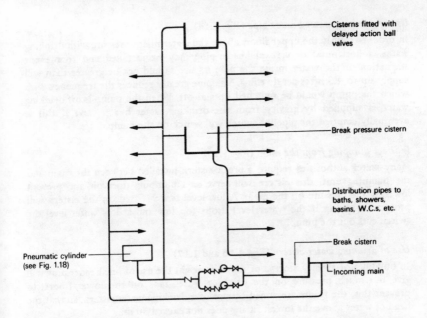

Fig. 1.20 Pneumatic cylinder for an office block

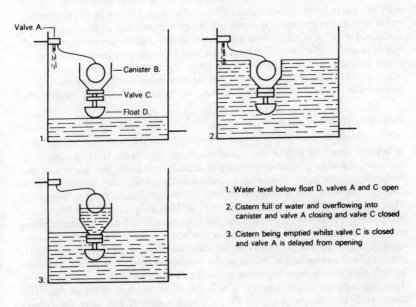

1. Water level below float D, valves A and C open

2. Cistern full of water and overflowing into canister and valve A closing and valve C closed

3. Cistern being emptied whilst valve C is closed and valve A is delayed from opening

Fig. 1.21 Delayed action ball valve

17

Use of drinking water header-pipe (Fig. 1.14)

In order to supply the upper floors above the water mains pressure with drinking water, a horizontal or vertical header-pipe may be installed and to prevent stagnation of the water inside the pipe its size should not be greater than will supply up to 4.5 litres per dwelling. The pipe greatly reduces the frequency with which the pump would be switched on and off. When the pump is off drinking water is supplied by gravity from the drinking water heater, and if this is eventually emptied the pipeline switch will switch on the pump.

Indirect pumping from the main (Fig. 1.15)

Many water authorities require a break cistern installed between the main and the pumping unit; this cistern will serve as a pumping reservoir and prevent lowering the pressure on the main. A low-level switch fitted on the cistern will protect the pump if the water level drops too low and at low water level the switch cuts out the pump.

Use of drinking water cistern (Figs 1.16 and 1.17)

In buildings of twenty storeys or more in height the use of one header-pipe will give too much pressure on the drinking water taps on the lower floors; to prevent this, the floors are zoned by use of a drinking water cistern, so that the head of water above the lowest fitting does not exceed 30 m.

Use of pneumatic cylinder (Figs 1.18, 1.19 and 1.20)

As an alternative to a drinking water header-pipe, a steel cylinder placed either vertically or horizontally may be used for boosting the drinking water to the upper floors. The cylinder contains a cushion of air under pressure, in contact with the water to be boosted; this cushion of air forces water up to the drinking water taps and as the water is drawn off the air expands and its pressure falls. At a predetermined low water level a low-level switch cuts in the pump, the pump will then satisfy the demand taking place and gradually increase the air pressure in the cylinder, until at a predetermined high water level a high-level switch cuts out the pump. The pressure switch settings are such that the minimum water pressures at the roof level cistern ball valve are 70 kPa and 100 kPa respectively.

Purpose of the air compressor

After a period of use some of the air is absorbed into the water and a gauge glass is usually fitted to give a visual indication of the water level. As more air becomes absorbed a smaller quantity is available to boost the water and the frequency of the pump operation is increased. To prevent this, a float switch is fitted in the vessel and is arranged to start the air compressor at a predetermined high water level. The compressor will force air into the cylinder until the correct water level is achieved, thus allowing the float switch to lower and thus cutting out the compressor. The ball valves in the water cisterns served from a pneumatic cylinder should preferably be the delayed action type to conserve the air pressure in the cylinder and minimise the number of pump operations. This type of ball-valve arrangement does not allow the valve to open until the cylinder is approximately two-thirds empty. It will also allow the ball valves to stay fully open until the cistern is almost full, whereas a normal ball valve closes very gradually and takes longer to fill the cistern (see Fig. 1.21).

Supply to baths, showers, W.C.s (Figs 1.14, 1.16, 1.18 and 1.20)

So far the problem of supplying drinking water to sinks or fountains has been considered. In high-rise buildings the water supply to baths, showers, W.C.s, etc., must also be considered. As already stated for drinking water fittings, the maximum head of water is 30 m and therefore the floors must be zoned, by use of break pressure cisterns or by pressure-reducing valves.

Taps and valves

The term 'taps', 'valves' and 'cocks' are used indiscriminately to name fittings required to control the flow of fluids, either along or at the end of a pipeline. Valves are usually used to control the flow along a pipeline, whilst taps are usually used at the end of a pipeline for draw-off purposes. Cocks consist of a body holding a tapered plug (see Fig. 1.22). The plug has a hole cast or drilled in the middle through which the fluid can flow. The cock can be fully opened or fully closed by turning the plug through an angle of 45° (quarter turn). It can be closed very quickly and may cause water hammer; it is therefore not usually permitted in water supply systems, but they are used extensively in gas installations.

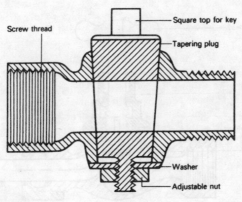

Fig. 1.22   Plug cock

Valves

Valves used to control the flow along a pipeline are known as the globe or gate types. Both types close slowly and therefore do not usually give rise to problems of water hammer.

Globe valves

These are used on high-pressure systems. Figure 1.23 shows a section of one type of globe valve; the metal-to-metal seating type is often used for heating systems and the composition valve for very high-pressure systems where a complete shut off is required. Figure 1.24 shows a section of a stopvalve used for domestic water installations. When the valve is used on cold water service pipework the jumper should be loose which tends to act as a non-return valve and prevent backflow into the main.

19

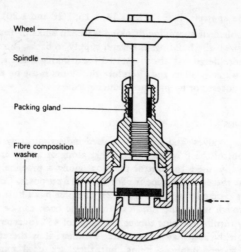

Fig. 1.23 Globe valve

Labels: Wheel, Spindle, Packing gland, Fibre composition washer

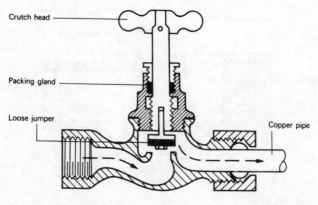

Fig. 1.24 Stop valve

Labels: Crutch head, Packing gland, Loose jumper, Copper pipe

Gate valves (see Fig. 1.25)

These are used for the control of fluids in low-pressure systems, such as on distribution pipework from storage cisterns, or on low-pressure heating systems. They offer much less resistance to the flow of fluids than the globe valve.

Drain valves (see Fig. 1.26)

These are used to drain boilers, cylinders and sections of pipework.

Safety valves

These are used to relieve excess pressure on boilers, tanks and pipework. Figure 1.27A, B shows spring and deadweight types of safety valves.

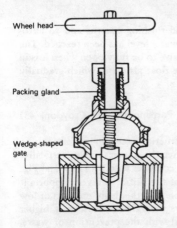

Fig. 1.25 Gate valve

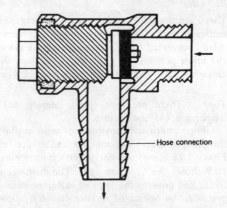

Fig. 1.26 Drain valve

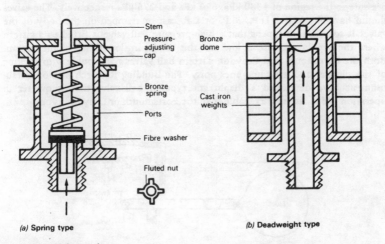

(a) **Spring type**

(b) **Deadweight type**

Fig. 1.27 Safety valves

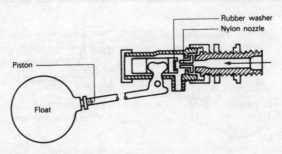

Fig. 1.28 Portsmouth ball valve – BS 1212

Ball valves

These are used to supply water to storage and flushing cisterns and to automatically shut off the supply when the correct water level has been reached. The valve is operated by a float which allows the valve to be fully open when it is in the lower position. As the water level rises, the float also rises which gradually closes the valve and shuts off the supply of water.

Types: There are four types, namely; (1) Portsmouth, (2) Croydon, (3) Diaphragm, (4) Equilibrium.

Portsmouth and Croydon are similar in construction except in the former type the plunger moves horizontally and in the latter the plunger moves vertically. Figure 1.28 shows the Portsmouth type, which complies with BS 1212, and Fig. 1.29 shows the Croydon type. The diameter of the orifice is a very important factor and governs the type of valve; for example, whether high, medium or low pressure. An orifice of smaller diameter allows the valve to close at a higher water pressure. The Model Bylaws (which deal with the prevention of waste, undue consumption, misuse and contamination of water) states that the high-pressure, medium-pressure and low-pressure ball valves should close at a test pressure in the region of 1380 kPa, 690 kPa and 276 kPa respectively. The valves should have the letters H.P., M.P. or L.P. cast or stamped on the body of the valve. It sometimes happens that a high-pressure ball valve is fitted to a cistern where the supply pressure is low and this results in slow filling of the cistern. Both the Portsmouth and Croydon pattern ball valves give trouble with sticking of the plunger and are sometimes noisy. The Building Research Station Establishment have developed a diaphragm type of ball valve that is quieter in operation and is also more reliable than the Portsmouth or Croydon types.

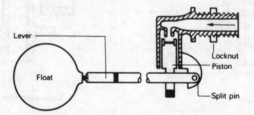

Fig. 1.29   Croydon ball valve

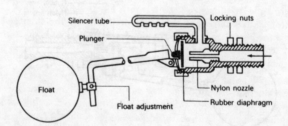

Fig. 1.30   B.R.E. diaphragm ball valve

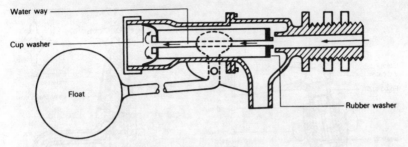

Fig. 1.31 Equilibrium ball valve – Portsmouth type

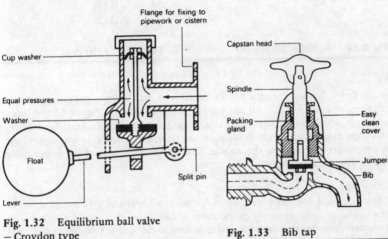

Fig. 1.32 Equilibrium ball valve – Croydon type

Fig. 1.33 Bib tap

Figure 1.30 shows a section of a diaphragm ball valve which is designed to have the working parts out of contact with the water. This prevents the working parts from sticking, due to the deposit of salts and rust from the water.

Equilibrium ball valve (see Fig 1.31, which shows a Portsmouth type, and Fig. 1.32, which shows a Croydon type).

The principle of the valve is to transmit equal water pressures at both ends of the piston and thus reduce the force produced by the float and level. The valve is used for large diameter supplies, or for very high water pressures.

Taps

There are several types of taps, sometimes referred to as 'screw down' types, which are designed to shut off the supply slowly and thus prevent water hammer. Figure 1.33 shows a 'bib tap' used for fitting over a sink, or for washing down purposes when it is then fitted with a hose outlet. The tap can be plain brass or chromium plated. Figure 1.34 shows a section of a 'Supatap' which incorporates a check valve. When the nozzle is removed the check valve prevents

23

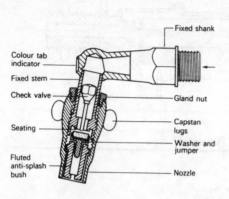

Fig. 1.34 'Supatap' bib tap

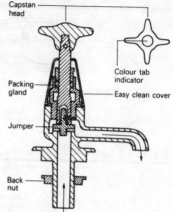

Fig. 1.35 Pillar tap

water from flowing through to the outlet and this permits the jumper to be changed without shutting off the supply at the stop valve. Figure 1.35 shows a pillar tap which can be used for baths, wash basins and sinks. Dual flow swivel sink taps may be used, which separate the flow of hot and cold water, until the water discharges through the nozzle. This prevents the risk of hot water being drawn into the cold-water main.

Spray taps

These are used for hand washing in factories, schools and offices and result in the saving of approximately 50 per cent of the water that would be used with ordinary taps; because less hot water is used there is also a saving in fuel. Hot and cold water supplies are connected to the same valve and are blended together before being discharged through a spray outlet.

Materials

Taps and valves are manufactured from either brass or gunmetal. English brass contains 64 per cent copper and 36 per cent zinc and is used for high grade fittings. Common brass contains 50 per cent copper and 50 per cent zinc and is used for lower grade fittings. Admiralty gunmetal contains 88 per cent copper, 10 per cent tin and 2 per cent zinc and is used for steam fittings. Leaded gunmetal contains 85 per cent copper, 5 per cent tin, 5 per cent zinc and 5 per cent lead and is used for high grade water fittings.

Materials for pipes

Lead and lead alloy

Lead is very resistant to corrosion by atmospheric gases or acid soils, but is affected by contact with cement mortar or concrete, and if there is a danger of corrosion the pipes should be wrapped with 'Denso' tape or coated with bitumen. The pipes are attacked internally by soft water which may cause

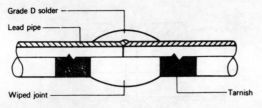

Fig. 1.36 Wiped underhand joint

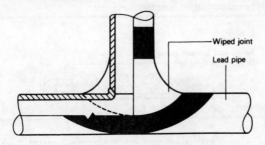

Fig. 1.37 Wiped branch joint

minute particles to pass into the water system and endanger the health of the user. Lead pipe is easily bent when cold, cut and jointed and for this reason was very useful for short connections to sanitary fittings and cisterns. Figures 1.36 and 1.37 show wiped soldered joints on lead pipes. The Water Byelaws 1986 prohibit the use of lead pipe. To carry out a repair, copper pipe may be inserted between lead pipe using brass couplings and wiped joints.

Specification: BS 602 covers pipes for other than chemical purposes and BS 1085 covers silver, copper, lead alloy pipes. BS 334 covers chemical lead used for waste pipes in chemical laboratories. Lead pipes up to 25 mm bore are obtainable in coils 18 m long; pipes up to 50 mm bore in coils 11 m long and pipes over 50 mm bore in straight lengths 3 m or 3.7 m long.

Copper

Copper pipes are used for hot and cold water, heating, gas and drainage installations. They have high tensile strength and may therefore be of thin walls, which make them comparatively cheap and light in weight. Some acid soils may attack copper, but if there is a danger of corrosion the pipes may be obtained with a plastic covering. The pipes have smooth internal surfaces and offer little resistance to flow of fluids and therefore smaller bore pipes may be used. Copper pipes are easily bent by a machine or spring, they are neat in appearance and if required may be chromium plated. Jointing can be achieved by non-manipulative compression joints (Fig. 1.38), manipulative compression joints (Fig. 1.39), or soldered capillary joints (Fig. 1.40).

The pipes may also be jointed by bronze welding or silver soldering. Where there is a risk of the joint being pulled out due to fibration or settlement, manipulative compression or soldered capillary joints should be specified and these types of joints are therefore used for underground service pipes.

25

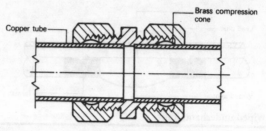

Fig. 1.38 Non-manipulative compression joint

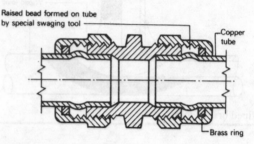

Fig. 1.39 Manipulative compression joint

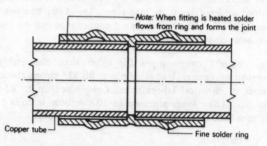

Fig. 1.40 Soldered capillary joint

Specification: BS 2871, Part 1, Table X applies to light gauge, half-hand temper tube, supplied in straight lengths of 6 m for use above ground. BS 2871, Part 1, Table Y applies to light gauge annealed tube, supplied in coils, in lengths of up to 60 m. The tube is used for underground water and gas services and for panel heating installations. BS 2871, Part 1, Table Z applies to hand-tempered, thin-walled tube supplied in straight lengths for use above ground. The tube is not suitable for bending, but has the same outside diameter of the other tubes and standard non-manipulative and capillary fittings may therefore be used.

Note: All tube sizes refer to the outside diameter and sizes from 6 mm to 159 mm O.D. may be obtained.

26

Mild steel

Mild steel pipes may be obtained galvanised or ungalvanised; the former type are used for hot- and cold-water installations and the latter for heating installations. The pipes are comparatively cheap and have a very high tensile strength, which enables them to be used for high pressures; they also resist external mechanical damage better than other pipes. They have, however, rougher internal surfaces than other pipes and offer greater resistance to the flow of fluids. The pipes may be easily bent by a hydraulic bending machine and readily jointed by means of screwed or flanged joints (see Figs 1.41, 1.42 and 1.43). Hemp and jointing paste is used between the threads of the screwed joints and a special jointing ring used between the flange joint. The union type joint provides for a lateral movement of about 5 degrees without leaking and the flange joint is used for large diameter pipes, especially where maintenance is of primary concern. Welded joints may also be used.

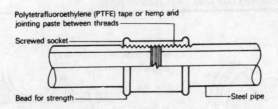

Fig. 1.41   Screwed joint on steel pipe

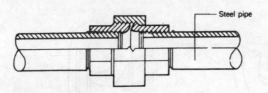

Fig. 1.42   Union type joint on steel pipe

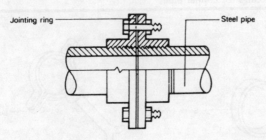

Fig. 1.43   Flange joint on steel pipe

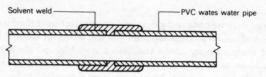

Fig. 1.44   Solvent weld joint on PVC pipe

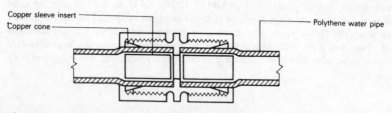

Fig. 1.45   Compression joint on polythene pipe

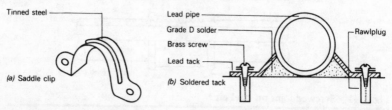

Fig. 1.46   Fixings for lead pipes

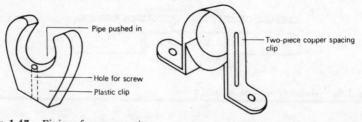

Fig. 1.47   Fixings for copper pipes

Fig. 1.48   Fixings for steel pipes

Specification: BS 1387 covers mild steel pipes, both galvanised and ungalvanised, in diameters from 6 mm to 150 mm. The standard covers three grades:

Grade A with thin walls banded brown;
Grade B with medium thick walls banded blue;
Grade C with thick walls banded red.

Grade A is used for waste, ventilating and overflow pipes, Grade B for hot and cold distribution and heating pipes and Grade C for underground service pipes and rising mains. Stainless steel pipes may be obtained which have thinner walls than mild steel pipes and may be bent and jointed in the same way as copper pipes.

Plastic

PVC (Polyvinyl chloride) is used for cold water service and distributing pipes, water mains and drainage pipe systems. It is not suitable for use with hot-water pipes, but may be used for short periods of discharge of hot waste water. The pipe is manufactured as unplasticised PVC and cut into 10 m lengths. It has a smooth internal surface, is light and easy to handle and can be obtained in various colours. The pipe may be jointed by means of a solvent cement, which is applied to the socket and spigot of the pipe, as shown in Fig. 1.44.

Specification: BS 3505 covers unplasticised PVC pipes for cold water supply and BS 3506 covers unplasticised PVC pipe for industrial purposes. The internal diameters range from 9 mm to 150 mm.

Polythene pipe is used for cold water services, especially underground mains, when it can be laid by mole ploughing. The pipe is not suitable for hot water as its softening temperature is low, it is not impervious to coal gas and a leak from a gas main may cause tainting of the water. The pipe has a smooth internal surface and offers little resistance to the flow of the fluids, it is light in weight and a non-conductor of electricity. Jointing can be made by use of a copper compression fitting, as shown in Fig. 1.45.

Specification: BS 1972 covers two grades of pipe, namely: normal gauge and heavy gauge. Normal gauge pipe may be obtained from 13 mm to 50 mm bore and heavy gauge from 6 mm to 25 mm bore.

Fixing of pipes

Various methods are used for pipe fixings to walls and brickwork, cement and timber surfaces. Figures 1.46, 1.47 and 1.48 show the fixing devices used for lead, copper and steel pipes. Plastic pipes may be fixed by means of saddle clips used for lead pipes, or plastic clips similar to those used for copper pipes.

Chapter 2

Hot-water supply

Systems

Centralised boiler systems

The boiler may be heated by gas, solid fuel or oil and should be positioned as close to the hot-water storage cylinder as possible, so that heat losses from the primary flow and return pipes are reduced to the minimum. The boiler and cylinder should be placed in a central position to reduce the length of the secondary circuit to the various hot-water draw-off points. This circuit may circulate hot water by gravity or by a pump and the pipes should be insulated wherever possible to conserve heat. The Building Regulations 1985 state the maximum lengths of pipes not requiring insulation (see Table 2.1).

Direct system (Fig. 2.1)

If central heating is not to be combined with the hot-water supply, or if the water is soft, the direct system may be used providing the boiler is rustprooved. The system is cheaper to install than the indirect system and the water in the cylinder will be heated quicker, due to 'direct' circulation between the boiler and cylinder.

Indirect system (Fig. 2.2)

This system is used in temporary hard water districts, or when heating is combined with the hot water supply system. An indirect cylinder is used which has an inner heat exchanger. The water from the boiler circulates through this heat exchanger and heats the water in the cylinder indirectly. Since the water in this heat exchanger and boiler is not drawn off through the hot-water taps, lime is precipitated only after the initial heating of the water, and afterwards (unless the system is drained) there is no further occurrence and therefore no scaling. This

30

Table 2.1 Building Regulations 1985 for the maximum lengths of hot water draw-off pipes (not requiring insulation)

Outside diameter of pipe in mm	Maximum length of uninsulated pipe in (m)
Not more than 12	20
More than 12 but not more than 22	12
More than 22 but not more than 28	8
More than 28	3

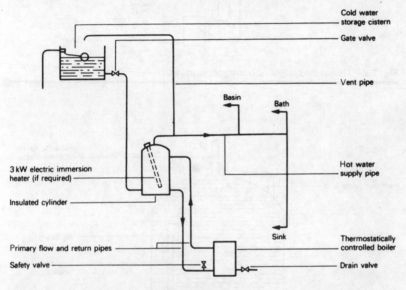

Fig. 2.1 'Direct' system of hot water supply

same water also circulates through the steel or cast iron radiators, and after heating the water is freed from carbon dioxide which then reduces corrosion of the radiators.

Primatic cylinder (Fig. 2.3)

For small installations. This type of self-venting indirect cylinder may be used. When the water is heated the heat exchanger has two air locks, which prevent the secondary water in the cylinder from mixing with the primary water in the heat exchanger and boiler. The cylinder is connected with pipework similar to the direct system and therefore there is a saving in cost, due to the absence of an expansion and feed cistern, primary cold feed and primary vent pipes (see Fig. 2.4).

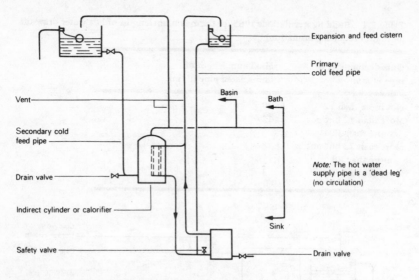

Fig. 2.2 'Indirect' system of hot water supply

Labels in figure:
- Expansion and feed cistern
- Primary cold feed pipe
- Basin
- Bath
- Vent
- Secondary cold feed pipe
- *Note:* The hot water supply pipe is a 'dead leg' (no circulation)
- Drain valve
- Indirect cylinder or calorifier
- Sink
- Safety valve
- Drain valve

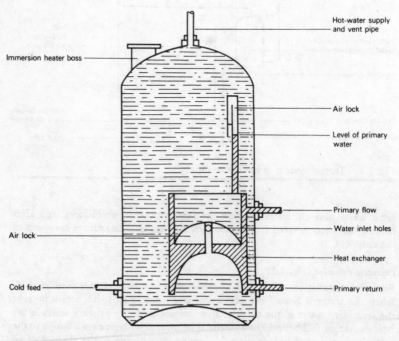

Fig. 2.3 Primatic cylinder

Labels in figure:
- Hot-water supply and vent pipe
- Immersion heater boss
- Air lock
- Level of primary water
- Primary flow
- Water inlet holes
- Air lock
- Heat exchanger
- Cold feed
- Primary return

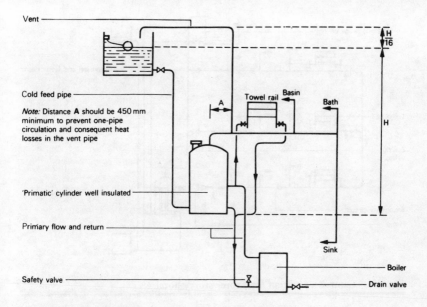

Fig. 2.4 The 'Primatic' cylinder

Vent

Cold feed pipe

Note: Distance **A** should be 450 mm minimum to prevent one-pipe circulation and consequent heat losses in the vent pipe

'Primatic' cylinder well insulated

Primary flow and return

Safety valve

Towel rail   Basin   Bath

H
16

A

H

Sink

Boiler

Drain valve

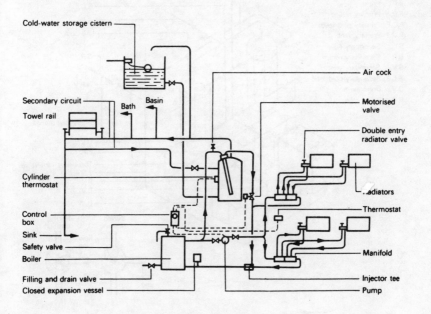

Fig. 2.5 Combined heating and hot water system

Cold-water storage cistern

Secondary circuit

Towel rail   Bath   Basin

Cylinder thermostat

Control box

Sink

Safety valve

Boiler

Filling and drain valve

Closed expansion vessel

Air cock

Motorised valve

Double entry radiator valve

Radiators

Thermostat

Manifold

Injector tee

Pump

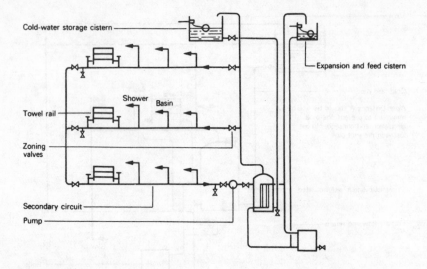

Fig. 2.6 Centralised system for a three-storey hotel

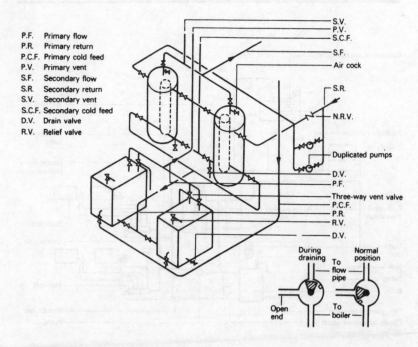

P.F. Primary flow
P.R. Primary return
P.C.F. Primary cold feed
P.V. Primary vent
S.F. Secondary flow
S.R. Secondary return
S.V. Secondary vent
S.C.F. Secondary cold feed
D.V. Drain valve
R.V. Relief valve

Fig. 2.7 Duplicated boilers and calorifiers

Combined system

Figure 2.5 shows a system having a 'closed' primary circuit, which, like the primatic cylinder, saves an expansion and feed cistern, primary cold feed and primary vent pipes. The closed expansion vessel contains air or nitrogen which takes up the expansion of the water when heated. A 'micro bore' heating system is shown, with the radiators served with 6, 8, 10 or 12 mm outside-diameter soft copper pipes, from a 22 mm outside-diameter copper manifold. The system saves about 15 per cent of costs when compared with a conventional system of heating with larger pipes. When the pump is working the injector tee draws water down from the return pipe and promotes better circulation through the heat exchanger in the cylinder.

Systems for larger buildings

Figure 2.6 shows a system for a three-storey hotel with bathrooms and towel rails on each floor. Each floor is zoned with valves, so that a repair on one floor may be carried out without draining the whole of the secondary pipework.

Figure 2.7 shows a duplicated plant which allows the repair or renewal of one of the boilers or calorifiers without shutting down and draining the others. This will provide a supply of hot water at all times, and in order to accomplish this every pipe connection to the boilers and calorifiers must be provided with valves for isolating purposes. The three-way vent valves will ensure that the boilers are open to atmosphere at all times and thus avoid the risk of an explosion. The plant is essential in hospitals, large factories, colleges, hotels and offices.

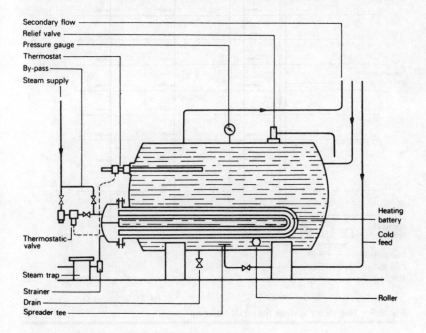

Fig. 2.8   Large horizontal steam heated calorifier

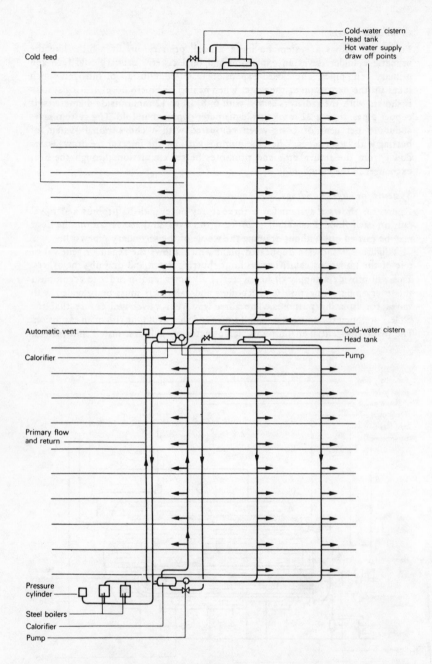

Fig. 2.9 Hot water system for a tall building

Figure 2.8 shows a detail of a large horizontal steam-heated calorifier, which is an ideal method of providing hospitals and factories with hot water when steam is used for space heating. The calorifiers may be sited at various strategic points in the building; for example, close to the various hot water draw-off points.

Figure 2.9 shows a hot-water system for a tall building. The floors are zoned, so that the maximum head of water on the lowest draw-off taps does not exceed 30 m. This will reduce noise and wear of valves on the lower floors. The head tank improves the flow of hot water to the taps on the upper floors of each zone.

Estimation of hot-water storage

The Code of Practice, hot water supply, gives the storage requirements shown in Table 2.2.

Table 2.2

Type of building	Storage per person (litres)	Type of building	Storage per person (litres)
Colleges and schools		Hospitals	
Boarding	23	General	27
Day	4.5	Infectious	45.5
Dwelling houses	45.5	Maternity	32
Factories	4.5	Nurses' homes	45.5
Flats	32	Hostels	32
Hotels (average)	35	Offices	4.5
		Sports pavilions	36

By use of Table 2.2, a dwelling house with three occupants will require 45.5 × 3 = 136.5 litres of hot-water storage. If the number of occupants of the building is not known Table 2.3 may be used.

Table 2.3 Volumes of water used at each appliance

Appliance	Volumes of hot water (litres)
Wash basin	
Hand wash	1.5
Wash	3
Hair wash	6
Shower	13
Bath	70
Washing machine	70
Sink	
Wash-up	15
Cleaning	5

By use of Table 2.3 a dwelling house requiring two consecutive baths during the peak demand period would require a hot-water storage of 140 litres.

Boiler power

Table 2.4 shows the boiler power recommended for various types of buildings in watt per person.

Table 2.4   Boiler power recommended for various buildings in watts per person

Boarding schools	750	General hospitals	1500
Day schools	90	Nurses' homes	900
Dwelling houses	1200	Hotels (average)	900
Factories	120	Hotels (first class)	1200
Flats	750	Hostels	750
		Offices	120

By use of Table 2.4 the boiler power required in kilowatt for a dwelling house with four occupants, when the heat losses are 20 per cent would be:

4 persons x 1200 watt = 4800 watt

$$\text{Boiler power} = \frac{4800}{1} \times \frac{100}{80}$$

Boiler power = 6000 watt

Boiler power = 6 kW

Electric water heating

At the present moment the cost of heating water by electricity is more expensive than heating by other fuels, and care is required when installing electric water heaters in order to conserve heat. *The following points therefore must be observed:*

1. The hot-water storage vessel must be well insulated, with a minimum thickness of 50 mm — preferably 75 mm — of good insulation.
2. The heated water must not circulate through towel rails or radiators.
3. The length of hot water draw-off points, particularly to the sink, should be reduced to the minimum.
4. Single-pipe circulation in the hot-water pipes, or vent pipes, must be avoided.
5. Airing cupboards should not be heated by leaving part of the hot-water storage vessel uninsulated.
6. An effective thermostat must control the temperature of the water at a maximum of 60 °C for temporary hard water and at a maximum of 71 °C for soft water. The lower temperature for temporary hard water greatly reduces the deposit of lime.

Pressure type heaters (Fig. 2.10)

These must always be supplied from a cold-water storage cistern. They are available in capacities from 50 to 450 litres. One of the most useful type is called 'U.D.B.', or under the draining board, type as shown in Fig. 2.11. It is fitted with two heating elements, one of which is near the top and maintains about 23 litres of hot water for general use. The bottom heater is switched on when larger

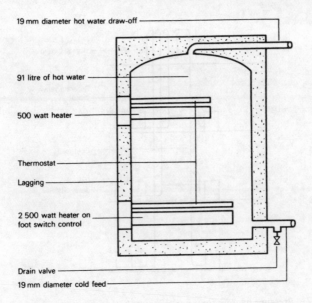

Fig. 2.10 Two-in-one pressure type heater

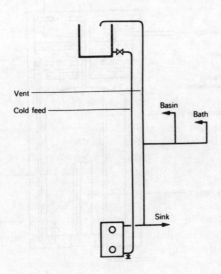

Fig. 2.11 Pressure heater for a house

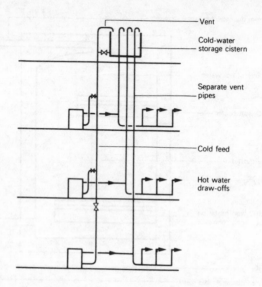

Vent

Cold-water storage cistern

Separate vent pipes

Cold feed

Hot water draw-offs

Fig. 2.12 Pressure heaters for a multi-storey building

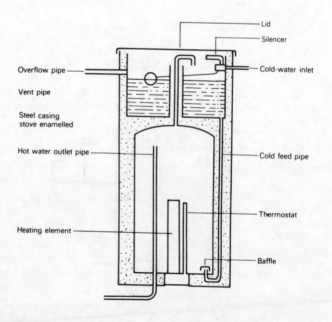

Lid

Silencer

Overflow pipe

Cold-water inlet

Vent pipe

Steel casing stove enamelled

Hot water outlet pipe

Cold feed pipe

Thermostat

Heating element

Baffle

Fig. 2.13 Cistern type water heater

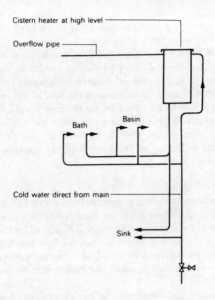

Fig. 2.14 Cistern heater for a house

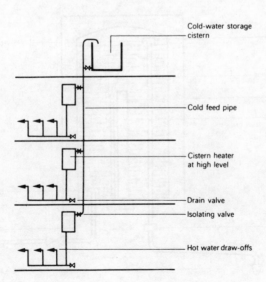

Fig. 2.15 Cistern heater for a multi-storey building

41

quantities of hot water are required for baths or laundry use. The heater can provide sufficient hot water for a small house.

If the heater is required for blocks of flats, a cold-water storage cistern may be installed on each floor and the pipework is similar to that required for a house. In order to save the cost of separate cold-water storage cisterns, the heaters may be supplied from one cistern on the roof as shown in Fig. 2.12. The cold feed branch to each heater must be taken from a higher level than the top of the heater, as this will prevent the water from the higher heaters draining down to the lower ones. A vent pipe on the cold-feed pipe as shown in Fig. 2.12 will also prevent the siphoning of hot water from the upper to the lower heaters when the stop valve is closed.

Cistern type heaters (Fig. 2.13)

These are available with hot-water capacities from 23 to 136 litres. They may be supplied with cold water direct from the main, or from a storage cistern. Upon opening one of the hot-water taps, hot water is displaced by the cold water from the cistern and since the head of water is small the flow rate will be limited.

Figure 2.14 shows the installation of the cistern type heater for a house. Because the cold-water cistern is small the cold water to the taps is supplied direct from the main.

Figure 2.15 shows the installation of the cistern type heater in a block of flats, where the Water Authority will not allow cold water to supply baths, basins and W.C.s direct from the main. The cold-water storage cistern will supply cold water to these fittings and also the cistern type heater. The vent pipe on the cold feed pipe is used for the same purpose as explained for the pressure heater installation.

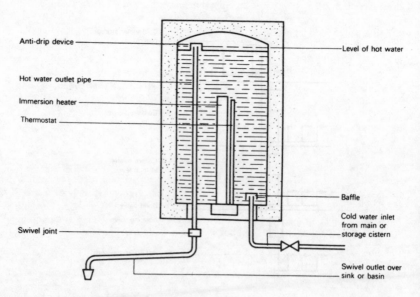

Fig. 2.16   Open outlet type electric water heater

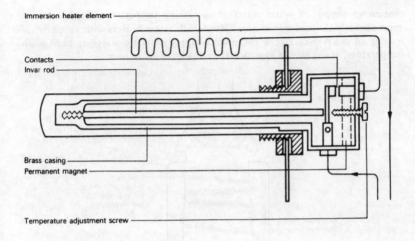

Immersion heater element

Contacts
Invar rod

Brass casing
Permanent magnet

Temperature adjustment screw

Fig. 2.17   Rod type thermostat

Open outlet type heaters (Fig. 2.16)

These are available in capacities from 6 to 136 litres and like the cistern type heater may be supplied with cold water, either direct from the main, or from a storage cistern. They are fitted over the bath, basin, sink or washing machine and one heater may be used to supply hot water to two basins or sinks. The 'anti-drip' device is used to prevent a drip of water through the outlet as the water expands on heating. The baffle on the cold-feed pipe prevents undue mixing of the cold water entering with the hot water in the heater.

Rod type thermostat (Fig. 2.17)

As mentioned earlier, all heating elements must be thermostatically controlled. The rod type thermostat uses the difference in expansion between brass and invar (nickel steel) for its operation. When the brass casing expands it pulls the invar rod (which expands very little) with it and breaks the electric contact. The permanent magnet ensures a snap action break.

Off peak electricity

In order to encourage the use of electricity during the 'off peak' period, usually between 23.00 hr and 07.00 hr, the Electricity Board offers a reduced tariff. Both cistern type and pressure type electric heaters are available, with storage capacities up to 225 litres and loadings up to 6 kW. These 'off peak' heaters are taller and smaller in diameter than the normal type of heaters, so as to maintain stratification of hot and cold water.

Instantaneous electric water heaters

These are designed for direct connection to the cold-water supply main, and are fitted with a pressure switch to prevent the element switching on before the water flows and vice versa. A thermal cut-out also prevents the water from over-heating. Shower water heaters with an electrical loading of 6 kW will give a continuous supply of warm water at showering temperature, at the rate of approximately 3 litres per minute. Hand-wash water heaters with an electrical loading of 3 kW will give a continuous supply of warm water at hand wash temperature, at the rate of approximately 1.4 litres per minute.

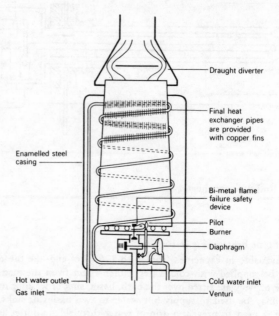

Draught diverter

Final heat exchanger pipes are provided with copper fins

Enamelled steel casing

Bi-metal flame failure safety device

Pilot

Burner

Diaphragm

Hot water outlet

Cold water inlet

Gas inlet

Venturi

Fig. 2.18

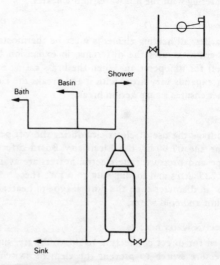

Bath

Basin

Shower

Sink

Fig. 2.19 Instantaneous gas water heater

Gas water heaters

There are three types of gas water heaters; instantaneous, storage and circulatory.

Instantaneous heaters

These give instant hot water day or night, the water being heated as it passes through a finned pipe heat exchanger. They are obtainable in the following classes;

1. *Sink heaters*, single or multipoint, to serve a sink, or basin, or a sink and basin where these are close together. They are fitted with a swivel spout outlet.
2. *Bath heaters*, a swivel spout can serve a wash basin in addition to the bath.
3. *Boiling water heaters*, will provide hot or boiling water for making beverages and a humming device fitted to the heater sounds when the water is boiling.
4. *Multipoint heaters*, will provide sufficient hot water to bath, basin and sink, or they may be used for several basins or sinks in larger buildings.

Figure 2.18 shows a detail of a multipoint instantaneous water heater, which operates as follows: When a hot-water tap is opened water flows through the venturi, which causes a differential pressure across a flexible diaphragm, causing the main gas valve to open, the burners are ignited and cold water flows through the finned pipe heat exchanger, where it is heated before leaving the heater. The flame failure device will shut off the gas supply to the burners should the pilot light be extinguished. The heater may be of the balanced flue type and will deliver about 5.6 litres per minute, with the water raised through a temperature of 38 °C.

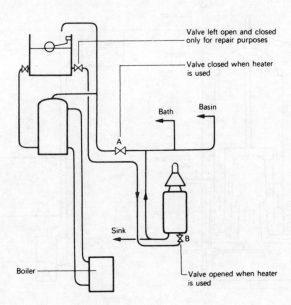

Fig. 2.20 Gas multipoint heater connected to an existing hot-water system

Figure 2.19 shows the method of installing the heater for a house; the head of water above the heater should not be less than 3 m. Figure 2.20 shows the method of installing the heater to an existing hot water system. To obtain hot water from the heater, stop valve A is closed and stop valve B opened.

Storage heaters (Fig. 2.21)

The hot water is stored in an insulated copper cylinder. There are two types:

1. *Sink heaters*, which are provided with a swivel spout outlet, usually of 9 to 23 litres capacity.
2. *Multipoint storage heaters*, which like the instantaneous multipoint heaters, may supply bath, basin and sink, as shown in Fig. 2.22. A common hot-water storage is 114 litres, but other capacities are obtainable.

Circulators

This type of heater should be fitted with its own flow and return pipe direct to the storage cylinder. The heater may be the sole means of providing hot water, as shown in Fig. 2.23. If possible the heater should be fitted close to the sink, but it may also be installed in the airing cupboard. Figure 2.24 shows the method of installing the heater to an existing hot-water system, to provide a boost to the boiler or an alternative means of heating the water during summer. The three-way economy valve permits the closing of the low-level return pipe, so that only a small quantity of water is heated for sink and basin use. When hot water is required for bath or laundry use, the valve can be operated so as to close the high-level return pipe and open the low-level return pipe, thus allowing the

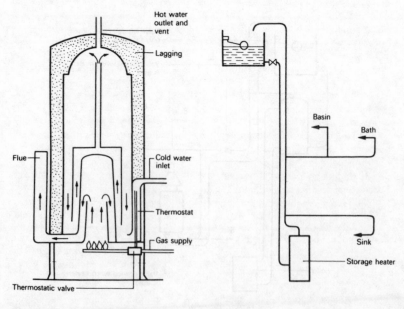

Fig. 2.21   Storage heater

Fig. 2.22

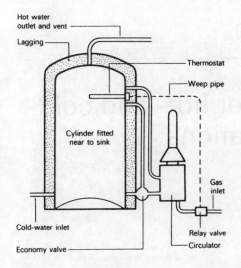

Fig. 2.23   Gas circulator

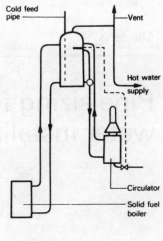

Fig. 2.24   Auxiliary circulator

whole of the water in the cylinder to be heated. Table 2.5 gives a comparison of heating water by centralised plant and electric or gas unit heaters.

Table 2.5   Summary of the hot-water heating systems

Centralised systems	Electric or gas water unit heaters
1. Provides large bulk storage for hospitals, hotels and factories	1. May be fitted close to the fittings being supplied, thus saving a great deal of pipework
2. One central boiler plant requires less maintenance than several unit heaters	2. Saving in boiler house space and possible fuel store
3. Cheaper fuel may be used	3. A number of heaters in large buildings require either separate gas or electrical connections
4. Requires long lengths of secondary pipework, which can lead to large heat losses	4. Greater risk of fire inside the building, due to more gas or electrical connections
5. Reduction in flue construction (unless electric heaters are used)	5. No need to pump the hot water supply circuit
6. Towel rails and airing coils may be connected to the secondary circuit	

Unvented hot-water storage systems

(For a discussion of this topic please see Appendix A).

Chapter 3

Pipe sizing for hot- and cold-water installations

Relative discharging power of pipes

Relative discharging power of pipes are as the square root of the fifth power of their diameters.

$$N = \sqrt{\left(\frac{D}{d}\right)^5}$$

where

N = number of branch pipes

D = diameter of main pipe

d = diameter of branch pipes

Table 3.1 has been based on the formula.

Determination of pipe diameter

Example 3.1. *Determine the number of 20 mm diameter branch pipes that may be supplied by a 50 mm diameter main pipe.*

From Table 3.1 ten branch pipes may be supplied by a 50 mm diameter main pipe.

Example 3.2. *Determine the diameter of a main pipe to supply thirty-nine 15 mm diameter branch pipes.*

From Table 3.1 the diameter of main pipe is 65 mm.

Table 3.1 Relative discharging power of pipes

Main pipe	Branch pipe						Internal diameter		
Nominal diameter of pipe size	Nominal diameter of pipe size (mm)								
Internal diameter (mm)	100	75	65	50	40	32	25	20	15
100	1	2	3	6	10	17	32	56	115
75		1	2	3	5	9	16	28	56
65			1	2	4	6	11	19	39
50				1	2	3	6	10	21
40					1	2	4	6	12
32						1	2	4	7
25							1	2	4
20								1	2
15									1

Number of branch pipes

Thomas Box formula

This is a well-known practical formula for pipe sizing given in the following expression:

$$q = \sqrt{\frac{d^5 \times H}{25 \times L \times 10^5}}$$

where

q = discharge through pipe in litres per second

d = diameter of pipe in millimetres

H = head of water in metres

L = total length of pipe in metres

Example 3.3. *Calculate the diameter of a pipe to discharge 1.25 litre/s when the head is 4 m and the effective length is 45.5 m.*

By transposition of formula:

$$q^2 = \frac{d^5 \times H}{25 \times L \times 10^5}$$

$$d = \sqrt[5]{\frac{q^2 \times 25 \times L \times 10^5}{H}}$$

$$d = \sqrt[5]{\frac{1.25^2 \times 25 \times 45.5 \times 10^5}{4}}$$

$$d = 33.85$$

The nearest pipe size is 32 mm which is approximately 2 mm undersize, the next size is 38 mm which is approximately 4 mm oversize and it would be left to the designer which size to choose, depending upon the circumstances.

Example 3.4. *Calculate the discharge in litre/s through a 50 mm bore pipe when the head of water is 8 m and the effective length of pipe is 15 m.*

$$q = \sqrt{\frac{50^5 \times 8}{25 \times 15 \times 10^5}}$$

$q = 8.2$ litre/s approx.

Example 3.5. *Calculate the head of water necessary to provide a discharge of 0.2 litre/s through a 13 mm diameter pipe 6 m long.*

$$q = \sqrt{\frac{d^5 \times H}{25 \times L \times 10^5}}$$

by transposition $H = \dfrac{q^2 \times 25 \times L \times 10^5}{d^5}$

$$= \frac{0.2^2 \times 25 \times 6 \times 10^5}{13^5}$$

$$= 1.616 \text{ m}$$
$$= 1.6 \text{ m (approx.)}$$

Example 3.6. *Calculate the maximum length of 25 mm diameter pipe that can be used when the discharge is to be 4 litre/s and there is a constant head of water of 30 m.*

$$q = \sqrt{\frac{d^5 \times H}{25 \times L \times 10^5}}$$

by transposition $L = \dfrac{d^5 \times H}{q^2 \times 25 \times 10^5}$

$$L = \frac{25^2 \times 30}{4^2 \times 25 \times 10^5}$$

$$L = 7.3 \text{ m approx.}$$

Example 3.7. *Calculate the discharge in litres per second through a 32 mm diameter pipe when the head is 5 m and the total length 20 m.*

$$q = \sqrt{\frac{d^5 \times H}{25 \times L \times 10^5}}$$

$$= \sqrt{\frac{32^5 \times 5}{25 \times 20 \times 10^5}}$$

$$= 1.8 \text{ litre/s (approx.)}$$

Chapter 4

Low-pressure hot-water heating

Systems

When low-pressure hot water is used for heating systems the temperature of the water is below boiling point, usually about 80 °C on the flow pipe and between 60 °C and 70 °C on the return pipe.

Water has the high specific heat capacity of 4.2 kJ/kg K and although it is more difficult to heat than other media, more heat can be transferred from the boiler to the various heat emitters with pipes of a relatively small diameter. The higher the temperature of the water the greater the amount of heat transferred, but some of this heat is lost by the higher heat losses on the pipework. This higher temperature may also cause injury to persons coming into contact with the radiators, etc., and special precautions must be taken.

Water circulation

Water may be circulated in the system either by natural convection (thermo-siphonage) or by means of a centrifugal pump. Thermo-siphonage is produced by the difference in temperature between the flow and return pipes. The denser cooler water in the return pipe forces the less dense hotter water in the flow pipe through the circuit. Pump circulation has now replaced thermo-siphonage circulation for all but the smallest house installation. It has the advantage of reducing the heating-up period and also smaller pipes may be used.

Circuit arrangement

Various circuits may be used depending upon the type and layout of the building. In some buildings two or more circuits may be used supplied from the same boiler plant. One-pipe or two-pipe circuits may be used and although the one-pipe is simpler than the two-pipe it has two disadvantages:

1. The cooler water passing out of each heat emitter flows to the next one, resulting in the emitters at the end of the circuit being cooler than those at the beginning. This can be reduced by shutting down the lock shield valves

at the start of the circuit thus allowing more water to pass to the emitters at the end of the circuit.

2. Even if the circuit is pumped, the pump pressure does not force water through the heat emitters. Water is induced to circulate through the emitters by thermo-siphonage created by the difference in density between the water entering and leaving the emitters. A one-pipe system therefore cannot be used to supply heat to various types of emitters that have a comparatively high resistance to the flow of water.

Injector tees can be used to induce water through emitters on a one-pipe circuit, but these increase the resistance to the flow of water.

The two-pipe system requires more pipework, but this can be reduced in diameter as it passes around the circuit. The pump pressure acts throughout the circuit and therefore any type of heat emitter can be used. There is much less cooling down of the emitters at the end of the circuit, due to the cooler water passing out of the emitters being returned to the boiler via the return pipe.

One-pipe ring circuit (Fig. 4.1):   suitable for small single-storey buildings and if the circuit is pumped the heat emitters may be on the same level as the boiler. All the other circuits shown may be used for multi-storey buildings.

One-pipe ladder (Fig. 4.2):   suitable when it is possible to use horizontal runs either exposed in a room or in a floor duct.

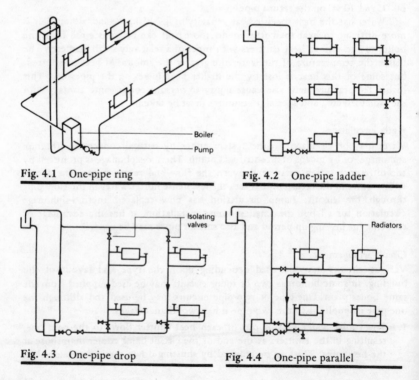

Fig. 4.1   One-pipe ring

Fig. 4.2   One-pipe ladder

Fig. 4.3   One-pipe drop

Fig. 4.4   One-pipe parallel

One-pipe drop (Fig. 4.3): this circuit requires provision at the top of the building, for a horizontal main distributor pipe and at the bottom of the building, for a main horizontal collector pipe. It is suitable for offices, etc., having separate rooms on each floor where the vertical pipe can be housed in a corner duct. It has the advantage of making the heat emitters self venting.

One-pipe parallel (Fig. 4.4): similar to the ladder system and is used when it is impractical to install a vertical main return pipe.

Two-pipe parallel (Fig. 4.5): again similar to the ladder system, but possessing the advantages of a two-pipe circuit.

Two-pipe upfeed (Fig. 4.6): suitable for buildings having floors of various heights, or for groups of buildings. An automatic vent valve can be used at the top of each flow pipe. The system is also used for embedded panel heating, using a panel of pipes instead of radiators.

Two-pipe high level return (Fig. 4.7): used when it is impractical to install a main horizontal collector pipe. The system is most useful when installing heating in existing buildings having a solid ground floor.

Two-pipe reverse return (Fig. 4.8): the predominant feature of this system is the equal travel to each heat emitter which provides a well-balanced circuit. Note that the length of the circuit for emitter A is the same as for emitter B.

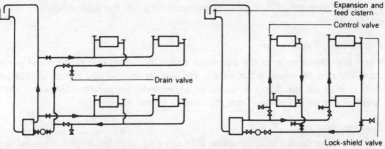

Fig. 4.5   Two-pipe parallel   Fig. 4.6   Two-pipe upfeed

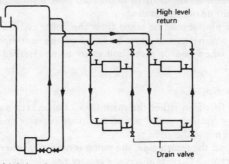

Fig. 4.7   Two-pipe, high-level return

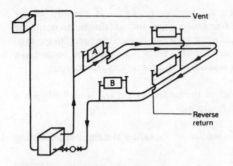

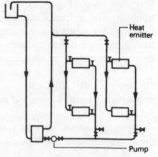

Fig. 4.8 Two-pipe reverse return   **Fig. 4.9** Two-pipe drop

Two-pipe drop (Fig. 4.9): suitable for buildings where it is possible to install a main horizontal distributor pipe and a main horizontal collector pipe in ducts. The system is self venting and therefore periodic venting of the radiators is unnecessary.

Isolating valves

Each heat emitter should be provided with a control valve on the inlet and a lock shield valve on the outlet. The lock shield valve is used by the heating engineer to balance the circuit as described earlier.

Isolating valves will also be required on the boiler, pumps and on all main branches. Drain valves must also be provided, to allow the various sections to be drained down.

Expansion and feed cistern

When the system is cold the ball valve should be set so that there is not more than 100 mm of water in the cistern and the capacity of the cistern should be such that when the water is raised to its working temperature the water level does not rise within 50 mm from the bottom of the warning pipe.

Feed and vent pipes

The feed pipe should be of adequate diameter and taken from the bottom of the expansion cistern, without any branch pipes, direct to the bottom of the boiler or return pipe. If a valve is fitted to the feed pipe, it should be of the lock shield type to prevent unauthorised use.

The vent pipe should be taken from the boiler and turned over the expansion cistern. A valve should never be fitted on the vent pipe, unless a three-way type is used when two or more boilers are to be installed (see centralised hot water supply).

Position of pump

This may be fitted on either the main flow or main return pipe. If fitted on the flow pipe, the heating system is under positive pressure and there is less risk of air being drawn into the circuit.

If fitted on the return pipe, the pump is normally easier to install and is at a lower temperature. There is however a greater risk of drawing air into the circuit, due to negative pump pressure.

Sealed systems (Fig. 4.10)

In place of an expansion and feed cistern, the expansion of the heated water may be accommodated in a closed expansion vessel fitted to the boiler. The vessel contains nitrogen or air above a neoprene diaphragm and as the water expands the gas is compressed and its pressure rises. The vessel should accommodate the expansion of the heated water in the system.

Small-bore heating systems (Fig. 4.11)

The system is used extensively for houses and other types of small buildings. Use is made of small-bore copper pipes, usually 13 mm or 19 mm bore, depending upon the heating load to be carried in the circuit.

The boiler also heats the hot-water calorifier by natural convection. Thermostatic control may be by zoning valves shown, separate thermostatic radiator valves, a three-way mixing valve or by switching on and off the pump by a wall thermostat.

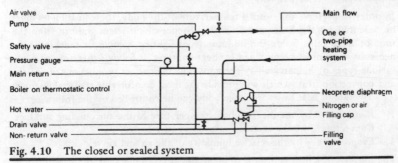

Fig. 4.10   The closed or sealed system

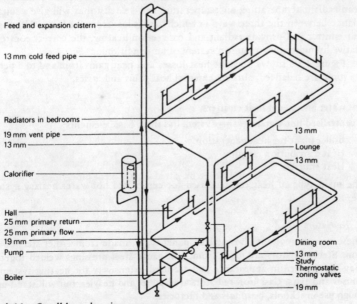

Fig. 4.11   Small-bore heating system

Thermal comfort, hot water and steam heat emitters

Thermal comfort

The thermal comfort of a human body is governed by the following factors:

1.   The heat lost in radiation from the body, through clothing and exposed skins surfaces to the cooler surroundings.
2.   The heat lost by convection from the body through clothing and exposed skin surfaces due to contact with the surrounding air, the temperature of which is considerably lower than that of the body.
3.   The heat lost from the body by evaporation from the skin, due to perspiring:

The normal losses from the body, from the above sources, approximate to the following:

Radiation	45 per cent
Convection	30 per cent
Evaporation	25 per cent

In order to preserve the normal temperature of the body, these heat losses must be balanced by the heat gained. In the absence of sufficient warmth from the sun, or heat gains inside the building from lighting, people or machines, the necessary heat must be provided by heat emitters. It follows therefore that for various types of human activity there must be the correct proportions of radiant and convection heat, which will provide the most comfortable artificial warmth.

The rate of heat losses from the body can be controlled by the following:

1.   *Radiation* — by the mean radiant temperature of the surrounding surfaces.
2.   *Convection* — by the air temperature and air velocity.
3.   *Evaporation* — by the relative humidity of the air and air velocity.

The purpose of a heat emitter is to maintain, at economic cost, the conditions of mean radiant temperature, air temperature and velocity that will give a suitable balance between the three ways in which heat is lost from the body. Although a heat emitter will provide radiant and convection heating, the correct control of relative humidity may require a system of air conditioning.

Figure 4.12 shows how the heat losses and heat gains from and to a person in a room are balanced, also the external heat gains and losses.

Hot water and steam heat emitters

A centralised hot-water heating system has three basic elements:

1.   Boiler plant for heat generation.
2.   Heat distribution circuit.
3.   Heat emitter.

The main type of heat emitters used for centralised hot water heating systems are:

1. *Radiators*

These may be column, hospital or panel types, made from either steel or cast iron. Steel radiators are made from light gauge steel pressings welded together, they are modern in appearance and are used extensively for heating systems in houses and flats. Cast iron radiators are bulkier and heavier, but will stand up to rough use in schools, hospitals and factories.

If a radiator is fitted against a wall, staining of the wall above the radiator

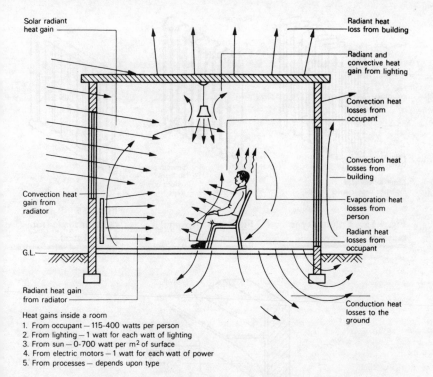

Solar radiant heat gain

Radiant heat loss from building

Radiant and convective heat gain from lighting

Convection heat losses from occupant

Convection heat losses from building

Convection heat gain from radiator

Evaporation heat losses from person

Radiant heat losses from occupant

G.L.

Radiant heat gain from radiator

Conduction heat losses to the ground

Heat gains inside a room
1. From occupant — 115-400 watts per person
2. From lighting — 1 watt for each watt of lighting
3. From sun — 0-700 watt per m^2 of surface
4. From electric motors — 1 watt for each watt of power
5. From processes — depends upon type

Fig. 4.12 Heat balance for an occupant in a room, and the external heat gains and losses

will occur due to convection currents picking up dust from the floor. To prevent this, a shelf should be fitted about 76 mm above the radiator, and the jointing of the shelf to the wall must be well made or otherwise black stains will appear above the shelf. End shields must be fitted to the shelf to prevent black stains at the sides.

Painting of radiators: The use of metallic paints reduce the heat emitted from a radiator and the best radiating surface is dead black. Any colour of non-metallic paints may be used, as these do not affect appreciably the amount of radiant heat emitted by the radiator. The heat emitted by convection is not affected by the painting of radiators. The name 'radiator' is misleading, for although heat is transmitted by radiation, a greater proportion of heat is transmitted by convection, depending upon the type of radiator used.

Position of radiators: The best position is under a window, so that the heat emitted mixes with the incoming cold air from the window and this prevents cold air passing along the floor, which would cause discomfort to the occupants of the room. Figures 4.13, 4.14 and 4.15 show column, hospital and panel types of radiators. Figure 4.16 shows a radiator shelf.

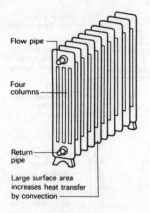

Fig. 4.13 Column type radiator

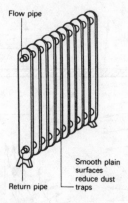

Fig. 4.14 Hospital pattern radiator

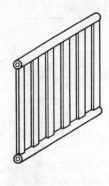

Fig. 4.15 Panel radiator made from pressed steel

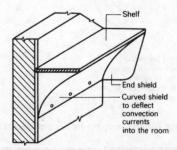

Fig. 4.16 Radiator shelf

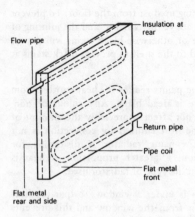

Fig. 4.17 Radiant panel

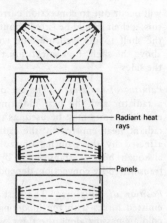

Fig. 4.18 Positions of radiant panels

2. Radiant panels

These have flat faced metal fronts and are similar to panel radiators, but transmit a greater proportion of heat by radiation. The panels are particularly suited to the heating of workshops, where they may be suspended at heights from 3 to 4 m above the floor level and arranged so that the heat is radiated downwards. They have the advantage of giving comfortable conditions to the occupants of the room by providing radiant heat at a lower air temperature. There is also a lower temperature gradient between the floor and the ceiling, which added to the lower air temperature reduces the cost of heating by about 15 per cent.

Figure 4.17 shows a radiant panel made from steel and Fig. 4.18 shows the various positions of the panels in a workshop.

3. Natural convection

These can be cabinet or skirting types: the cabinet type comprises a finned tubular heating element fitted near to the bottom of the casing, so that a stack effect is created inside the cabinet. The column of warm air above the heating element is displaced through the top of the cabinet by the cool air entering at the bottom. The greater the height of the cabinet the greater will be the air flow through it. Skirting types provide a good distribution of heat in a room and are very neat in appearance. If the floor is to be carpeted care should be taken to ensure that a gap is left at the bottom of the heater casing or convection through the heater will be prevented. Figure 4.19 shows a cabinet type convector and Fig. 4.20 shows a skirting type convector.

4. Fan convectors

These have a finned tubular heating element, usually fitted near the top of the casing. The fan or fans fitted below the element draw air in from the bottom of the casing, the air is then forced through the heating element, where it is heated, before being discharged through the top of the cabinet into the room. The fans may have two- or three-speed control and thermostatic control of the heat output is often by switching off, or a change of speed of the fans. If required, a clock can also control the switching on and off of the fans. The convector may be fitted with an air filter below the heating element, which is not possible with the natural convector. They also have the advantage of quickly heating the air in the room and give a good distribution of heat. Figure 4.21 shows a fan convector incorporating an air filter.

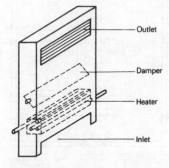

Fig. 4.19 Cabinet type convector

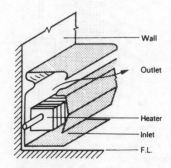

Fig. 4.20 Skirting type convector

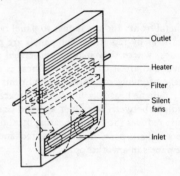

Fig. 4.21 Fan convector

5. Overhead unit heaters

These are similar to the fan convector and have a finned tubular heating element with a fan to improve the circulation of warm air. The method of fixing the fan and the heating element however differs from the fan convector to permit the overhead installation of the heater in factories, garages and warehouses, so that the warm air is blown down on to the working area. They usually operate on high temperature hot water or steam and the louvres can be adjusted so as to alter the direction of the warm air. Figure 4.22 shows an overhead unit heater and Fig. 4.23 shows how several heaters may be used to heat a workshop.

Note: The heating efficiency of both types of convectors and unit heaters is lowered more quickly than that of radiators, due to a drop in temperature of the heating element. For this reason, it is better to use a two-piped pumped distribution system.

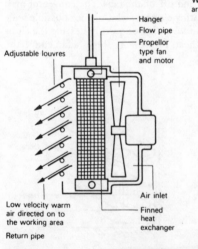

Fig. 4.22 Overhead unit heater

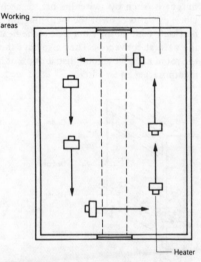

Fig. 4.23 Arrangement of unit heaters

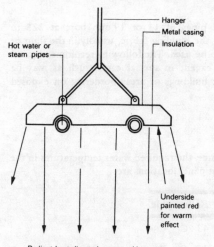

Fig. 4.24 Overhead radiant strip

Hanger
Metal casing
Insulation
Hot water or steam pipes
Underside painted red for warm effect
Radiant heat directed onto working area

Fig. 4.25 Arrangement of radiant strips

6. Overhead radiant strips

These overcome the difficulty and cost of connecting separate radiant panels at high level. They consist of heating pipes, up to 30 m long, fixed to an insulated metal plate which also becomes heated by conduction from the pipe. The minimum mounting height of the strips is governed by the heating system temperature and ranges from about 3 m for low temperature hot water, to about 5 m for high temperature hot water and steam. Figure 4.24 shows a radiant strip having two heating pipes; one-to-four heating pipes may also be used. Figure 4.25 shows how radiant strips may be installed in a workshop.

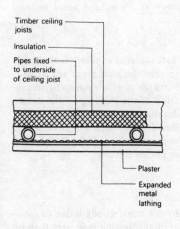

Timber ceiling joists
Insulation
Pipes fixed to underside of ceiling joist
Plaster
Expanded metal lathing

Fig. 4.26 Ceiling panel

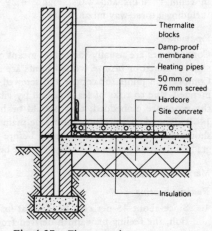

Thermalite blocks
Damp-proof membrane
Heating pipes
50 mm or 76 mm screed
Hardcore
Site concrete
Insulation

Fig. 4.27 Floor panel

7. Embedded pipe panels

Continuous coils of copper or steel pipes of 13 or 19 mm bore at 225 to 300 mm centres are embedded inside the building fabric, usually in the floor or ceiling, although wall panels may also be used. The following recommend panel surface temperatures may be used, except in special cases, such as may be required for entrance halls to public buildings or areas bordering on exposed outside walls.

Floors   26.7 °C
Ceilings   49 °C
Walls   43 °C

With regards to these panel temperatures, the required water temperatures in the flow and return mains for the different panel locations are:

Panel location	Flow pipe	Return pipe
Ceilings	54 °C	43 °C
Floor	43 °C	35 °C
Wall	43 °C	35 °C

In order to control the temperature of the pipe panel, a modulating three-way mixing valve is used which allows the cooler water in the return pipe to mix with the hotter water in the flow pipe. The amount of radiant heat given off to the room, from different panel locations, is as follows:

Ceilings   65 per cent
Floors   50 per cent
Walls   50 per cent

Since radiant heat provides a feeling of warmth at a lower temperature than heat provided by convection, ceiling panels are to be preferred.

Figures 4.26, 4.27 and 4.28 show the methods of embedding the pipes in ceilings, floors and walls. Figure 4.29 shows an embedded panel system, including a three-way mixing valve.

Pipework

Copper pipes are usually jointed by means of soft soldered capillary fittings, but silver soldered or bronze welded joints are also suitable; steel pipes are welded. Compression joints for copper and screwed joints for steel are not to be recommended, due to risks of leaks caused by vibration of the building fabric. Before the pipes are embedded, they should be hydraulically tested at a pressure of 1400 kPa and this pressure should be maintained for 24 hours. The floor screed should be allowed to cure naturally before the pipes are heated and then heated gradually over a period of 10 days, before being put on full load.

Merits of heating by radiation

Radiant heating

1. Since about 45 per cent of the heat lost by the human body is due to radiation, the feeling of warmth derived from radiant heating is greater than by convection.

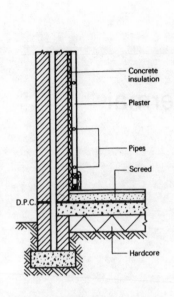

Concrete insulation

Plaster

Pipes

Screed

D.P.C.

Hardcore

Fig. 4.28 Wall panels

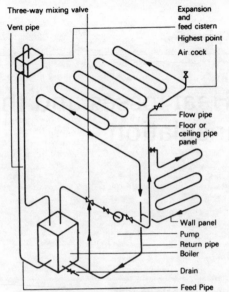

Three-way mixing valve

Vent pipe

Expansion and feed cistern

Highest point

Air cock

Flow pipe

Floor or ceiling pipe panel

Wall panel

Pump

Return pipe

Boiler

Drain

Feed Pipe

Fig. 4.29 Embedded panel system

2. The radiant heat gives a greater feeling of warmth with a lower air temperature and this achieves about a 15 per cent saving in fuel costs.
3. In factories the lower air temperature gives a greater feeling of freshness, and production is known to increase.
4. The draughts are reduced to a minimum and dust is also kept down to a minimum.
5. Radiant heat does not heat the air through which it passes, but heats solid objects on which it falls, and so floors and walls derive warmth from the radiant heat rays. These warm surfaces set up convection currents, which reduce the heat lost from the human body by convection.

Chapter 5

Heat losses and thermal insulation

Heat loss calculations

Definition of terms

1. *Thermal conductivity (k)*

The thermal transmission in unit time through unit area of a slab, or a uniform homogeneous material of unit thickness, when the difference of temperature is established between its surfaces.

The unit is W/m K

2. *Thermal resistivity (r)*

The reciprocal of the thermal conductivity.

The unit is m K/W

3. *Thermal conductance (c)*

The thermal transmission is unit time, through a unit area of a uniform structural component of thickness L per unit of temperature difference, between the hot and cold surfaces.

The unit is W/m² K

4. *Thermal resistance (R)*

The reciprocal of the thermal conductance.

$$R = \frac{L}{k}$$

where:

R = Thermal resistance of a material (m² K/W)

L = Thickness of the material in metres

k = Thermal conductivity of the material (W/m K)

Note: If the thickness L is given in millimetres, it must be converted to metres.

5. *Thermal transmission* (U)

The thermal transmission in unit time through unit area of a given structure, divided by the difference between the environmental temperature on either side of the structure.

The unit is W/m² K

6. *Standard thermal transmission* (Standard U)

The value of the thermal transmission of a building element related to standard conditions.

7. *Design thermal transmission* (Design U)

The value of the thermal transmission of a building element for prevailing design conditions.

8. *Emissivity* (e)

The ratio of the thermal radiation from unit area of a surface, to the radiation from unit area of a black body at the same temperature.

9. *Environmental temperature* (t_e)

A balanced mean, between the mean radiant temperature and the air temperature. It may be evaluated approximately from the following formula:

$$t_{ei} = \frac{2}{3} t_{ri} + \frac{1}{3} t_{ai}$$

where

t_{ri} = mean radiant temperature of all the room surfaces in °C

t_{ai} = inside air temperature in °C

The concept of environmental temperature for heat loss calculations provides a more accurate assessment of steady state heat loss than the conventional procedure that uses air temperature as a basis. The internal environmental temperature is also better than the internal air temperature as an index of the thermal comfort of the internal environment. This places the designer in a more favourable position for assessing the internal thermal comfort than is possible employing the air temperature. Conventional methods however may be followed when the difference between the mean radiant temperature and the air temperature is quite small. This occurs when rooms have little exposure to the outside and the standard of building thermal insulation is very high.

10. *Sol-air temperature* (t_{eo})

The outside air temperature which in the absence of solar radiation would give the same temperature distribution and rate of heat transfer, through the wall or roof, as exists with the actual outdoor temperature and the incidence of solar radiation.

11. *Mean radiant temperature* (t_{rm})

The temperature of a uniform block enclosure, in which a solid body or occupant would exchange the same amount of radiant heat as in existing non-uniform environment.

12. Degrees Kelvin (K)

This is defined in terms of the triple point of water as the fundamental fixed point, attributing to it the temperature of 273.16 K. Absolute zero is defined as 0 K. The unit may also be used for temperature interval.

13. Degrees Celsius (°C)

Degrees Celsius 0 °C = 273.16 K and the intervals on the Celsius and Kelvin scales are identical.

14. Heat

Heat is a form of energy, its quantity is measured in joules (J).

15. Power

Power is measured in watts (W). One watt is equal to one joule per second.

16. Heat transfer

There are three ways in which heat may be transferred from a material: (a) conduction, (b) convection and (c) radiation.

Conduction. The molecules of a material at a higher temperature will vibrate more than the molecules of a material at a lower temperature and this vibrational heat energy is transferred from the higher temperature to the lower temperature. This heat transfer takes place without movement of the hotter molecules to the cooler molecules, and the greater the temperature difference the greater the transfer of heat by conduction.

Conduction is greater in solids than in gases. Still air conducts heat very slowly and an unventilated cavity provides a good insulator. Still air pockets in insulating materials provide good heat-insulating characteristics.

Convection: this is the transfer of heat in a fluid. The hotter less dense liquid or gas is displaced by the more dense liquid or gas surrounding it, thus creating circulation. The natural circulation of air in a room, or water in a heating system, is brought about by convection.

Radiation: this is the transfer of heat in the form of electro-magnetic radiation from one body to another, without the need of a conducting medium. All bodies emit radiant heat and receive radiant heat back from other bodies. The higher the temperature of the body, the greater the radiant heat emitted. Matt black surfaces generally radiate or receive more heat than white, or bright shiny surfaces. White chippings on roofs will help to prevent a roof slab receiving radiant heat from the sun and aluminium foil will reflect radiant heat back from a heated room and this will act as a heat insulator. Figure 5.1 shows the transfer of heat through a wall by conduction, convection and radiation.

Temperature distribution

Figure 5.2 shows the temperature distribution for a solid wall. The wall with a high thermal conductivity will have a higher outside surface temperature than the wall with a low thermal conductivity and therefore the temperature distribution will be greater. Figure 5.3 shows the temperature distribution for a cavity wall with a plastered aerated inner leaf, with a low thermal conductivity and a brick external leaf, and a fairly high thermal conductivity. In Fig. 5.4 the cavity is

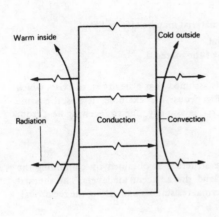

Fig. 5.1 Heat transfer through a wall

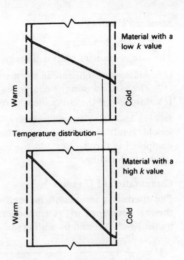

Fig. 5.2 Temperature distribution through wall

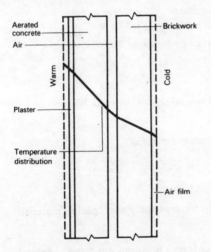

Fig. 5.3 Temperature distribution with air cavity

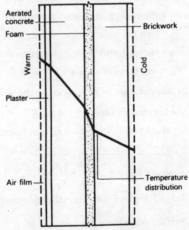

Fig. 5.4 Temperature distribution with urea-formaldehyde foam-filled cavity

filled with urea formaldehyde foam, which will improve the thermal insulation and the temperature distribution through the cavity will be greater than the air cavity.

Standard U values

Steady state conditions

The rate of transfer of heat through a material may be affected by:

(a) Amount of moisture in the material.
(b) The variations in the composition of the material.
(c) Jointing of the component parts.

In heat loss calculations, however, it is assumed that a steady state exists which would result if the material is homogeneous; for example, it has the same composition throughout and the material is also dry, due to receiving heat from inside the building.

Computation of U values

The thermal transmission through the structure is obtained by combining the thermal resistance of its components and the adjacent air layers. The thermal transmission is found by adding the thermal resistances and taking the reciprocal.

$$U = \frac{1}{R_{si} + R_{so} + R_1 + R_2 + R_3 + R_a}$$

where

U = thermal transmission W/m^2 K

R_{si} = inside surface resistance m^2 K/W

R_{so} = outside surface resistance m^2 K/W

R_1 = thermal resistance of the structural components m^2 ° K/W

R_2 = thermal resistance of the structural components m^2 ° K/W

R_3 = thermal resistance of the structural components m^2 ° K/W

R_a = resistance of air space m^2 K/W

In computation of U values, the thermal resistances L/k are used. Where

k = thermal conductivity W/m K

L = thickness in (m) of a uniform homogeneous material

$$U = \frac{1}{R_{si} + R_{so} + \dfrac{L_1}{k_1} + \dfrac{L_2}{k_2} + \dfrac{L_3}{k_3} + R_a}$$

Table 5.1 gives the thermal conductivity for commonly used building materials.

Surface resistances

The transfer of heat by convection to or from a homogeneous material depends upon the velocity at which the air passes over the surface of the material and the roughness of the surface. An internal wall may have a smooth plastered surface with very little air movement and an external wall may have a rough exterior surface and a high air movement.

The smooth internal surface will have a small amount of heat transfer by convection. The air forms a stagnant film, which tends to insulate the wall surface from the warmer air in the room. On the external surface of the material, the wind forces acting on a rough surface will cause eddy currents and heat will be transferred at a higher rate. Table 5.2 gives the inside surface resistances.

68

Table 5.1 Thermal conductivities of common building materials

Material	k value W/m K
Asbestos cement sheet	0.40
Asbestos insulating board	0.12
Asphalt	1.20
Brickwork (commons)	
light	0.80
average	1.20
dense	1.47
Brickwork (engineering)	1.15
Concrete	
structural	1.40
aerated	0.14
Cork slab	0.40
Clinker block	0.05
Glass	1.02
Glass wool	0.034
Gypsum plasterboard	0.15−0.58
Linoleum (inlaid)	0.20
Plastering	
gypsum	0.40
vermiculite	0.20
Plywood	0.138
Polystyrene foam slab	0.04
Polyurethane foam	0.020−0.025
Foamed urea formaldehyde	0.030−0.036
Hair felt	0.43
Rendering (cement and sand)	0.53
Roofing felt	0.20
Rubber flooring	0.40
Slates	1.50
Soil	1.00−1.15
Stone	
granite	2.90
limestone	1.50
sandstone	1.30
Strawboard	0.09
Tiles	
burnt clay	0.83
plastic	0.50
Timber	
softwood	0.14
hardwood	0.16
Vermiculite	0.36−0.58
Wood	
chipboard	0.108
wool slabs	0.09

Table 5.2   Inside surface resistances R_{si} in m² K/W

Building element	Heat flow	Surface resistance in m² K/W	
		High emissivity	Low emissivity
Walls	Horizontal	0.123	0.304
Ceilings, flat or pitched roofs, floors	Upward	0.106	0.218
Ceilings and floors	Downward	0.150	0.562

Table 5.3 gives the external surface resistance.

Table 5.3   External surface resistance R_{so} in m² K/W for various exposures and surfaces

Building element	Emissivity of surface	Surface resistance for stated exposure (m² K/W)		
		Sheltered	Normal (standard)	Severe
Wall	High	0.08	0.055	0.03
	Low	0.11	0.067	0.03
Roof	High	0.07	0.045	0.02
	Low	0.09	0.053	0.02

Sheltered: up to third-floor buildings in city centres.
Normal: most suburban and country premises and the fourth to eighth floors, of buildings in city centres.
Severe: buildings on the coast, or exposed hill sites and above the fifth floor of buildings in suburban, or country districts, or above the ninth floor of buildings in city centres.

Thermal resistances of air spaces

Air spaces can be regarded as a further thermal resistance and an unventilated space offers more resistance than a ventilated one. Table 5.4 gives the standard unventilated resistances of unventilated air spaces.

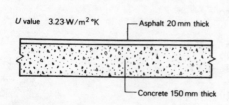

U value   3.23 W/m² °K — Asphalt 20 mm thick
— Concrete 150 mm thick

Fig. 5.5   Concrete flat roof covereds covered with asphalt

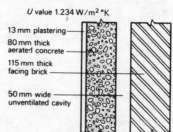

U value 1.234 W/m² °K
13 mm plastering
80 mm thick aerated concrete
115 mm thick facing brick
50 mm wide unventilated cavity

Fig. 5.6   Cavity wall — aerated concrete — brickwork

Table 5.4

Air space thickness	Surface emissivity	Thermal resistance (m² °C/W)	
		Heat flow horizontal or upwards	Heat flow downwards
5 mm	High	0.11	0.11
	Low	0.18	0.18
20 mm	High	0.18	0.21
	Low	0.35	1.06

Example 5.1 (Fig. 5.5). *A flat roof consists of 150 mm thick concrete covered by 20 mm of asphalt and sheltered conditions exists. Calculate the thermal transmittance (U) for the roof.*

Thermal conductivities

Concrete	1.4 W/m K
Asphalt	1.2 W/m K

Thermal resistances

Inside surface	0.11 m² K/W
Outside surface	0.07 m² K/W

$$U = \frac{1}{R_{si} + R_{so} + \dfrac{L_1}{k_1} + \dfrac{L_2}{k_2}}$$

$$U = \frac{1}{0.11 + 0.07 + \dfrac{0.15}{1.4} + \dfrac{0.02}{1.2}}$$

$$U = \frac{1}{0.11 + 0.07 + 0.11 + 0.02}$$

$$U = \frac{1}{0.31}$$

$$U = \underline{3.23 \text{ W/m}^2 \text{ K}}$$

Example 5.2 (Fig. 5.6). *A cavity wall consists of 13 mm thick plaster, 80 mm thick aerated concrete, 50 mm wide unventilated air space and 115 mm of external facing brick. Calculate the thermal transmission (U) for the wall.*

Thermal conductivities

Plaster	0.4 W/m K
Cellular concrete	0.25 W/m K
Brick	1.15 W/m K

71

Thermal resistances

Inside surface	0.123 m² K/W
Air space	0.18 m² K/W
Outside surface	0.055 m² K/W

$$U = \cfrac{1}{R_{si} + R_{so} + \cfrac{L_1}{k_1} + \cfrac{L_2}{k_2} + \cfrac{L_3}{k_3} + R_a}$$

$$U = \cfrac{1}{0.123 + 0.055 + \cfrac{0.013}{0.4} + \cfrac{0.08}{0.25} + \cfrac{0.115}{1.15} + 0.18}$$

$$U = \cfrac{1}{0.123 + 0.055 + 0.0325 + 0.32 + 0.1 + 0.18}$$

$$U = \cfrac{1}{0.8105}$$

$$U = \underline{1.234 \text{ W/m}^2 \text{ K}}$$

Example 5.3 (Fig. 5.7). *One wall of a building consists of 25 mm thickness of cedar boarding, 76 mm thickness of glass wool insulation and 13 mm thickness of plasterboard. Compare the overall thermal transmission of the wall, with the wall given in Example 5.2.*

Thermal conductivity

Cedar wood	0.14 W/m K
Glass wool	0.042 W/m K
Plasterboard	0.58 W/m K

Thermal resistances

Inside surface	0.123 m² K/W
Outside surface	0.055 m² K/W

$$U = \cfrac{1}{R_{si} + R_{so} + \cfrac{L_1}{k_1} + \cfrac{L_2}{k_2} + \cfrac{L_3}{k_3}}$$

$$U = \cfrac{1}{0.123 + 0.055 + \cfrac{0.013}{0.58} + \cfrac{0.076}{0.042} + \cfrac{0.025}{0.14}}$$

$$U = \cfrac{1}{0.123 + 0.055 + 0.0224 + 1.809 + 0.178}$$

$$U = \cfrac{1}{2.188}$$

$$U = 0.457$$

$$U = \underline{0.457 \text{ W/m}^2 \text{ K}}$$

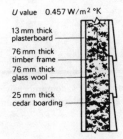

U value   0.457 W/m² °K

13 mm thick
plasterboard

76 mm thick
timber frame

76 mm thick
glass wool

25 mm thick
cedar boarding

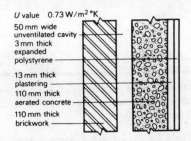

U value   0.73 W/m² °K

50 mm wide
unventilated cavity
3 mm thick
expanded
polystyrene

13 mm thick
plastering
110 mm thick
aerated concrete

110 mm thick
brickwork

Fig. 5.7   Lightweight wall

Fig. 5.8   Cavity wall — aerated concrete
— brickwork and expanded polystyrene

If the inside and outside environmental temperatures are 20 °C and −2 °C respectively, the rate of heat loss per metre squared would be:

For solid wall

Heat loss = 1.234 × 1.0 × [20 − (−2)]

Heat loss = 27.148 W

For lightweight wall

Heat loss = 0.457 × 1.0 × [20 − (−2)]

Heat loss = 10.054 W

The heat loss through the solid wall is approximately 2.7 times greater than through the lightweight wall.

Example 5.4.   *Figure 5.8 shows a section of a wall. Using the following data, calculate the thermal transmission (U) for the wall.*

Thermal conductivities

Brick	1.0 W/m K
Aerated concrete	0.14 W/m K
Plaster	0.7 W/m K
Expanded polystyrene	0.04 W/m K

Surface resistances

R_{si} External surface layer 0.12 m² K/W

R_{so} Internal surface layer 0.08 m² K/W

R_a Air space   0.18 m² K/W

$$U = \frac{1}{R_{si} + R_{so} + R_a + \dfrac{L_1}{k_1} + \dfrac{L_2}{k_2} + \dfrac{L_3}{k_3} + \dfrac{L_4}{k_4}}$$

$$U = \frac{1}{0.12 + 0.08 + 0.18 + \dfrac{0.11}{1} + \dfrac{0.11}{0.14} + \dfrac{0.013}{0.7} + \dfrac{0.003}{0.04}}$$

$$U = \frac{1}{0.12 + 0.08 + 0.18 + 0.11 + 0.78 + 0.02 + 0.08}$$

$$U = \frac{1}{1.37}$$

$$U = \underline{0.73 \text{ W/m}^2 \text{ K}}$$

The Chartered Institution of Building Services Guide Book gives a comprehensive table of U values for various types of structures. Table 5.5 gives U values for common types of structures.

Table 5.5 U values for common types of structures

Construction	U value (W/m² K)		
	Sheltered	Normal	Severe
Walls (brickwork)			
220 mm solid brick wall unplastered	2.2	2.3	2.4
222 mm solid brick wall with 16 mm plaster	2.0	2.1	2.2
220 mm solid brick wall with 10 mm plaster-board on inside face	1.9	2.0	2.1
260 mm cavity wall (unventilated with 105 mm outer and inner leaves, with 16 mm plaster on inside face	1.4	1.5	1.6
Walls (brickwork)			
lightweight concrete block 260 mm cavity unventilated with 105 mm brick outer leaf, 100 mm lightweight concrete block inner leaf and 16 mm dense plaster on inside face	0.93	0.96	0.98
Walls, but with 13 mm expanded polystyrene board in cavity	0.69	0.70	0.71
Walls (lightweight concrete block)			
150 mm solid wall with 150 mm aerated concrete block, with tile hanging externally and with 16 mm plaster on inside face	0.95	0.97	1.0
Cavity wall (unventilated)			
with 76 mm aerated concrete block outer leaf, rendered externally 100 mm aerated concrete inner leaf and with 16 mm plaster on inside face	0.82	0.84	0.86
Concrete			
150 mm thick cast	3.2	3.5	3.9
200 mm thick cast	2.9	3.1	3.4
150 mm thick cast, with 50 mm woodwool slab permanent shuttering on inside face and 16 mm plaster	1.1	1.1	1.1

Table 5.5 – *continued*

Construction	U value (W/m² K)		
	Sheltered	Normal	Severe
Roofs (flat or pitched)			
19 mm asphalt on 150 mm solid concrete	3.1	3.4	3.7
19 mm asphalt on 150 mm hollow tiles	2.1	2.2	2.3
19 mm asphalt on 13 mm cement and sand screed on 50 mm metal edge reinforced woodwool slabs on steel framing, with vapour barrier at inside	0.88	0.90	0.92
19 mm asphalt on 13 mm cement and sand screed, 50 mm woodwool slabs on timber joists and aluminium foil – backed 10 mm plasterboard ceiling, sealed to prevent moisture penetration	0.88	0.90	0.92
Roofs, but with 25 mm glass fibre insulation laid between joists	0.59	0.60	0.61
Tiles on battens, roofing felt and rafters, with roof space and aluminium foil-backed 10 mm plasterboard on ceiling joists	1.4	1.5	1.6
Tiles, but with boarding on rafters	1.4	1.5	1.6
Corrugated asbestos cement sheeting	5.3	6.1	7.2
Floors			
Suspended timber floor above ground:			
150 mm x 60 mm	–	0.14	–
150 mm x 30 mm	–	0.21	–
60 mm x 60 mm	–	0.16	–
60 mm x 30 mm	–	0.24	–
30 mm x 30 mm	–	0.28	–
30 mm x 15 mm	–	0.39	–
15 mm x 15 mm	–	0.45	–
7.5 mm x 7.5 mm	–	0.68	–
3 mm x 3 mm	–	1.05	–
Glass			
Single glazing	5.0	5.6	6.7
Double glazing with 20 mm air space	2.8	2.9	3.2
Double glazing with 12 mm air space	2.8	3.0	3.3
Double glazing with 6 mm air space	3.2	3.4	3.8
Double glazing with 3 mm air space	3.6	4.0	4.4
Triple glazing with 20 mm air space	1.9	2.0	2.1
Triple glazing with 12 mm air space	2.0	2.1	2.2
Triple glazing with 6 mm air space	2.3	2.5	2.6
Triple glazing with 3 mm air space	2.8	3.0	3.3

Heat loss through solid ground floor

A solid ground floor is exposed to the external air on one side near the wall and this is the point where the greatest heat loss will occur. The rate of heat loss decreases as the distance from the wall increases and therefore the rate of heat loss per unit area decreases as the floor area increases. The rate of heat loss through a solid ground floor therefore must be based on the floor area and the number of edges exposed. Figures 5.9 and 5.10 show how heat loss is lost through both narrow and wide solid ground floors respectively.

Table 5.6 shows U values for solid floors in contact with the earth.

Table 5.6

Dimensions of floor (metres)	Four exposed edges (W/m² K)	Two exposed edges at right angles (W/m² K)
150 × 60	0.11	0.06
150 × 30	0.18	0.10
60 × 60	0.15	0.08
60 × 30	0.21	0.12
30 × 30	0.26	0.15
30 × 15	0.36	0.21
15 × 15	0.45	0.26
15 × 7.5	0.62	0.36
7.5 × 7.5	0.76	0.45
3 × 3	1.47	1.07

Examples of heat loss calculations

In normal design situations the Chartered Institution of Building Services Guide proposes two classifications of heat emitters: (a) convective, (b) radiant. In the former type, it is considered that the heat input to the space is at air temperature, while in the latter type it is considered to be at the environmental temperature. Heat emitters however do not fall rigidly into these classifications, but the guide suggests that heat emitters such as natural or forced convectors, overhead unit heaters,

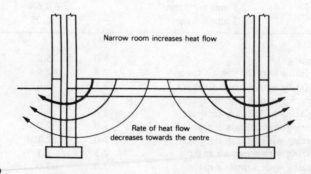

Fig. 5.9

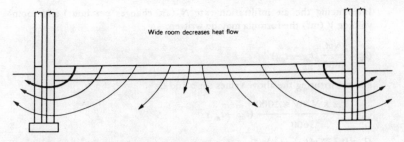

Wide room decreases heat flow

Fig. 5.10   Heat flow through solid ground floor

radiators and low temperature panel heaters should be considered as convective heaters. Heated floors and ceilings, high temperature radiant panels and strips should be considered as radiant heaters.

The formula heat loss = U value × area × temperature difference still applies.

Convective heating, using the environmental temperature concept

The following steps are taken:

(a) Calculate the heat loss through the various elements of the structure, using the difference between the inside and the outside environmental temperatures and the sum of these to produce $\Sigma \, Q_f$.

(b) Calculate the area of the entire enclosure to produce ΣA (this should include any partitions, floors, or ceilings, gaining heat from or losing heat to the adjacent rooms).

(c) Calculate $\Sigma \, Q_f / \Sigma \, A$ and from the following equation find the difference between the inside air temperature and inside environmental temperature.

$$t_{ai} - t_{ei} = \Sigma \, Q_f / 4.8 \, \Sigma \, A$$

where

t_{ai} = inside air temperature °C

t_{ei} = inside environmental temperature °C

$\Sigma \, Q_f$ = rate of heat transfer through the building fabric W

$\Sigma \, A$ = total area of room surfaces in m²

(d) Calculate the heat loss by ventilation. The heat loss due to infiltration may be found from the formula:

$$Q_v = pVC(t_{ai} - t_{ao})$$

where

p = density of air which may be taken as 1.2 kg/m³

V = infiltration rate m³/s

C = specific heat capacity of air, which may be taken as 1000 J/kg | K

t_{ai} = inside air temperature °C

t_{ao} = outside air temperature °C

Introducing the air infiltration rate N (air changes per hour) and room volume V (m³) the formula may be written,

$$Q_v = \frac{pNvC}{3600}(t_{ai} - t_{ao})$$

and substituting the above values for p and C,

$$Q_v = \frac{1.2 \times N \times V \times 1000}{3600}(t_{ai} - t_{ao})$$

$$Q_v = 0.33Nv(t_{ai} - t_{ao})$$

where

N = rate of air change per hour

v = volume of room in m³

t_{ai} = inside air temperature °C

t_{ao} = outside air temperature °C

(e) Find $\Sigma Q_f + \Sigma Q_v$ to give the total heat loss.

Worked examples on convective heating

Example 5.5. *Figure 5.11 shows the plan of an office on the second floor of a four-storey building. The other floors have the same construction and heating design conditions. From the data given below calculate the total rate of heat loss and the surface area of the radiator required.*

Office internal environmental temperature = 20 °C

Corridor environmental temperature = 16 °C

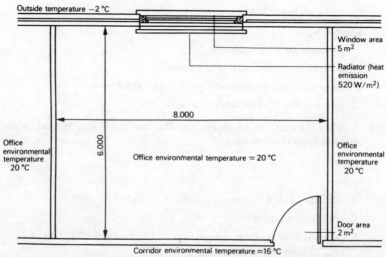

Fig. 5.11   Plan of office

Design outside air temperature	$= -2\ ^{\circ}\mathrm{C}$
Area of door	$= 2\ \mathrm{m}^2$
Area of window	$= 5\ \mathrm{m}^2$
Height of office	$= 3\ \mathrm{m}$
Air change	$= 1\ \text{per hour}$
Ventilation allowance	$= 0.33\ \mathrm{W/m^3\ K}$

U *values*

External wall	$=\ 1.5\ \mathrm{W/m^2\ K}$
Internal partition	$=\ 1.6\ \mathrm{W/m^2\ K}$
Door	$=\ 2.3\ \mathrm{W/m^2\ K}$
Window	$=\ 5.6\ \mathrm{W/m^2\ K}$
Heat emission from radiator	$=\ 520\ \mathrm{W/m^2}$

Heat loss through the structure

Type of structure	Area (m^2)	U value $(\mathrm{W/m^2\ K})$	Temperature difference $(^{\circ}\mathrm{C})$	Total heat loss (watts)
External wall (less window)	19	1.5	22	627
Window	5	5.6	22	616
Internal partition (less door)	22	1.6	4	140.8
Door	2	2.3	4	18.4
Floor	48	—	—	—
Ceiling	48	—	—	—
Other partition	36	—	—	—
ΣA	180		ΣQ_f	1402.2

Internal air temperature

$$t_{ai} - t_{ei} = \frac{\Sigma Q_f}{4.8\ \Sigma A}$$

$$t_{ai} - t_{ei} = \frac{1402.2}{4.8 \times 180}$$

$$t_{ai} - t_{ei} = 1.6$$

$$t_{ai} = 20 + 1.6$$

$$t_{ai} = 21.6\ ^{\circ}\mathrm{C}$$

Heat loss by ventilation

$$Q_v = 0.33 Nv(t_{ai} - t_{ao})$$

$$Q_v = 0.33 \times 144[21.6 - (-1)]$$

$$Q_v = 0.33 \times 144 \times 22.6$$

$Q_v = 1073.9W$

Total heat loss Q_t

$Q_t = \Sigma Q \Sigma Q_v$

$Q_t = 1402.2 + 1073.9$

$Q_t = 2476.1$

Area of radiator

$$\text{Area} = \frac{\text{Total heat loss W}}{\text{Heat emission W/m}^2}$$

$$\text{Area} = \frac{2426}{520}$$

$$\text{Area} = \underline{4.66 \text{ m}^2}$$

Example 5.6 (Convective heating). *Figure 5.12A, B, C shows the elevations and plan of a small detached classroom, to be heated by means of two convector heaters. Calculate the total heat loss for the classroom.*

Classroom internal environmental temperature   20 °C

Design outside air temperature   1 °C

		U values	
Area of door	2 m²	External wall	1.40 W/m² K
Area of windows	12 m²	Window	5.60 W/m² K
Height of classroom	3 m	Door	2.30 W/m² K
Air change	3 per hour	Floor	0.45 W/m² K
Ventilation allowance	0.33 W/m³ K	Ceiling	0.49 W/m² K

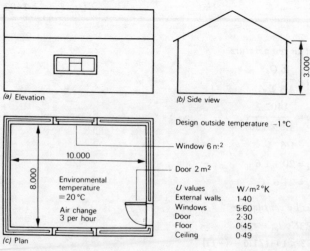

(a) Elevation

(b) Side view

3.000

Design outside temperature −1 °C

Window 6 n:²

Door 2 m²

10.000

8.000

Environmental temperature = 20 °C

Air change 3 per hour

U values	W/m²°K
External walls	1.40
Windows	5.60
Door	2.30
Floor	0.45
Ceiling	0.49

(c) Plan

Fig. 5.12   Detached classroom

Heat loss through structure

Type of structure	Area (m²)	U value (W/m² K)	Temperature difference (°C)	Total heat loss (watts)
External wall (less windows and doors)	$(36 \times 3) - (12 + 2)$ 94	1.4	21	2763.60
Window	12	5.6	21	1411.20
Door	2	2.3	21	96.60
Floor	80	0.45	21	756.00
Ceiling	80	0.49	21	823.20
ΣA	268		ΣQ_f	5850.60

Internal air temperature

$$t_{ai} - t_{ei} = \frac{\Sigma Q_f}{4.8\, \Sigma A}$$

$$t_{ai} - t_{ei} = \frac{5850.6}{4.8 \times 268}$$

$$t_{ai} - t_{ei} = 4.548$$

$$t_{ai} = 20 + 4.5$$

$$t_{ai} = 24.5\,°C$$

Heat loss by ventilation

$$Q_v = 0.33 Nv(t_{ai} - t_{ao})$$

$$Q_v = 0.33 \times 3 \times 240[24.5 - (-1)]$$

$$Q_v = 0.33 \times 3 \times 240 \times 25.5$$

$$Q_v = 6058.8\ W$$

Total heat loss Q_t

$$Q_t = \Sigma Q_f + \Sigma Q_v$$

$$Q_t = 5850.6 + 6058.8$$

$$Q_t = 11\,909.4\ W$$

$$Q_t = 12\ kW$$

Each convector would require a heat output of 6 kW.

Radiant heating

In order to find the total heat requirements, the following steps are necessary.

(a) Calculate the heat loss through the structure as for convective heating to produce ΣQ_f.

(b) Calculate the surface area of the entire enclosure, as for convective heating to produce ΣA.

(c) Find the ventilation conductance C_v from:

$$\frac{1}{C_v} = \frac{1}{0.33Nv} + \frac{1}{4.8 \Sigma A}$$

where N = number of air changes per hour

where v = volume of enclosure m².

(d) Calculate ventilation loss Q_v from:

$$Q_v = C_v(t_{ei} - t_{eo})$$

(e) Add the results of steps (a) and (d) to give the total heat loss.

Example 5.7 (Radiant heating). *Calculate the total heat loss for the classroom given in Example 5.6 but assume that in this case the heating is to be in the form of a heated ceiling.*

Note: Since a heated ceiling is to be employed, there is no need to consider heat loss from the classroom through the ceiling.

$\Sigma Q_f = 5850.6 - 823.2$

$\Sigma Q_f = 5019.4$ W

Also

$\Sigma A = 268$ m², $v = 240$, $N = 3$

Ventilation conductance

$$\frac{1}{C_v} = \frac{1}{0.33 \times Nv} + \frac{1}{4.8 \Sigma A}$$

$$\frac{1}{C_v} = \frac{1}{0.33 \times 3 \times 240} + \frac{1}{4.8 \times 268}$$

$$\frac{1}{C_v} = 0.0042 + 0.000\,77$$

therefore

$C_v = 201.2$ W K

Heat loss by ventilation

$Q_v = C_v(t_{ei} - t_{eo})$

$Q_v = 201.2\,[20 - (-1)]$

$Q_v = 201.2 \times 21$

$Q_v = 4225.2$ W

Total heat loss Q_t

$Q_t = \Sigma Q_f + \Sigma Q_v$

$Q_t = 5850 + 4225.2$

$Q_t = 10\ 075.8$

$Q_t = 10$ kW.

Pitched roofs

The U values for common types of pitched roofs can be found in the Institution of Heating and Ventilating Engineers Guide Book A. There may be occasions, however, when some special type of construction is to be used and a U value for the roof will have to be calculated. The following equation gives the method of calculating the U value for a pitched roof with a horizontal ceiling below. The values in the equation are shown in Figure 5.13.

$$U = \frac{U_r \times U_c}{U_r + U_c \cos \infty}$$

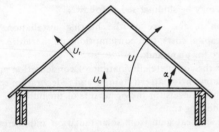

Fig. 5.13 Thermal transmission (U value) pitched roof

Example 5.8. *A pitched roof inclined at 40° has a horizontal ceiling below. If U_c and U_r are found to be 1.60 W/m² K and 3.20 W/m² K respectively, calculate the value of* U.

$$U = \frac{3.20 \times 1.60}{3.20 + (1.60 \times 0.766)}$$

$U = 1.157$ W/m² K

Example 5.9. *A pitched roof inclined at 45° has a horizontal ceiling below. If U_c and U_r are found to be 4.60 W/m² K and 7.38 W/m² K respectively, calculate the value of* U.

$$U = \frac{7.38 \times 4.60}{7.38 + (4.60 \times 707)}$$

$U = 3.19$ W/m² K

Alternatively, the U value for the total construction may be calculated by the use of the following formula:

83

$$U = \frac{1}{R_c + R_r \times \text{Cos} \infty}$$

where

R_c = thermal resistance of ceiling

R_r = thermal resistance of roof

The formula only applies where the roof space is unventilated: it can be used when considering the improvement made by adding an insulating lining to the roof by expressing the U value of the insulating material as a thermal resistance; the reciprocal of the total resistance gives the U value of the total construction.

Thermal insulation

Thermal insulation reduces the flow of heat through the structure of a building and its advantages may be summarised as follows:

1. The reduction in the size of the heating installation, resulting in the reduction in capital costs, fuel consumption and therefore running costs.
2. Saving in space for plant and fuel.
3. Reduction, or the complete elimination, of condensation problems.
4. Reduction of unsightly pattern staining and redecoration costs.
5. Improved comfort levels for the occupants of the building.
6. Reduced pre-heating time.
7. Reduced rate of heat gain from solar radiation and therefore reduction in size of cooling plant.

The inclusion of thermal insulation within the structure of a heated building can be regarded as an investment, from which an annual return on capital can be derived. The cost of insulation can also be largely offset by the saving in the cost of the heating installation.

The heat losses from a building having a compact layout are less than those from a straggling layout of the same floor area and volume. A room of square proportions on plan also has less heat losses than a room of rectangular proportions on plan. For example, a room measuring 6 m x 6 m has a perimeter of 24 m, while a room measuring 9 m x 4 m will have a perimeter of 26 m. The square room therefore will have less heat losses through the walls and floor perimeter than the rectangular room of the same floor area and volume.

Building Regulations 1985 Conservation of Fuel and Power

Exposed elements

Means in relation to a dwelling:

(a) exposed to the outside air; or

(b) separating a dwelling from part of a building which is ventilated by means of an opening or duct to the outside air, the aggregate area of which exceeds 5 per cent of the area of the walls enclosing the space, and which allows a passage of air at all times.

In relation to a building not consisting of a dwelling:

(c) exposed to outside air; or

(*d*) separating a part of the building which is heated from a part which is not and which is wholly or partly exposed to the outside air.

The area of perimeter wall used to calculate the areas of windows should include all openings in the wall, and:

(*a*) an external door with 2 m² or more of glazed area should be counted as part of the window area; and

(*b*) any part of a roof which has a pitch of 70° or more should be counted as walling; and

(*c*) any opening in a wall other than a window opening and a meter cupboard recess may be counted as part of the wall area; and

(*d*) lintels, jambs and sills associated with windows and roof lights may be counted as part of the window and roof light area; and

(*e*) areas of walls, floors and roofs should be between finished internal faces of the building and in the case of a roof, in the plane of the insulation.

Note

A good deal of heat loss through window openings may be saved if the windows having the larger areas have a southern aspect.

In winter, south-facing windows during daytime may provide a useful degree of solar heating and buildings are sometimes constructed having most of the windows facing south.

This type of solar heating is known as 'passive' and another type, which circulates water through a solar collector, is known as 'active'. Both types of solar heating are dealt with in detail in Building Services and Equipment Volume 3.

'*U* value' means thermal transmittance coefficient, that is to say, the rate of heat transfer in watts through 1 m² of a structure when the combined radiant and air temperatures at each side of the structure differ by 1 °C and is expressed in W/m² K.

Requirement for dwellings

1. The calculated rate of heat loss (WK) through any windows and roof lights shall be no greater than it would be if:

(*a*) the aggregate of the areas of windows and roof lights were 12 per cent of the area of the walls bounding the dwelling; and

(*b*) the windows and roof lights had a *U* value of 5.7.

2. The calculated rate of heat loss through the solid parts of the exposed elements shall be not greater than it would be if:

(*a*) the exposed walls and exposed floors had a *U* value of 0.6; and

(*b*) the roof had a *U* value of 0.35.

3. The extent that the calculated rate of heat loss through the solid parts of exposed elements is less than the maximum permitted under sub-paragraph (2) the calculated rate of heat loss through windows and roof lights may be greater than the maximum permitted under paragraph (1).

Table 5.7 Maximum U value of walls, floors and roofs

Type of building	Exposed walls	Roofs	Exposed floors
Dwellings	0.6	0.35	0.6
Other residential buildings including hotels and institutional	0.6	0.6	0.6
Places of assembly, offices and shops	0.6	0.6	0.6
Industrial and storage	0.7	0.7	0.7

Note: Display windows in shops are not included.

Example 4.10. *A detached house has an area of exposed walls of 200 m² and the area of windows is 50 m². The walls and ceiling have U values of 0.5 W/m² K and 0.4 W/m² K respectively.*
If the area of the ceiling is 84 m² and double glazing is to be used, calculate if the levels of insulation meet the requirements of the Regulations.

Area of exposed walls including windows	$= 200\,m^2$
Area of exposed walls to be insulated	
= 96 – area of windows = 200 – 50	$= 150\,m^2$
Area of roof to be insulated	$=\ \ 84\,m^2$

From Table 4.7 the U value of exposed walls and roof are $0.6\,W/m^2$ K and $0.35\,W/m^2$ K respectively

Allowable rate of heat loss through exposed walls (150 × 0.6)	$=\ \ 90\,W/K$
Allowable rate of heat loss through roof (84 × 0.35)	$=\ \ 29.4\,W/K$
Total allowable rate of heat loss through walls and roof	119.4 W/K

In proposed house rate of heat loss through exposed walls = (150 × 0.5)	$=\ \ 75$
Rate of heat loss through roof (84 × 0.4)	$=\ \ 33.6$
Total heat loss through walls and roof	108.6 W/K

(The proposed insulation levels are satisfactory)

It is sometimes necessary to check if the type of construction has a U value that does not exceed the U value specified in the Regulations.

Example 4.11. *The exposed wall of a dwelling consists of 113 mm brick outer leaf; 25 mm air space; 25 mm insulation; 100 mm aerated concrete inner leaf; and 16 mm internal plastering. Calculate the thermal transmission U value for the wall.*

Thermal conductivities

Brick	0.8 W/m K
Aerated concrete	0.14 W/m K
Insulation	0.04 W/m K
Plaster	0.20 W/m K

Surface resistances

R_{si} External surface layer	0.12 m² KW
R_{so} Internal surface layer	0.08 m² KW
R_a Air space	0.18 m² KW

The thermal is obtained by dividing the thickness of the material in (m) by the thermal conductivity and the U value is obtained by adding the thermal resistances and taking the reciprocal of the result.

$$U = \cfrac{1}{R_{si} + R_{so} + R_a + \dfrac{L_1}{k_1} + \dfrac{L_2}{k_2} + \dfrac{L_3}{k_3} + \dfrac{L_4}{k_4}}$$

$$U = \cfrac{1}{0.12 + 0.08 + 0.18 + \dfrac{0.113}{0.8} + \dfrac{0.025}{0.04} + \dfrac{0.1}{0.14} + \dfrac{0.016}{0.2}}$$

$$U = \cfrac{1}{0.12 + 0.08 + 0.18 + 0.14 + 0.625 + 0.714 + 0.08}$$

$$U = \frac{1}{1.939}$$

$$U = 0.516 \text{ (approx)}$$

The construction is below 0.6 (see Table 4.7) and is therefore satisfactory.

Insulating materials

Insulating materials may be divided broadly into two groups:

1. Non-loadbearing.
2. Loadbearing.

Non-loadbearing materials generally have a low density and make use of still air cells and usually possess a greater thermal resistance than loadbearing materials. The rate of heat loss through modern non-loadbearing lightweight structures is less than the heat losses through heavier loadbearing structures and this has led to a wider use of lightweight prefabricated sections in buildings. Curtain wall structures use lightweight non-loadbearing panels between heavy frames of reinforced concrete, or structural steel. Some materials are organic in origin, or contain organic materials and the subject of fire spread must be considered in conjunction with that of insulation when proposing to use these materials. The hazards of smoke and toxic fumes produced in fires where foamed plastics are used for insulating materials must also be considered. The Building Regulations (England and Wales) 1985 covers the spread of fire in buildings and the local Fire Prevention Officer should also be consulted where any doubt exists regarding the choice of materials. When selecting a suitable insulating material, the following points must be considered:

1. The risk of spread of fire, or the production of toxic fumes when fixed.
2. Whether the material required, is non-loadbearing or loadbearing.
3. The cost and thickness in relation to the saving in fuel and capital cost of the heating installation.
4. The availability of the material and the ease of fixing.

Foamed plastics

Foamed plastics are the most effective of all materials used for thermal insulation and their thermal conductivities are as follows:

Foamed polyurethane	0.020–0.025 W/m K
Expanded polystyrene	0.029–0.04 W/m K
Foamed urea formaldehyde	0.030–0.036 W/m K

Cavity fill

The insulation of an external wall can be improved by about 50 per cent by blowing non-toxic insulating material into the cavity (see Fig. 5.14).

Mineral wool may be used which does not shrink or crack and also prevents the penetration of water. The material is fire resisting and can be used with absolute safety.

Resin-coated expanded polystyrene beads can be blown into the cavity to improve the insulation. The beads bond together by the resin and they are resistant to water.

On new work, expanded polystyrene board 25 mm thick may be fixed to the inner leaf of the cavity, thus leaving 25 mm of an air cavity (see Fig. 5.15). Alternatively, on new work, the cavity may be filled with mineral wool quilt, or semi-rigid glass wool slab treated with a water-repellent binder.

Insulating boards or slab are used for insulating all various types of structures and these include the following types:

1. Wood wool slabs.
2. Compressed strawboard.
3. Insulating plasterboard.
4. Aluminium foil-backed plasterboard.
5. Mineral wool slabs.
6. Expanded polystyrene slabs.
7. Corkboard.
8. Insulating wood fibre board.

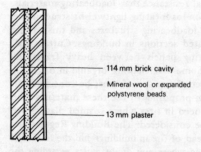

Fig. 5.14 Cavity wall with foam insulation

114 mm brick cavity
Mineral wool or expanded polystyrene beads
13 mm plaster

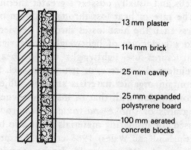

Fig. 5.15 Expanded polystyrene board insulation

13 mm plaster
114 mm brick
25 mm cavity
25 mm expanded polystyrene board
100 mm aerated concrete blocks

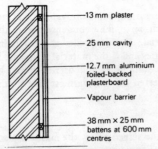

Fig. 5.16 Solid wall with internal lining

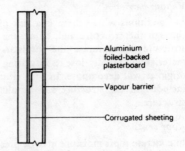

Fig. 5.17 Corrugated sheet with internal lining

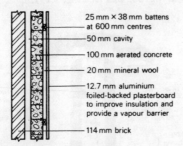

Fig. 5.18 Cavity wall with internal lining

9. Cellular glass rigid slabs.
10. Semi-rigid slabs of glass fibre, treated with a water repellent.

Before the boards or slabs are fixed they must be conditioned for at least 24 hours, by exposing them on all sides to the same air temperature and humidity as would exist when they are fixed on site or otherwise distortion of the boards would occur after fixing.

Internal linings

Insulation board fixed to battens on the inside walls enables a room to warm up quickly and helps to prevent condensation when intermittent heating is used. The insulation will reduce the radiant heat loss from the body and therefore provides better conditions of thermal comfort. The insulation, however, should be considered with the risk of spread of fire since the temperature of the combustible materials inside the room will reach ignition point more quickly if a fire occurs.

Figures 5.16, 5.17 and 5.18 show the methods of fixing internal linings to brick and corrugated asbestos cement sheet walls.

Insulating plasters

Insulating plasters containing lightweight perlite and vermiculite as aggregates are produced ready for use and require only the addition of clean water before use. They have three times the insulating value and are only one-third the density of ordinary plasters.

Vapour barriers

In conditions where there is a risk of condensation, moisture vapour will rise through the structure and, being unable to disperse, may condense within the structure and saturate the insulating material. If this occurs the insulating material will rapidly lose its insulating properties and if the material is organic in origin it will decompose. In such situations a suitable vapour barrier should be included in the structure and should be inserted on the warmest side of the structure.

Roof vents

In concrete roofs moisture may be present in the screed below the mastic asphalt or felt covering. During hot weather this moisture may vaporise and cause an upward pressure, resulting in the lifting of the roof covering. To prevent this occurrence roof ventilators are fixed to relieve this pressure. It is usual to fix one ventilator to every 20 m^2 of roof area (see Fig. 5.19).

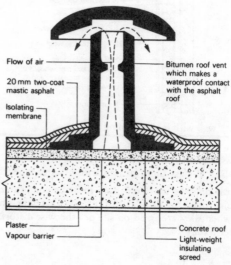

Fig. 5.19   Roof vent

Solid ground floors

Since the greatest heat loss is around the perimeter of the floor, it is essential to provide insulation at this location. For wide floors, a horizontal strip of insulation, may be extended 1 m from the wall and a vertical strip of insulation material should be extended through the thickness of the floor slab, around all exposed edges (see Fig. 5.20). For narrow floors, the horizontal strip insulation may be carried under the entire floor slab, with vertical strip insulation material extended through the thickness of the floor slab, as before. If the cavity is to be filled with semi-rigid slabs of glass fibre, specially treated with a water-repellent binder, horizontal strip insulation may be omitted (see Fig. 5.21). The slabs are available in three thicknesses, 50, 65 and 75 mm, and they provide a moisture

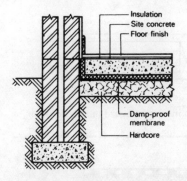

- Insulation
- Site concrete
- Floor finish
- Damp-proof membrane
- Hardcore

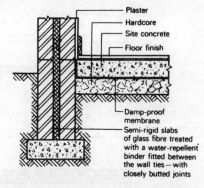

- Plaster
- Hardcore
- Site concrete
- Floor finish
- Damp-proof membrane
- Semi-rigid slabs of glass fibre treated with a water-repellent binder fitted between the wall ties — with closely butted joints

Fig. 5.20 Solid ground floor with horizontal insulation

Fig. 5.21 Solid ground floor with edge insulation

barrier between the outer and inner leaf of the cavity wall. If required, a horizontal strip 1 m from the wall may also be included, to provide additional insulation for the floor.

Suspended timber ground floor
A suspended ground floor above an enclosed air space is exposed to air on both sides, but the air temperature below the floor is higher than the external air because the ventilation rate below the floor is very low. Additional thermal insulation of a suspended timber ground floor may be provided either in the form of a continuous layer of semi-rigid or flexible material laid over the joists (see Figs 5.22 and 5.23). Alternatively, a semi-rigid material may be laid between the joists (see Fig. 5.24). A vapour barrier should never be included in suspended timber ground floors as this would prevent the escape of water above and evaporation, which could lead to the dangerous conditions conductive to fungal attack on the timber floor.

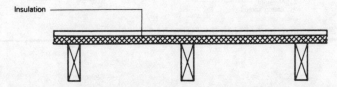

Insulation

Fig. 5.22 Hollow timber ground floor with insulation board or slab above joists

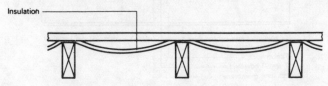

Insulation

Fig. 5.23 Hollow timber ground floor with insulating quilt above joists

91

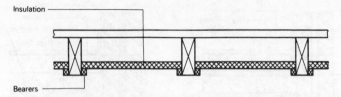

Fig. 5.24 Hollow timber ground floor with insulation board or slab between joists

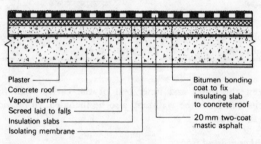

Plaster
Concrete roof
Vapour barrier
Screed laid to falls
Insulation slabs
Isolating membrane

Bitumen bonding coat to fix insulating slab to concrete roof
20 mm two-coat mastic asphalt

Fig. 5.25 Concrete roof with insulation slabs

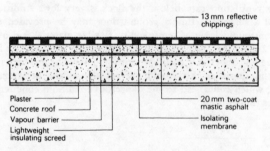

13 mm reflective chippings

Plaster
Concrete roof
Vapour barrier
Lightweight insulating screed

20 mm two-coat mastic asphalt
Isolating membrane

Fig. 5.26 Concrete roof with insulating screed

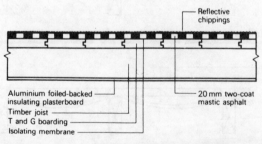

Reflective chippings

Aluminium foiled-backed insulating plasterboard
Timber joist
T and G boarding
Isolating membrane

20 mm two-coat mastic asphalt

Fig. 5.27 Timber roof with insulated ceiling

Flat roofs

These are usually constructed of reinforced concrete or timber and may be covered with mastic asphalt, roofing felt, lead, copper, aluminium or zinc. To prevent radiant heat gain, mastic asphalt and felt roofs have a layer of reflective chippings spread over the external surface. Figure 5.25 shows a section through a concrete flat roof, insulated with mineral wool slabs and Fig. 5.26 shows an alternative method of insulating a concrete flat roof with an aerated concrete screed. Figure 5.27 shows a section through a timber roof, insulated with aluminium foil-backed plasterboard. The aluminium foil acts as both a thermal insulator and a vapour barrier.

Aerated concrete

Aerated concrete may be used for inside work as a screed to a concrete roof, or as concrete blocks for walls. The concrete uses lightweight aggregates such as foamed slag, sintered pulverised fuel ash, exfoliated vermiculite, expanded perlite or expanded clay. Alternatively, aerated concrete may be made by forcing air or gas into a concrete mix, and in both types the concrete is of a low density, containing a large number of still air pockets which provide good insulating properties.

Pitched roofs

Pitched roofs with a ceiling below may have a glass fibre or mineral wool quilt laid over the ceiling joists, or between them. If the roof space is to be used for habitation, the insulating quilt is laid between the roof rafters under the tiles, with a vapour barrier laid between the quilt and the plasterboard (see Fig. 5.28).

Figure 5.29 shows a method of insulating a corrugated asbestos cement roof. When the insulation is laid between the roof rafters, the cold water storage cistern may be left without insulation. Exfoliated vermiculite, or granulated cork, may also be used for insulating a ceiling, by pouring this loose fill material between the ceiling joists directly from a paper bag and levelling off with a shaped template. The position of electric ceiling roses and junction boxes should be marked by painting arrows on the roof timbers prior to insulating the ceiling. The thickness of ceiling insulation should be at least 50 mm, but preferably 76 mm.

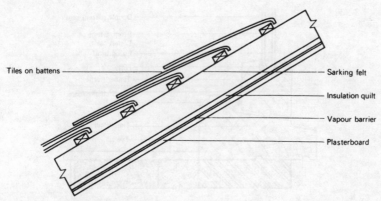

Tiles on battens — Sarking felt — Insulation quilt — Vapour barrier — Plasterboard

Fig. 5.28   Insulation of tiled roof

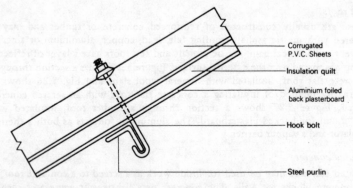

Corrugated
P.V.C. Sheets

Insulation quilt

Aluminium foiled
back plasterboard

Hook bolt

Steel purlin

Fig. 5.29   Insulation of corrugated polyvinyl chloride roof

Reflective insulation

Reflective insulation consists of reinforced aluminium foil, which may be used for ceiling and walls to reflect radiant heat. The foil is also bonded to one surface of plasterboard, which increases thermal insulation of the board.

Double glazing

Double glazing for thermal insulation consists of separate panes of glass 20 mm apart, with each pane in a separate frame, or factory-made hermetically sealed units. For sound insulation, sealed glazing units having double panes 200 mm apart should be used, but this distance is not so effective for thermal insulation as the 20 mm air space. Figure 5.30 shows a detail of a factory-made all glass unit. The internal air is dried to such a degree that condensation within the cavity wall will not occur in any condition likely to be encountered when the glass is in service. Figure 5.31 shows a detail of a double glazing unit, which may be either screwed, or hinged, to an existing window frame. Figure 5.32 shows a detail of an aluminium alloy double glazing bar. The bars are fitted at the top and bottom ends, with slipper sections for fixing to a steel or timber frame.

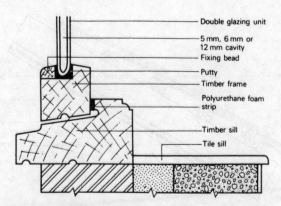

Double glazing unit

5 mm, 6 mm or
12 mm cavity

Fixing bead

Putty

Timber frame

Polyurethane foam
strip

Timber sill

Tile sill

Fig. 5.30   Pilkington insulight double glazing units

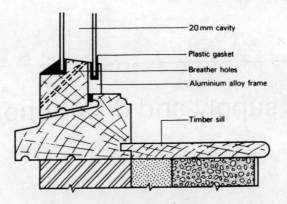

Fig. 5.31 Double glazing an existing window frame

- 20 mm cavity
- Plastic gasket
- Breather holes
- Aluminium alloy frame
- Timber sill

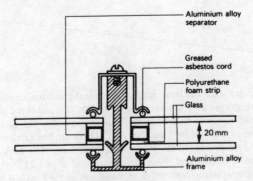

Fig. 5.32 Aluminium alloy double glazing frame

- Aluminium alloy separator
- Greased asbestos cord
- Polyurethane foam strip
- Glass
- 20 mm
- Aluminium alloy frame

Chapter 6

Gas supply and distribution

Gas supply

Natural gas

Almost all the gas used in Great Britain is natural gas from beneath the North Sea. Liquid natural gas at a temperature of −160 °C is imported in special ships from Algeria and is stored in frozen earth underground tanks on Canvey Island and Ambergate in Derbyshire (see Fig. 6.1). These frozen earth tanks are kept hard by the liquid gas at −160 °C contained in them. The tanks are approximately 40 m in diameter and 40 m deep and hold about 21 000 t (tonnes) of liquid natural gas which is 600 times as much gas as they would hold if the gas was not liquefied. The liquid is converted into a gas and transmitted through a pipeline to Leeds, with branches to provide bulk supplies to eight of the twelve Area Gas Boards. This Algerian gas is used with natural gas from beneath the North Sea and it represents about 10 per cent of the gas supply for the UK.

Formation

Plankton and other minute organisms that flourished in the seas, and the trees and plants which grew in the earth's swamps millions of years ago, died and sank to the sea-bed. They were buried and sank deeper below the surface of the sea-bed, became compacted and subjected to increased pressure and temperature. The minute organisms, trees and plants were converted into coal, petroleum and natural gas. Far beneath the bed of the North Sea, the gas is trapped below an impermeable layer of rock and salt. It is tapped, brought ashore by a pipeline and fed into the pipe mains supplying the eight Area Gas Boards in England, Scotland and Wales. Figure 6.2 shows the rock strata below the North Sea with dome traps for natural gas.

Composition and characteristics

Table 6.1 gives the compositions of natural gas and coal gas and Table 6.2 a comparison of their characteristics.

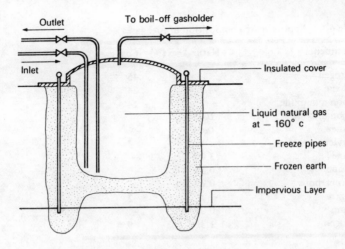

Fig. 6.1 Frozen ground liquid gas storage tank

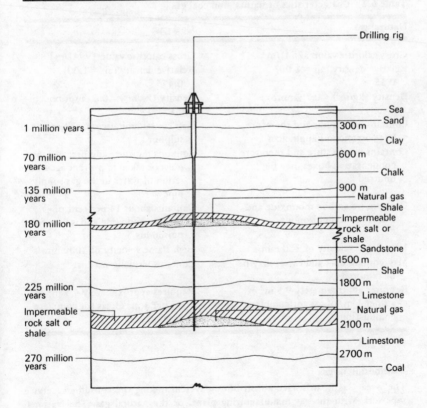

Fig. 6.2 Rock strata below the North Sea with salt dome traps for gas

Table 6.1 Approximate composition of fuel gases

Constituents	Natural gas (%)	Coal gas (%)
Hydrogen	–	45
Methane	94.7	24
Carbon monoxide	–	14
Carbon dioxide	0.05	–
Butane	0.04	–
Propylene	–	3
Ethane	3.00	–
Propane	0.51	–
Hydrocarbons	0.27	–
Oxygen	–	2
Helium	0.03	–
Nitrogen	1.30	9

Table 6.2 Characteristics of natural and coal gas

Natural gas	Coal gas
Gross calorific value 37 MJ/m^3	Gross calorific value 19 MJ/m^3
Relative density (air = 1.00) 0.55	Relative density (air = 1.00) 0.475
Density (kg/m^3) = 0.7 (approximately)	Density (kg/m^3) = 0.6 (approximately)
Contains no sulphur and therefore less corrosion of appliances	May contain minute quantities of sulphur
Contains no moisture and therefore condensation boxes may be omitted	Contains moisture and precautions must be taken to prevent accumulation of water in the gas supply pipe
Contains no carbon monoxide and therefore non-poisonous	Contains about 14 per cent of carbon monoxide and is therefore poisonous
Low flame velocity of 350 mm/s	High flame velocity of 1000 mm/s
May contain dust and filters may be be required	Contains virtually no dust
Requires approximately 9.5 m^3 of air per 1 m^3 of gas for complete combustion	Requires approximately 4.5 m^3 of air per 1 m^3 of gas for complete combustion

Distribution of gas

The Area Gas Boards have a distribution system linking the consumers' service pipework with the gas manufacturing plant, or the natural gas. The National Transmission System links up the Area Boards' system and also the shore terminals of the natural gas fields (see Fig. 6.3).

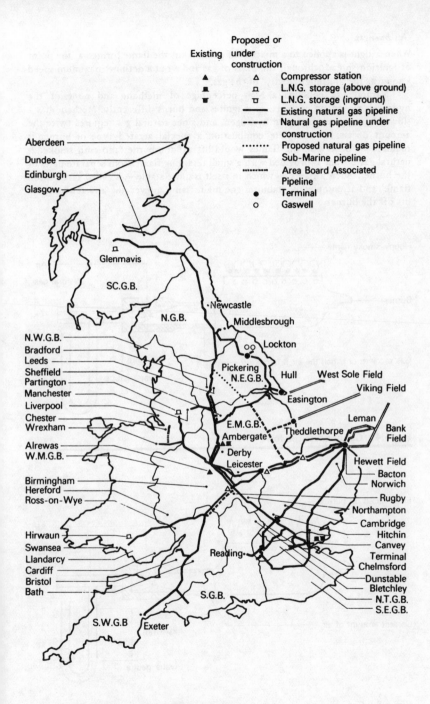

Fig. 6.3 The National Transmission System

Gas burners

When a light is applied to a mixture of gas and air, the flame formed at the point of ignition spreads through the mass of gas and air at a definite maximum speed known as the 'burning velocity' of the gas.

Natural gas contains a high percentage of methane and none of the hydrogen present in coal gas, so it ignites and burns differently. Methane has a slower burning velocity than hydrogen, and since natural gas requires twice the amount of air for complete combustion a special aerated type of burner is required or otherwise the flames would lift off the burner and emit smoke. A natural-gas burner is provided with a small retaining flame from separate parts of the burner. Such a flame — which in itself is quite stable — is called a 'retention flame' and it completely stabilises the main flame, preventing any tendency to lift off the burner.

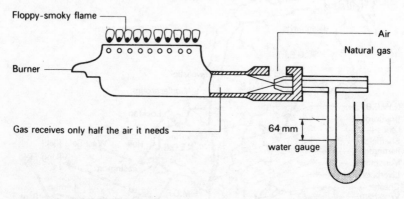

Fig. 6.4   Gas pressure too low

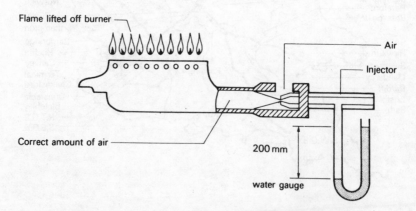

Fig. 6.5   Gas pressure correct but no retention flame

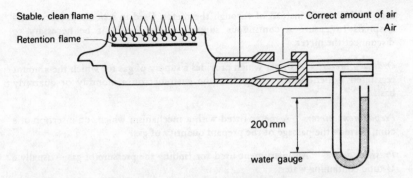

Fig. 6.6 Gas pressure correct and retention flame incorporated in the burner

Figure 6.4 shows a burner without a retention flame and with the gas pressure too low. The velocity of the gas passing through the injector is also too low, thus allowing only half the amount of air required for correct combustion to be mixed with the gas, resulting in a smoky flame.

Figure 6.5 shows a burner without a retention flame, but having the correct gas pressure; the flame is clean, but lifts off the burner and is therefore unstable. Figure 6.6 shows a burner incorporating a retention flame and also the correct gas pressure, thus resulting in a stable, clean flame.

Note: The tendency of natural gas flames to lift off the burner may also be prevented by increasing the number of burner ports and therefore the total flame port area. This slows down the speed of the gas/air mixture and stabilises the flames.

Gas services in buildings

Definitions

Condensate receiver: A receptacle fitted at the lowest part of the gas-line pipe to collect any liquid or deposit which might otherwise form in the pipe.

Control cock: A cock or valve fitted at the inlet of the meter to control the supply of gas from the Board's main to the consumer.

Governor: A regulating device for reducing the high transmission pressures to normal requirements.

Installation pipe: Every pipe between any meter and the point at which the appliance is connected.

Meter compartment: An enclosure in which one or more meters are accommodated. The compartment should be well ventilated and if situated on a public stairway or corridor, be constructed of fire-resisting materials.

Meter bypass: An arrangement of pipes, and cocks or valves whereby the gas

101

may be led round instead of through the meter. Used in schools, factories and hospitals to ensure a continuous supply of gas·should it be necessary to disconnect the meter.

Ordinary meter: A meter which provides a supply of gas for which the amount registered is periodically charged to the customer on a monthly or quarterly basis.

Prepayment meter: A meter fitted with a mechanism which, on insertion of a coin, permits the passage of the prepaid quantity of gas.

Pressure gauge: An instrument used for finding the pressure of gas — usually a U tube containing water.

Pressure point: A small plug-type fitting on a gas pipe to which a pressure gauge may be attached for taking pressure readings.

Primary meter: A meter connected to the service pipe, the index reading of which constitutes the basis of the charge by the Board for gas used on the premises, and where there may or may not be a secondary or subsidiary meter.

Secondary meter: A subsidiary meter for measuring gas used on separate parts of premises or on separate appliances, the whole of which has passed through the primary meter.

Secondary supply pipe: The pipe connecting the inlet of a secondary meter to the outlet pipe from a primary meter.

Service pipe: The pipe between the gas main and the customer's control cock (normally at the meter). In large buildings with more than one tenancy, there may be several service pipes entering at different points in the building.

Service valve: A valve inserted in the service pipe close to the site boundary. The valve allows the supply of gas to the building to be turned off in an emergency. A key to operate the valve must be kept available.

Design considerations

Consultation with the Gas Board in the early stages of design and planning of a building is essential to ensure that adequate provision is made for the gas services. All necessary information regarding the position of the meter, controls and installation points to serve the appliances should be made as early as possible by means of drawings and specifications. Figure 6.7 shows the graphical symbols used for gas installation drawings.

The drawings should show the following:

1. The position of ducts, chases and channels required when the pipes are to be concealed.
2. The position of control cocks or valves.
3. The routes and diameters of all installation pipework.

Note: Except where a pipe has to be exposed on the internal surfaces, or laid in prepared ducts or channels permitting access, pipes should be tested as the erection of the building proceeds.

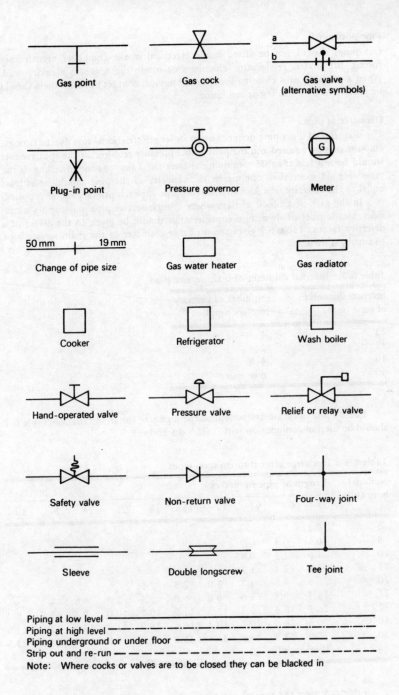

Gas point

Gas cock

Gas valve
(alternative symbols)

Plug-in point

Pressure governor

Meter

50 mm   19 mm

Change of pipe size

Gas water heater

Gas radiator

Cooker

Refrigerator

Wash boiler

Hand-operated valve

Pressure valve

Relief or relay valve

Safety valve

Non-return valve

Four-way joint

Sleeve

Double longscrew

Tee joint

Piping at low level ————————————————
Piping at high level ————————————————
Piping underground or under floor — — — — — — —
Strip out and re-run — — — — — — — — — — — —
Note: Where cocks or valves are to be closed they can be blacked in

Fig. 6.7 Graphical symbols

Pipe positions

Gas pipes should not be fitted inside electrical intake chambers, transformer rooms, lift shafts, refrigerator chambers or inside the space in a cavity wall. When a gas pipe runs close to some other service, contact between them should be prevented by a spacing or insulation.

Diameter of pipes

The diameter of a gas pipe depends upon its length, frictional loss due to fittings, amount of gas required and the permissible pressure required at the appliance. It should be not less than 25 mm nominal bore for a single family dwelling. If the pipe supplies more than one meter, the capacity of the pipe should be at least equal to the capacity of a 25 mm diameter pipe for each primary meter supplied.

In the case of a block of flats where a single service pipe may supply a considerable number of dwellings, consideration should be given to the effect of a diversity factor. Table 6.3 gives the probable diameter of the main service pipe to small gas meters.

Table 6.3 Internal diameter of main service pipe

Internal diameter of pipe (mm)	Number of primary meters supplied
25	1
32	2
40	4–6
50	6 or more

For a more accurate assessment of the pipe size for an installation Table 6.4 should be used in conjunction with Tables 6.5 and 6.6.

Table 6.4 Discharge rates through steel pipes

Nominal bore (mm)	Length of pipe in metres									
	3	6	9	12	15	18	21	24	27	30
6	0.1									
8	0.1	0.3								
10	1.6	1.3	0.85							
15	3.0	2.1	1.71							
20	6.5	4.5	3.7	3.0	2.8	2.5				
25	13.3	9.4	7.6	6.8	6.0	5.4	5.0	4.8	4.5	
32	26.3	18.4	15.3	13.3	11.9	10.7	10.0	9.3	8.7	8.2
40	36.8	26.0	20.7	18.4	16.4	15.0	13.8	13.0	12.0	11.6
50	73.6	53.8	42.5	36.8	34.0	31.0	28.0	26.3	25.0	23.8
	Discharge (m³/h)									

Table 6.5 gives the typical gas consumption at appliances and Table 6.6 the additions to the net pipe run for fittings.

Table 6.5   Gas consumption of appliances

Appliance	Consumption (m^3/h)
Refrigerator	0.10
Wash boiler	1.13
Sink water heater	2.30
Instantaneous multi-point water heater	5.70
Cooker	3.70
Warm-air heater	2.30

Table 6.6   Additions to pipe run

Nominal bore	Elbows	Tees	90° bends
15—25	0.6	0.6	0.3
32—40	1.0	1.0	0.3
50	1.6	1.6	0.6

Example 6.1.   *Find the internal diameter of a gas pipe to supply two sink water heaters, one instantaneous multi-point water heater and two cookers. The net length of the pipe required is 20 m and there will be six 90° bends and four tees in the pipe run.*

Gas consumption (Table 6.5).

$$\text{Sink water heaters} = 2 \times 2.3 = 4.6 \ m^3/h$$
$$\text{Instantaneous multi-point water heaters} = 5.7 \ m^3/h$$
$$\text{Cookers} = 2 \times 3.7 = 7.4 \ m^3/h$$
$$\text{Total} \quad 17.7 \ m^3/h$$

Resistance of pipe fittings assuming a 50 mm diameter pipe (see Table 6.6).

$$90° \text{ bends} = 6 \times 0.6 = 3.6 \ m$$
$$\text{Tees} = 4 \times 1.6 = 6.4 \ m$$
$$\text{Total} \quad 10.0 \ m$$

Total length of pipe = 20 + 10 = 30 m

Table 6.4 shows that a 50 mm diameter pipe 30 m long will discharge 23.80 m^3/h and is therefore adequate.

Domestic installations

The service pipe should be laid at least 375 mm below ground and if possible with a fall towards the main of 1 in 120. At the point of entry into the building a 76 mm diameter sleeve should be provided for the pipe. The service pipe should be set centrally in the sleeve by means of a bituminous or similar non-setting material filling the space between the pipe and the sleeve throughout the length of the sleeve. The space between the sleeve and the wall should be filled with cement mortar throughout the thickness of the wall. A service pipe, when laid with screwed joints, should be jointed to the main by a connector or coupling for the purpose of facilitating connection or disconnection.

The use of sharp bends or square elbows should be avoided and the pipe should not be restricted by bending or cutting. It is not usual practice to insert a service valve on the service pipe for domestic installations.

Figure 6.8 shows the method of laying the service pipe when it is possible to obtain a fall towards the main. Figure 6.9 shows the method of laying a service pipe when it is not possible to provide a fall from the entry into the building and the gas main. A condensate receiver should be fitted at the lowest point of the service pipe so that any water in the pipe may enter the receiver.

Natural gas does not contain moisture and therefore water from condensation of the gas will not be present. However, it may be necessary to fit a condensate receiver to prevent the service pipe from flooding from extraneous causes, such as water from a broken water main entering a broken gas main. The receiver is emptied by a pump connected to the suction pipe. When a condensate receiver is fitted, a notice to this effect should be mounted on the service pipe adjacent to the consumer's control cock.

The service pipe may be of mild steel to BS 1387, Grade B (medium) with screwed joints protected from corrosion with bituminous paint or hessian

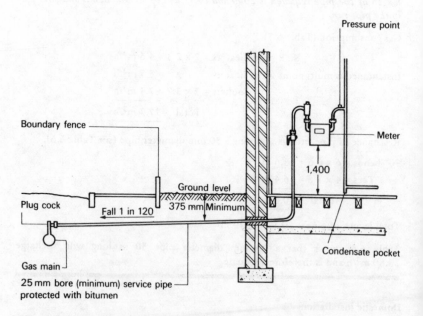

Fig. 6.8 Normal service pipe installation

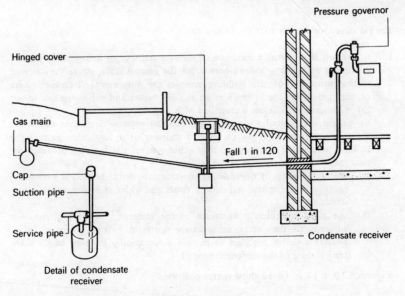

Fig. 6.9   Service pipe with condensate receiver

wrapping. A PVC pipe may be used from the main to the point of entry into the building, and steel pipe connected to this for entry into the building up to the control cock.

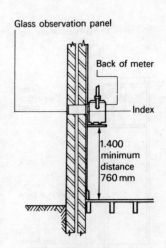

Fig. 6.10   Meter in dry, well-ventilated outbuilding

Note: Gas safety regulations 1972

(1) No meter shall be installed in a building, which has two or more floors above the ground floor of the building, on or under a stairway or elsewhere, where the stairway or other part of the building provides the only means of escape in case of fire.

(2) Every meter and its connections installed in a building other than one mentioned in paragraph (1) on or under a stairway or elsewhere, where the stairway or other part of the building provides the only means of escape in case of fire, shall either be of fire-resistant construction or be housed in a compartment of which the enclosing sides, top and bottom including the doors have a fire resistance of not less than half an hour and of which the doors shall be fitted with automatic self-closing devices or the meter shall be connected to a service pipe which incorporates a thermal cut-off device near the meter.

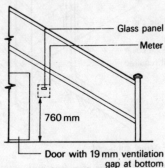

Fig. 6.11   Meter under staircase

107

The gas safety regulations state the following:

1. No person shall install a meter on or under a stairway or in any other part of a building with two or more floors above the ground floor, where the stairway or that other part of the building provides the only means of escape in case of fire, unless the meter replaces an existing meter and sub-paragraph (*a*) or (*b*) of paragraph (2) below is complied with.

2. No person shall install a meter in any building with no more than one fooor above the ground floor on or under a stairway or in any other part of the building where the stairway or that other part of the building provides the only means of escape in case of fire, unless:
   (*a*) the meter is: (i) of fire-resisting construction; or (ii) housed in a compartment with automatic self-closing doors and which is of fire-resisting construction; or
   (*b*) the pipe immediately upstream of the meter or, where a governor is adjacent to the meter, immediately upstream of that governor, incorporates a device designed to cut off automatically the flow of gas if the temperature of the device exceeds 95°C.

Figures 6.10, 6.11 and 6.12 show meter positions.

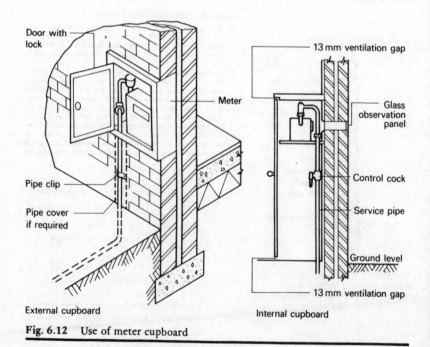

Fig. 6.12 Use of meter cupboard

Types of meters

Domestic meters are available in two basic sizes, D1 and D2. The normal D1 size will supply cooker, washing machine or boiler, refrigerator, poker, water heater and two gas fires. The D2 size should be used when central heating or warm-air heating units are to be installed in addition to other appliances.

Installation pipework

Materials

The larger diameter pipes are usually of mild steel to BS 1387, Grade B (medium) with screwed joints or light-gauge copper pipe to BS 659 with capillary fittings. Semi flexible stainless steel pipe is used for the short connections to the meter to give some degree of flexibility at the meter connections. Brass pipe, which may be chromium plated, is used for short connections to appliances such as fires and refrigerators. Flexible steel pipe is used for connections to movable appliances such as castor-mounted gas cookers.

Method of installation

The pipework should be installed with a fall to a pocket fitted with a tap or plug to facilitate the removal of any condensation. A pressure test point should be fitted in a convenient position on or near to the outlet of the meter as possible. Pipes should be laid between and parallel with the floor joists and provided with good supports. Where this is not possible, they may be laid across the joists, provided that the depth of notch does not exceed one-sixth of the depth of the joists and that the notch is no nearer than one-sixth the span, or further away than one-quarter of the span from the end of the joists.

Other points and angles increasing pressure loss should be avoided.

1. Sharp bends and angles increasing pressure loss should be avoided.
2. Each end of the pipe should be provided with sufficient connectors or unions to permit its removal, cleaning or alteration with minimum damage to the structure or decoration.
3. Pipes should be well supported with clips or brackets that will prevent the pipe being in contact with the finished surfaces of the building.
4. Where a pipe passes through a wall or floor, a sleeve should be provided and the space between the sleeve and the pipe filled with incombustible material.
5. Pipes in contact with any material likely to cause their corrosion should be protected with a coating of bitumen.
6. Pipes should not be placed within a cavity.
7. Where copper popes are run under timber floors, care should be taken to avoid puncturing the pipe when nailing the floorboards to the joists.
8. Pipes should not be installed near any source of heat.

Figure 6.13 shows the service and installation pipework for a small house.

Meter pipework

The traditional method of installing the meter pipework is by an inlet and outlet connection at either side of the meter, as shown in Fig. 6.14. A single annular connection may also be used which permits a more compact installation (see Fig. 6.15).

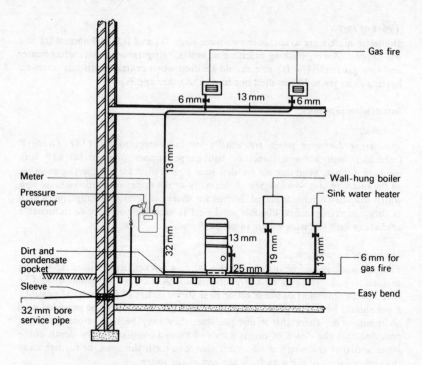

Fig. 6.13 Gas installation for a small house

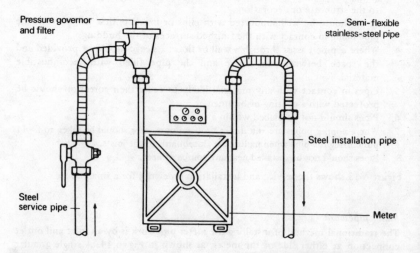

Fig. 6.14 Traditional meter installation

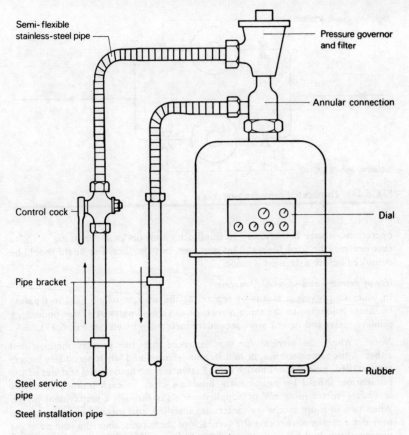

Semi-flexible stainless-steel pipe

Pressure governor and filter

Annular connection

Control cock

Dial

Pipe bracket

Rubber

Steel service pipe

Steel installation pipe

Fig. 6.15 Meter with single annular connection

Installations for large buildings

Service pipe and valve

Where the service pipe has an internal diameter of 50 mm or more, or where a hazardous trade is carried out in the building or in the area in which it is situated, or its form of construction constitutes a special risk, a service valve of a type approved by the local Gas Board should be fitted in the service pipe. The valve should be sited outside but as near as is practicable to the property boundary and should be fitted with a surface box and cover. Then, by reason of special circumstances, for example in blocks of flats or buildings with a large forecourt, a service valve is sited within the property boundary. It should be placed outside the building in a readily accessible position.

Service governors

A valve or cock which may be the consumer's control, should be fitted between the governor and the service pipe to enable the gas to be shut off for inspection and repair of the governor. In large buildings where the gas is used in continuous

111

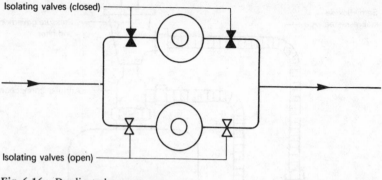

Isolating valves (closed)

Isolating valves (open)

Fig. 6.16 Duplicated pressure governors

operations, it may be necessary to duplicate governors as shown in Fig. 6.16, so that one may be used for stand-by purposes, but the local Gas Board should be consulted before a decision is made.

Use of primary and secondary meters

In order to provide a means of registering the amount of gas used in separate buildings belonging to the same owner, or in various parts of a large building, a primary meter and two or more secondary meters are fitted (see Fig. 6.17).

Note: Where the service pipe supplies more than one primary meter, fitted either in the same premises, or in different premises and where secondary meters are installed, a permanent notice calling attention to these special features of the installation should be prominently mounted close to each primary meter. A secondary meter must not be supplied with gas through a prepayment meter. When two or more secondary meters are installed, this method of metering also provides a means of checking the accuracy of the meters, since the volume of gas passing through the primary meter should be equal to the total volume of gas passing through the secondary meters.

Ring circuit

The service pipe from the primary to the secondary meters may be in the form of a ring, also shown in Fig. 6.17 and this has the following advantages over secondary meters supplied from a radial circuit shown in Fig. 6.18:

1. If the underground service pipe fails at any point, the zoning valves at each end of the pipe may be closed and the other valves left open so that each building may still be supplied with gas. However, radial system uses less pipework and fewer valves.
2. Gas can flow in both directions, thus providing a better distribution of gas to each secondary meter.

Bypass to meter

In order to avoid interrupting the supply of gas to hospitals, schools, office blocks and factories when it is necessary to take out the meter for replacement, a system of pipes and valves (known as a bypass) should be fitted. The pressure governor should control both the main supply and the bypass supply and the bypass valve should be sealed in a closed position in a manner approved by the

112

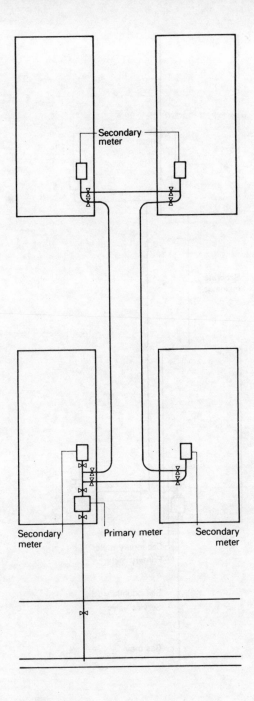

Fig. 6.17 Ring circuit with primary and secondary meters

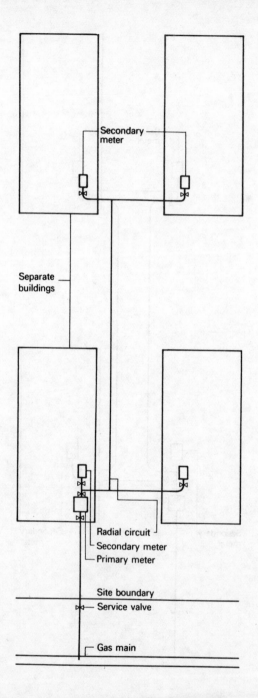

Fig. 6.18 Radial circuit with primary and secondary meters

114

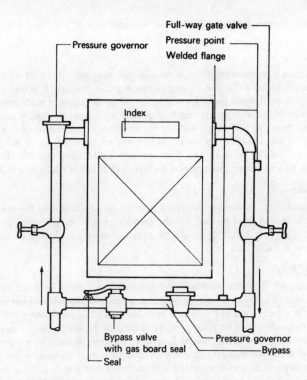

Fig. 6.19 Bypass to meter

Labels on figure:
- Pressure governor
- Full-way gate valve
- Pressure point
- Welded flange
- Index
- Bypass valve with gas board seal
- Seal
- Pressure governor
- Bypass

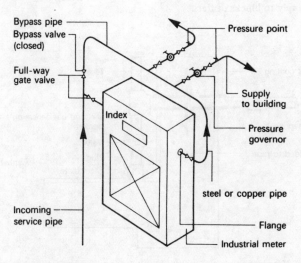

Fig. 6.20 Bypass to meter

Labels on figure:
- Bypass pipe
- Bypass valve (closed)
- Full-way gate valve
- Pressure point
- Supply to building
- Pressure governor
- Index
- steel or copper pipe
- Incoming service pipe
- Flange
- Industrial meter

Gas Board. Figures 6.19 and 6.20 show two methods of providing a bypass to a meter.

Large meters

Large meters for commercial or industrial gas supplies are fitted with flanged side connections suitable for 76 mm, 100 mm, 150 mm and 200 mm pipe connections. These flanged pipes are welded to the steel casing of the meter and the connections have sufficient strength to permit rigid steel or copper pipes to be connected direct to the meter, without the need for short lengths of flexible lead pipes which are required for small meters having soldered meter connections. The meter should be mounted level on a suitable base and should not be subjected to an internal gas pressure greater than that for which it was designed.

Meter housing

A ventilated, dry, incombustible compartment of adequate size for the housing of meters should be provided by the builder as part of the structure of the building. The compartment should be provided with a locked door to prevent unauthorised entry.

Blocks of flats

For blocks of flats the underground service pipe should be provided with a service valve fitted with a surface box and cover. The pipe should rise inside the building in a duct sited in a common corridor or landing, and where the riser has to pass through a wall or floor a sleeve should be provided. If the service pipe enters the flats through a tanked basement a flange should be welded on the pipe, and both the flange and the pipe coated with bituminous paint before being set in position and surrounded with concrete (see Fig. 6.21).

Tees for the gas supply to each floor should be fitted at suitable levels with connectors for accessibility. Meters should be installed in a dry, ventilated cupboard inside the flats, with the index visible from the outside so that the gas registered can be read from a common corridor or landing. Figure 6.22 shows the gas supply to blocks of flats.

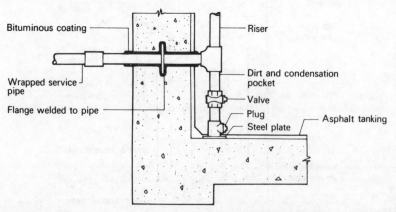

Fig. 6.21   Entry of service pipe through tanked basement

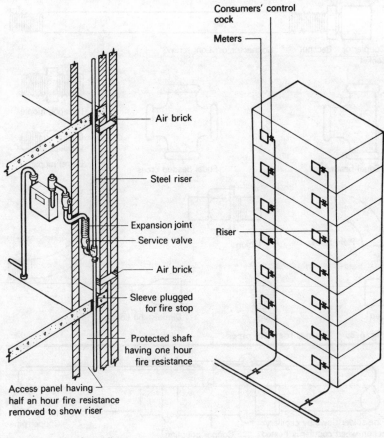

Consumers' control cock

Meters

Air brick

Steel riser

Expansion joint

Service valve

Air brick

Riser

Sleeve plugged for fire stop

Protected shaft having one hour fire resistance

Access panel having half an hour fire resistance removed to show riser

Fig. 6.22   Supply to flats

Purging

Before a meter is fitted, the gas control cock or valve should be fully opened to allow gas to pass through and at the same time clear any dirt in the service pipe. After the meter is fitted, the installation pipe should be purged before connection of the appliances.

Types of pipe fitting and joints

Various types of fittings are obtainable for use with mild steel pipe and these are commonly made from malleable iron, with the exception of connectors and bends which are made from mild steel. Figure 6.23 shows some common types of fittings for steel pipes; fittings for use with copper pipes take similar forms but are of the soldered type shown in Fig. 6.24. Alternatively, silver soldered joints may be used on copper pipes as shown in Fig. 6.25.

117

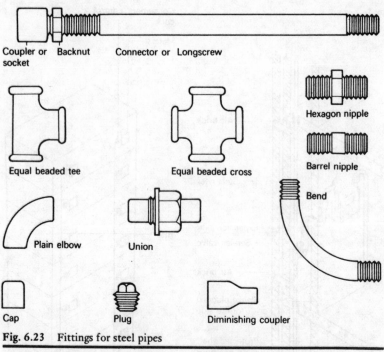

Fig. 6.23 Fittings for steel pipes

Coupler or socket · Backnut · Connector or Longscrew

Equal beaded tee · Equal beaded cross · Hexagon nipple · Barrel nipple

Plain elbow · Union · Bend

Cap · Plug · Diminishing coupler

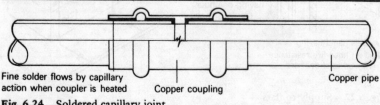

Fine solder flows by capillary action when coupler is heated · Copper coupling · Copper pipe

Fig. 6.24 Soldered capillary joint

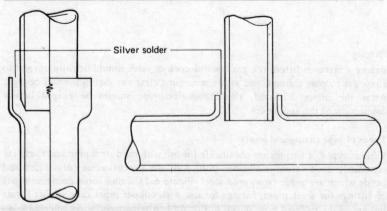

Silver solder

Fig. 6.25 Silver soldered joints on copper pipe

Pipe fixing

Gas piping should be fixed so as to be secure and prevent sagging, the spacing of the pipe supports depends upon the type of material and the diameter of the pipe (see Chapter 12). Figure 6.26 shows a variety of pipe fixings.

Protection of pipes

Pipes that may come into contact with composition floors, walls and skirtings, particularly those of magnesium oxychloride, should be protected from corrosion by painting them with bituminous paint. Pipes which need to pass vertically through corrosive floors may be protected by use of a short lead sleeve, shown in Fig. 6.27.

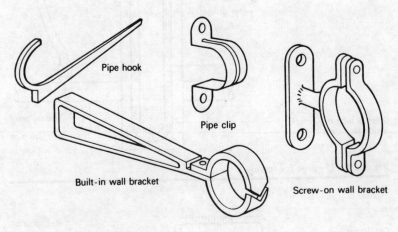

Fig. 6.26   Types of pipe fixings

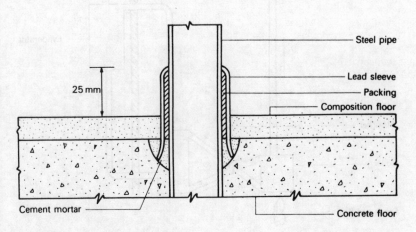

Fig. 6.27   Protection of steel pipe

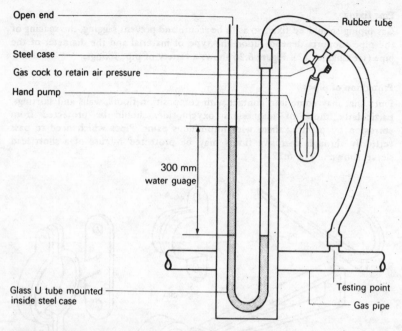

Fig. 6.28 U gauge for testing

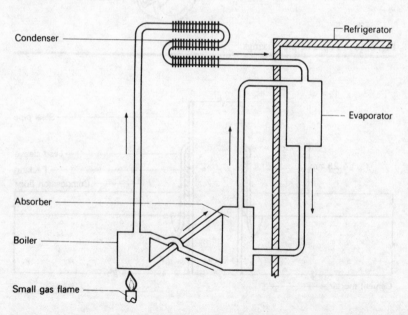

Fig. 6.29 The gas refrigerator (By Courtesy of the British Gas Corporation)

Installation testing

Immediately on completion, whether or not gas is available, any new installation or extension of an existing installation should be tested under air pressure. In installations where the pipes are covered with concrete, etc., it is desirable to test each section of pipework as the work proceeds. Air is used because it is possible to test at a greater pressure than that to which the installation would normally be subjected to when containing gas.

To test the installation all outlet pipes must be capped off, except the test point and a U gauge is connected to this point. Air is then pumped into the pipework through the test point until 300 mm water gauge or twice the normal gas pressure (whichever is the greatest) is registered on the U gauge. The air supply is then shut off and 10 min allowed for the adjustment of the air temperature. The air supply is reinstated and the test left for a further 15 min, when there should be no fall of the water level inside the U gauge. Figure 6.28 shows the U gauge and the method of testing.

The gas refrigerator

The principle on which gas refrigeration is based is that when a liquid evaporates it extracts heat from its surroundings. Figure 6.29 shows the components of a gas refrigerator which operates as follows:

1. A solution of ammonia in water is heated in the boiler by a small gas flame and the ammonia gas driven off is condensed to liquid ammonia in the air-cooled condenser.
2. The gases produced are led to the absorber and the ammonia absorbed by some weak liquid trickling down the absorber.
3. The strong ammonia solution produced is driven back into the boiler while the hydrogen gas, which is not absorbed, is led into the evaporator.

Note: The weak liquid trickling down the absorber is provided from the boiler, and in this way a complete cycle is obtained and refrigeration produced by heating only. There are no mechanical moving parts and refrigeration is produced continuously as long as heat is supplied to the boiler. The amount of cooling is automatically controlled by a thermostat inside the refrigerator.

Chapter 7

Gas controls, safety devices, heating and flues

Gas cocks

The simplest and most common form of gas control is the gas cock. This usually consists of a tapered plug which fits into a tapered body, the two connecting surfaces being machined to provide a gas-tight seal. The two surfaces should be smeared with grease to act as a lubricant. The cock is restricted to a 90° movement between being fully closed or fully opened. Figure 7.1 shows the customer's main control cock which incorporates a union to facilitate the removal of the meter.

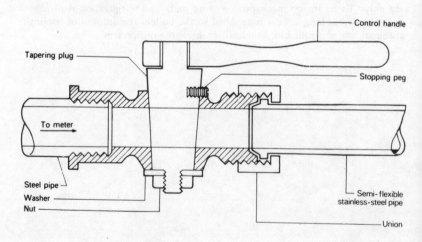

Fig. 7.1 Customer's control cock

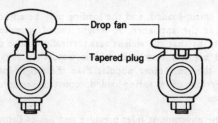

Fig. 7.2 Drop-fan safety cock

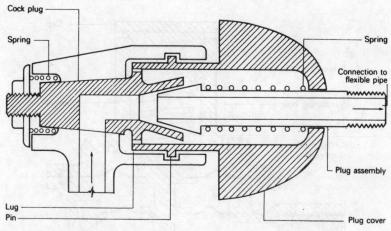

Fig. 7.3 Plug-in safety cock

For safety reasons, a drop-fan cock may be used as shown in Fig. 7.2. The fan is hinged to the turning head of the plug and has lugs which are arranged to hold the fan upright when the gas is on. When the cock is in the OFF position, the fan falls and the lugs engage with a slot in the body of the cock. The plug in this OFF position cannot be turned to the ON position until the fan is deliberately held upright, thus preventing the cock from being turned on accidentally.

The plug-in safety cock shown in Fig. 7.3 ensures that the cock cannot be turned to the ON position without first connecting the outlet pipe to the cock. The end of the plug assembly has two lugs which engage inside notches on the outside of the cock plug. When the plug assembly is inserted and turned to engage the lugs, two pins on the plug cover also engage a groove, and a gas-tight connection between the two components is made by compressing the spring which forces the two conical surfaces together.

Pressure governor

Pressure control of gas may be achieved by use of a constant pressure governor fitted on the inlet pipe to the meter and to each appliance. The governor may be weight-loaded or spring-loaded, and the loading may be adjusted to provide the correct pressure at the appliance. A weight-loaded governor must always be fitted horizontally so that the weight acts vertically on the diaphragm. Spring-loaded governors are not restricted in this way, they may be fitted in any position and are therefore more popular than the weight-loaded types. Figure 7.4 shows a section of a spring-loaded, constant-pressure governor which operates as follows:

1. Gas enters the governor at inlet pressure and passes through valve A to the appliance and also through the bypass to space B between the two diaphragms.

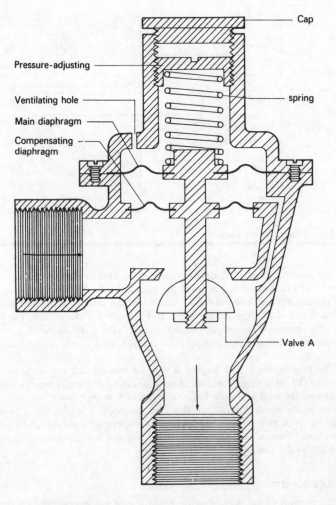

Fig. 7.4 Spring-loaded pressure governor

2. The main diaphragm is loaded by the spring and the upward and downward forces acting upon the diaphragm are balanced. The upward and downward forces acting upon the compensating diaphragm are also balanced and this has a stabilising affect on the valve and counteracts any tendency to oscillation.
3. Any fluctuation of inlet pressure will inflate or deflate the main diaphragm, thus raising or lowering valve A and altering the resistance to the flow of the gas, and thus ensuring a constant pressure at the outlet to the appliance.

Note: The space above the main diaphragm is ventilated to atmosphere to allow unrestricted movement of the valve. The diaphragms may be made from rubber, leather or plastic. A filter may be fitted on the inlet side of the governor.

Thermostats

A thermostat is a device which opens or closes a gas valve in accordance with the temperature it senses. The action of the thermostat depends upon the expansion of metals, liquids or vapours when heated.

Rod-type thermostat

This type of thermostat is used for cookers and storage-type water heaters (see Fig. 7.5). The brass tube shown in the diagram encloses an Invar steel rod to which is attached a valve. When the gas is burning, the brass tube becomes hot and as it expands it carries with it the Invar rod which expands very little. This brings the valve closer to its seating, thus reducing the flow of gas. Should the air or water cool down the brass tube also cools down and contracts, thus moving the valve away from its seating and so allowing more gas to flow to the burner until once again the temperature setting is reached. The bypass permits a small amount of gas to flow when the valve is closed and maintains a small flame at the burner.

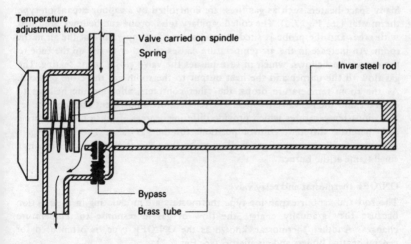

Fig. 7.5   Rod-type thermostat

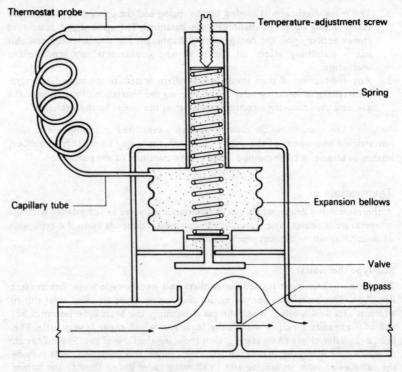

Fig. 7.6 Vapour expansion thermostat

Vapour expansion thermostat

Many space heaters such as gas fires, are controlled by a vapour expansion-type thermostat (see Fig. 7.6). The coiled capillary tube, probe and bellows, are filled with ether and the probe is sited so as to sense the temperature of the air in the room. An increase in the air temperature causes the ether to rise up the tube to the expansion bellows, which in turn pushes the valve closer to its seating. The gas flow to the burner and the heat output to the room are therefore reduced. As the room temperature drops, the ether contracts, allowing the bellows to contract and the gas valve to open. The temperature-adjustment screw can be set to various temperatures which provide differing degrees of tension on the spring and therefore different control positions for the gas valve. The bypass again permits a small amount of gas to flow when the valve is closed and maintains a small flame at the burner.

ON/OFF thermostat and relay valve

The rod and vapour expansion-type thermostats are modulating in their action because they gradually change the flow of gas in response to temperature changes. Another thermostat, known as the ON/OFF type, is often used for central heating boilers and circulators (see Fig. 7.7).

The relay-valve system shown, operates as follows:

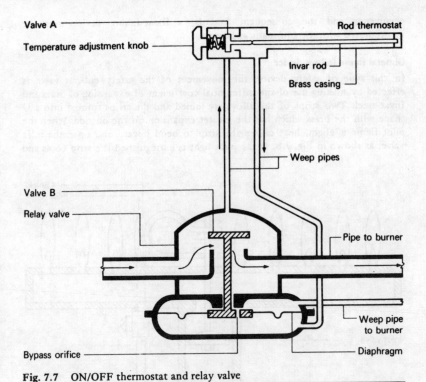

Valve A
Temperature adjustment knob
Rod thermostat
Invar rod
Brass casing
Weep pipes
Valve B
Relay valve
Pipe to burner
Weep pipe to burner
Bypass orifice
Diaphragm

Fig. 7.7 ON/OFF thermostat and relay valve

1. When the boiler or circulator is operated, the gas flows through to the burner because valves A and B are open and the gas pressures above and below the diaphragm are equal.
2. When the water reaches the required temperature, the brass casing expands sufficiently to draw valve A, connected to the Invar rod, to a closed position. The closing of valve A prevents gas from passing through the weep pipe to the underside of the diaphragm.
3. The gas pressure then builds up above the diaphragm in the relay valve and allows the valve assembly to fall under its own weight; valve B is thus closed.
4. When the water cools, valve A is again opened, allowing gas to flow to the underside of the diaphragm; valve B is again opened, which allows gas to again flow to the burner and be ignited by a pilot flame.

Note: The bypass allows gas below the diaphragm to escape through the weep pipe to the burner. This removes the pressure below the diaphragm and allows the valve assembly to fall under its own weight, aided by the gas pressure above the diaphragm.

Flame-failure device

It is essential to prevent unburnt gas reaching the burner of an automatic appliance in the event of failure of a pilot flame. In order to prevent the occurrence and the consequent hazards, a flame-failure device must be incorporated with the automatic appliance.

Bimetal flame-failure device

In this type of safety device, the movement of the safety cut-out valve is effected by making use of the differential coefficient of expansion of brass and Invar steel. Two strips of the alloys are joined and the strips formed into a U shape with the brass which has the greater expansion on the outside. When the pilot flame is alight, heat causes the strip to bend inward and open the inlet valve, as shown in Fig. 7.8. If the pilot light is extinguished the strip cools and

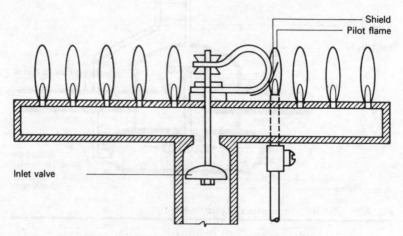

Fig. 7.8 Bimetal flame-failure device with pilot flame in operation

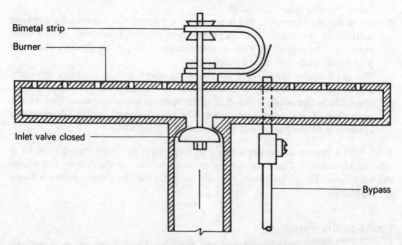

Fig. 7.9 Bimetal flame-failure device with pilot flame extinguished

reverts to its former shape, thus closing the inlet valve as shown in Fig. 7.9. This device is normally used for water heaters.

Magnetically operated flame-failure safety device

This type of safety device makes use of the fact that a small amount of electric current is generated between a hot and cold body and this current is used to energise a magnet (see Fig. 7.10). The thermocouple is heated by a pilot flame which also ignites the burner flames and the magnet holds the safety cut-out valve in an open position and allows gas to flow to the burner.

To light the burner, the following procedure is carried out:

1. The starter button is pressed down to the full length of its travel. This first closes the main gas valve and sets the lower end of the valve against the electromagnet.
2. The pilot cock is opened and the pilot flame established.
3. The starter button is kept depressed for about 30 s, in which time the magnet should be sufficiently energised to hold open the gas valve.
4. The button is released and the open interrupter valve allows gas to flow to the burner which is ignited by the pilot.

Note: As long as the pilot flame remains alight, electric current is generated and the electromagnet will hold the safety cut-out valve open. If the pilot flame is extinguished, the thermocouple no longer produces electricity and the spring underneath the safety cut-out valve closes the valve, thus cutting off the gas supply to the burner. The device is normally used with boilers and air heaters.

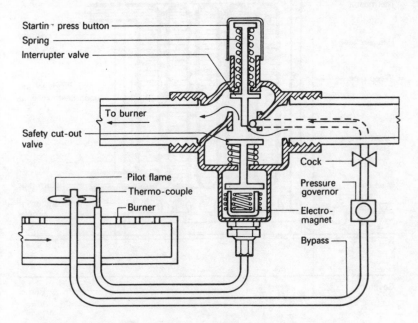

Fig. 7.10   Magnetically operated flame-failure safety device

Gas space heating

Boilers

Gas-fired, wall-hung boilers are popular because of saving in floor space. They can be obtained with either a conventional or a balanced flue. The heat exchanger of the boiler consists of a stainless steel or copper tube which holds approximately 0.7 litre of water, and this low water content permits a rapid thermal response. A typical wall-hung boiler has a heat output of 15 kW which is sufficient to heat domestic hot water and up to 20 m² of radiator surface, including the pipe runs.

Hearth-mounted boilers have heat outputs ranging from 8.8 kW for a small

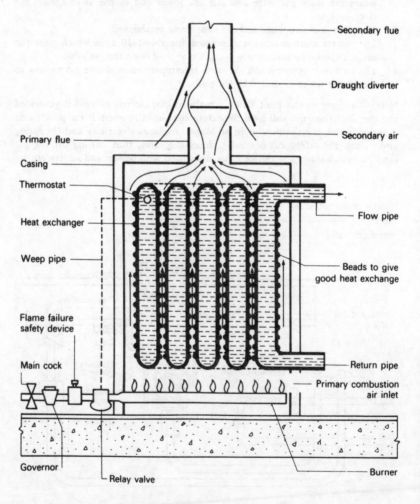

Secondary flue

Draught diverter

Secondary air

Primary flue

Casing

Thermostat

Heat exchanger

Weep pipe

Flow pipe

Beads to give
good heat exchange

Flame failure
safety device

Main cock

Return pipe

Primary combustion
air inlet

Governor

Relay valve

Burner

Fig. 7.11 Floor-mounted gas boiler

house to 1760 kW for a large building. The smaller boilers can be obtained with either a conventional or a balanced flue, but larger boilers are normally provided with a conventional flue. Figure 7.11 shows a small gas-fired, hearth-mounted boiler including the controls. These have been shown outside the boiler for clarity, but they are usually fitted inside the boiler casing.

Position

The boiler can be placed on the rooftop or in any other convenient position since there is no storage of fuel and removal of ashes are no problem. This is of great value since ground-floor and basement space is exceptionally valuable. A shorter conventional flue is also possible which saves on construction costs and space. There is also less pressure on the boiler. All types of boilers are fully automatic in operation and incorporate thermostatic and clock control, a flame-failure device which ensures a 100 per cent gas cut-off in the event of pilot failure, and a constant pressure governor.

Efficiencies are high — of the order of 75—80 per cent — and space requirements per unit of heat output is slightly less than for solid fuel and oil-fired boilers.

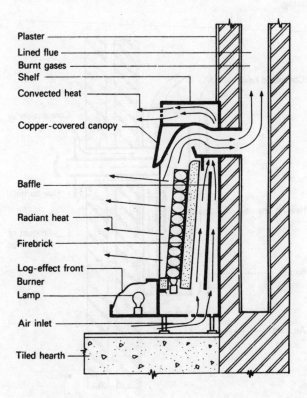

Fig. 7.12   Built-in-type gas fire

Construction

Sectional cast-iron boilers are available with heat outputs of between 8.8 and 440 kW. It is possible to erect the boilers in confined spaces and a single section can be readily replaced.

Welded plate steel boilers are normally fabricated in one piece, which reduces site work. Heat outputs of up to 180 kW are available. Welded tubular-steel boilers are available for larger installations, with heat outputs of up to 1760 kW. Steel boilers can withstand higher pressures than cast-iron boilers.

Fires

These are usually designed to provide both radiant and convective heating to the room; in addition they can incorporate a back boiler at the rear which can be easily fitted into a standard fireplace opening.

A typical fire has a heat output of 3 kW, and a gas-fired back boiler a heat output of 12 kW, which is sufficient to heat the normal domestic hot water and up to 18 m² of radiator surface, including the pipe runs. If domestic hot water is not required a back boiler will heat up to 20 m² of radiator surface, including the pipe runs. Fires can be either hearth- or wall-mounted. Figure 7.12 shows a section through a hearth-mounted gas fire providing both radiant and convective space heating.

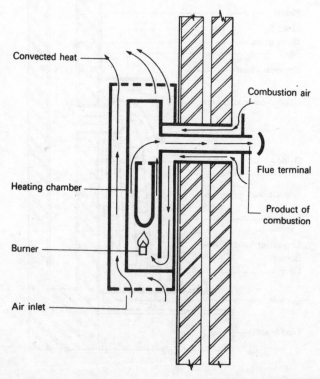

Fig. 7.13 Natural convector

Convector heaters

These are usually room-sealed combustion units, incorporating a balanced flue. The heat output from the convector is almost all by convection although some radiant heat is given off from the hot casing, usually about 10 per cent. They provide a simple, flexible space heating system and are usually cheaper to install than a boiler and radiator system. Figure 7.13 shows a natural convector and Fig. 7.14 a fan-assisted convector which gives a rapid thermal response. Heaters are available with heat outputs of between 5 kW and 7 kW.

Warm-air units (see Fig. 7.15)

These are free-standing, self-contained packaged units which combine controlled heating, ventilation and air movement. They are provided with a silent fan and built-in noise attenuators which make them suitable for the space heating of houses, schools, churches and libraries. The warm air may be ducted from the unit to the various rooms, as shown in Fig. 7.16. The ducts must be well insulated to prevent heat loss. Units are available having heat outputs from 6 kW to 50 kW.

A warm-air space heating system provides a good distribution of heat and the air movement gives the required feeling of freshness. The system can be used in hot weather to circulate the air in the rooms. However, criticism of the system

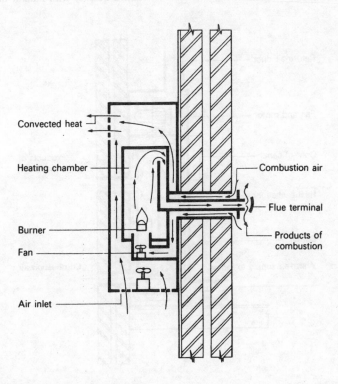

Fig. 7.14   Fan-assisted convector

is that there is no radiant heating and a gas fire may be required to provide this, especially in the lounge.

Unit heaters for overhead use

These are suitable for factories, churches and assembly halls and two types are available:

1. Indirect, which have a flue to carry off the products of combustion and have a heat output of up to 230 kW at 75 per cent efficiency.
2. Direct or flueless heater, in which the products of combustion are circulated together with the heated air and have a heat output of up to 41 kW at 90 per cent efficiency.

Figure 7.17 shows a direct overhead unit heater installed in a factory or assembly hall.

Radiant heaters

Thermal comfort may be provided for the occupants of a room at comparatively low capital and running costs, by use of radiant heaters mounted either on the wall or ceiling. They can be installed in factories, churches and assembly halls and are used as an alternative to the convector heaters for heating these buildings. Thermal comfort conditions can be obtained quicker with radiant heaters

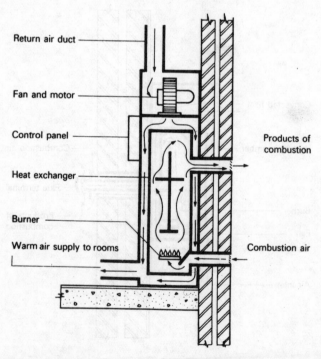

Fig. 7.15 Gas warm-air unit

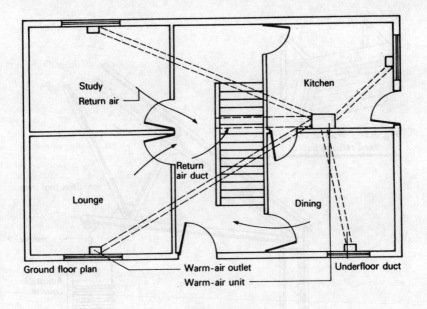

Study
Return air

Kitchen

Lounge

Return air duct

Dining

Ground floor plan

Warm-air outlet
Warm-air unit

Underfloor duct

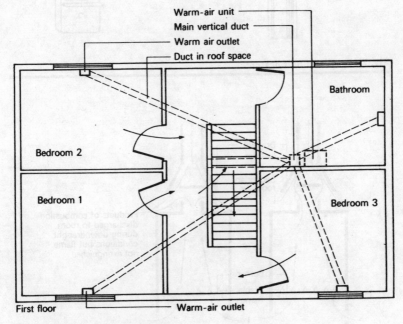

Warm-air unit
Main vertical duct
Warm air outlet
Duct in roof space

Bathroom

Bedroom 2

Bedroom 1

Bedroom 3

First floor

Warm-air outlet

Note: When the doors are closed the air
returns through grills in the doors

Fig. 7.16 Warm-air system

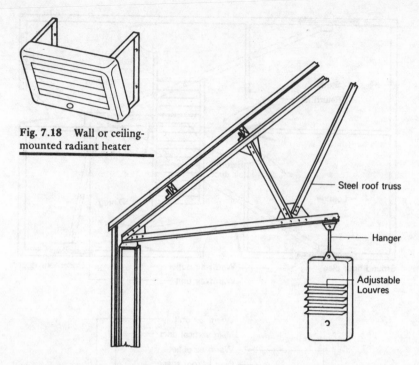

Fig. 7.18 Wall or ceiling-mounted radiant heater

Steel roof truss

Hanger

Adjustable Louvres

Fig. 7.17 Direct-unit heater

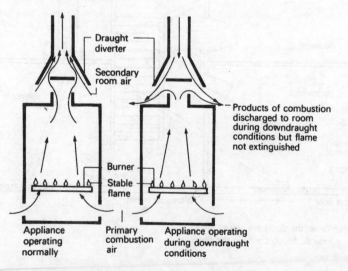

Draught diverter

Secondary room air

Products of combustion discharged to room during downdraught conditions but flame not extinguished

Burner

Stable flame

Appliance operating normally

Primary combustion air

Appliance operating during downdraught conditions

Fig. 7.19 Operation of draught diverter

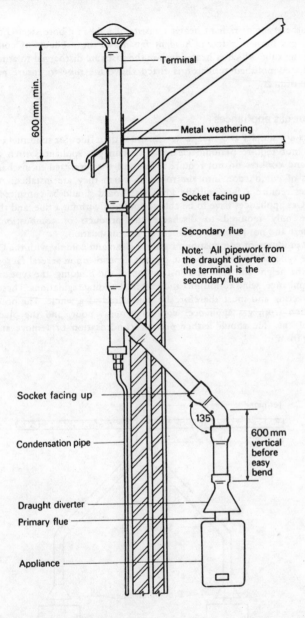

Terminal

600 mm min.

Metal weathering

Socket facing up

Secondary flue

Note: All pipework from
the draught diverter to
the terminal is the
secondary flue

Socket facing up

135°

600 mm
vertical
before
easy
bend

Condensation pipe

Draught diverter

Primary flue

Appliance

Fig. 7.20 Primary and secondary flue

than with convector heaters and the pre-heating time and fuel costs are therefore
reduced to a minimum. Figure 7.18 shows a wall- or ceiling-mounted radiant
heater.

Another type of radiant heater consists of a 64 mm bore steel U tube into which a gas burner is fixed. A silent fan draws the products of combustion through the tube which is heated before the gases are discharged to atmosphere. An insulated polished reflector is fitted above the tube to ensure maximum radiation of heat.

Flues for gas appliances

Gas flues are simpler and cheaper to construct than flues for solid fuel or oil and they do not require periodic cleaning. Certain gas appliances such as space heaters and cookers do not require a flue and are permitted to discharge their products of combustion into the room in which they are installed. All other appliances require a flue and the local Gas Board should be consulted on this matter. Gas appliances have to be able to function without a flue, and the flue is therefore only required to discharge the products of combustion to the atmosphere and not to create a draught to aid combustion.

The products of combustion of gas are clean and comply with the Clean Air Act. The type of flue for a specific project depends upon several factors which include the height and type of construction of the building, the type and siting of the appliance, wind conditions and current building regulations. These factors are interacting and must therefore be considered as a whole. The products of combustion from gas appliances contain water vapour, and the placing and design of the flue should either prevent condensation or remove any water resulting from it.

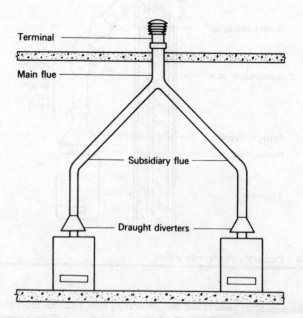

Fig. 7.21 Main and subsidiary flues

Terms used

Draught diverter. A device designed for preventing downdraught or static conditions in the secondary flue of an appliance from interfering with the combustion of gas within the appliance. It also prevents excessive draught conditions by

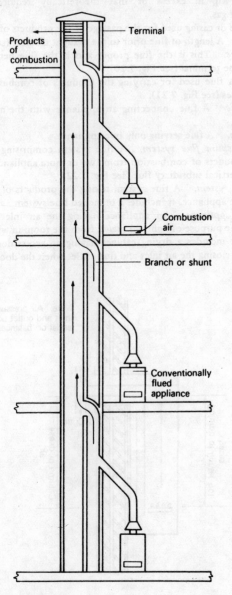

Fig. 7.22 Branch and shunt flue

allowing the air in the room to mix with the products of combustion in the secondary flue and then cool down these hot gases. Figure 7.19 shows the operation of a draught diverter.

Duct. A tube or casing used for the passage of the products of combustion or air.

Excess air. Air in excess of that theoretically required for complete combustion of gas.

Flue. A tube or casing used for the passage of the products of combustion.

Primary flue. A length of flue prior to the draught diverter (see Fig. 7.20).

Secondary flue. This is the flue proper and is the flue between the draught diverter and the terminal (see Fig. 7.20).

Main flue. A flue used for carrying the products of combustion from two or more appliances (see Fig. 7.21).

Subsidiary flue. A flue connecting an appliance with the main flue (see Fig. 7.21).

Individual flue. A flue serving only one appliance.

Branched or shunt flue system. A flue system comprising a main flue into which the products of combustion from two or more appliances discharge, each by way of a vertical subsidiary flue (see Fig. 7.22).

Common flue system. A flue system taking the products of combustion from more than one appliance. It includes a branched flue system.

Room-sealed appliance. An appliance having the air inlet and flue outlets (except for the purpose of lighting) *sealed* from the room in which the appliance is installed. It includes a drying cabinet having an access door, with means of automatically closing the air inlet and flue outlet when the door is opened.

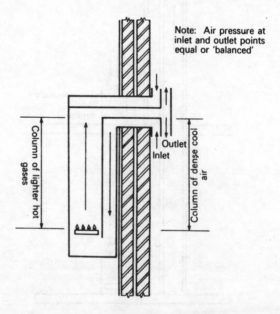

Fig. 7.23 Principle of operation of balanced-flue appliance

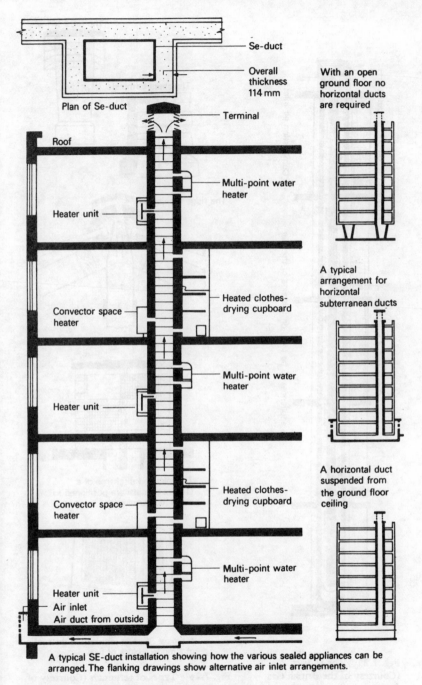

A typical SE-duct installation showing how the various sealed appliances can be arranged. The flanking drawings show alternative air inlet arrangements.

Fig. 7.24 The Se-duct (Courtesy of the British Gas Corporation)

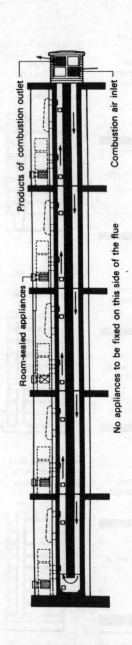

The G.C.1 terminal

The shunt terminal

The ridge terminal

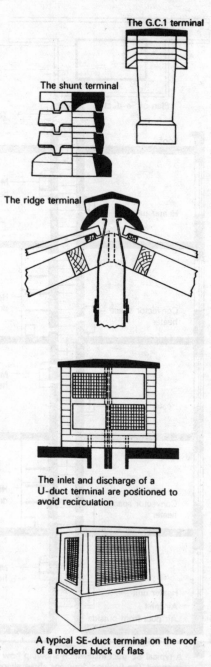

The inlet and discharge of a U-duct terminal are positioned to avoid recirculation

A typical SE-duct terminal on the roof of a modern block of flats

Fig. 7.25 The U duct (Courtesy of the British Gas Corporation)

Fig. 7.26 Types of terminals (Courtesy of the British Gas Corporation)

Balanced-flue appliance. An appliance designed to draw in combustion air from a point immediately adjacent to where it discharges its products of combustion. The inlet and outlet points are incorporated in a windproof terminal, which is sited outside the room in which the appliance is fitted (see Fig. 7.23 which shows the principles of operation of a balanced-flue appliance).

SE duct. A duct rising vertically which is open at the bottom and top, serving to bring combustion air to and take the products of combustion from room-sealed appliances to the external air (see Fig. 7.24).

U duct. A duct in the form of a U to one limb of which are fitted room-sealed appliances, while the other limb provides combustion air (see Fig. 7.25).

Terminal. A device fitted at the termination of the flue, designed to allow free passage of the products of combustion, to minimise downdraught and to prevent the entry of foreign matter which might cause restriction of the flue. Figure 7.26 shows various types of terminals.

Venting. The removal of the products of combustion from an appliance.

Principles of design of flues

A gas flue in a building may serve two purposes namely:

1. To remove the products of combustion from an appliance.
2. To assist in the ventilation of the room in which the appliance is installed.

The force causing the movement of the gases inside a flue is usually due to the difference in density between the hot gases in the flue and the cooler air inside the room. This force is small and it is therefore essential that bends and terminals used in the construction of the flue should offer low resistance to the flow of gases. The flue should also terminate in such a position in the open air that the effects of wind pressure will aid the updraught and not act adversely.

Note: Some gas flues use a fan to extract the products of combustion from the appliance, and therefore the force causing the movement of the gases in the flue is not due solely to the differences in density between the hot gases and the cooler air inside the room. However, this natural convection will reduce the power required for the fan. The size of a flue for a gas appliance is dependent upon the kilowatt rating of the appliance and the ventilation standard of the room in which the appliance is installed.

Materials for flues

1. Asbestos-cement pipes and fittings suitable for internal and external work and should conform to BSS 567.
2. Steel or cast-iron pipes protected by a good-quality vitreous enamel.
3. Sheet aluminium (except where temperatures and condensation is liable to be excessive, e.g. a water-heater flue in a cold position).
4. Sheet copper protected by chromium plating after fabricating.
5. Stainless steel.
6. Precast concrete flue blocks (see Fig. 7.27) made of acid resisting cement and pointed by acid resisting cement mortar.
7. Brick flue, lined with precast concrete made of acid resisting cement and pointed with acid resisting cement mortar, or glazed stoneware pipes pointed with high-acid resisting mortar.

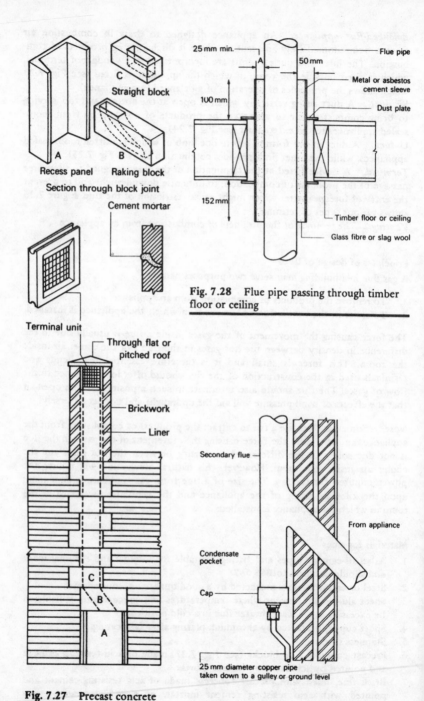

Straight block

Raking block

A

Recess panel

Section through block joint

Cement mortar

Terminal unit

Through flat or
pitched roof

Brickwork

Liner

C

B

A

**Fig. 7.27 Precast concrete
flue blocks**

25 mm min.

A

50 mm

100 mm

152 mm

Flue pipe

Metal or asbestos
cement sleeve

Dust plate

Timber floor or ceiling

Glass fibre or slag wool

**Fig. 7.28 Flue pipe passing through timber
floor or ceiling**

Secondary flue

Condensate
pocket

Cap

From appliance

25 mm diameter copper pipe
taken down to a gulley or ground level

Fig. 7.30 Condensate removal

Planning of flues

All necessary information with regards to the installation of gas flues, should be made at the early design stage of the building. The local Gas Board should be consulted before any drawings and specifications are made and also during the execution of the work. The drawings should show the proposed positions of appliances and full details of the routes of all flues, from the point of connection to the appliances to the position of termination.

Flue installations must conform with the Building Regulations, | 1985. The following points must be considered when planning a flue:

1. The flue should rise progressively towards its terminal.
2. The primary flue should be as short as possible.
3. The secondary flue should be of adequate height and kept inside the building so far as is possible.
4. In many appliances the draught diverter is an integral part of the appliance and permits easy disconnection of the flue from the appliance. Where an appliance is not fitted with a draught diverter, a disconnecting device should be fitted as near as is practicable to the appliance.
5. Routes which expose the flue to rapid cooling should be avoided, or thermal insulation afforded to the flue external surface.
6. Horizontal flues and fittings having sharp angles must be avoided.
7. The joints of asbestos-cement pipes and fittings should be made by caulking with slag wool for about 25 per cent of the depth of the socket. The remaining 75 per cent of the socket should be filled with a good-quality fire cement and the outside edge neatly chamfered. All socket joints should face upwards.
8. Exterior flue pipes should be supported by brackets fitted throughout the height of the flue at intervals of not more than 2 m, preferably immediately below the pipe socket.
9. Where a flue passes through combustible material, it must be covered by a metal or asbestos cement sleeve, with an annular spacing of 25 mm packed with incombustible material (see Fig. 7.28).

Terminal position

The terminal of a gas flue should be placed in such a position that the wind can blow freely across it, the best positions being above the ridge of a pitched roof or above the parapet wall of a flat roof. Figure 7.29 shows the usual requirements for flues passing through a flat roof.

High-wind-pressure regions must be avoided and therefore terminals must not be placed below the eaves, in a corner or adjacent to another pipe. However, a terminal can be placed above the level of the eaves (as shown in Fig. 7.20) or on the unobstructed portion of a wall.

Condensate and its removal

Some initial condensation in a gas flue will occur immediately after the appliance has been lit and it tends to persist in flues placed on the external walls or in flues attached to appliances of high efficiencies, especially if these are run for long periods at much less than their rated maximum output. Well-insulated internal flues are preferable to external flues which increase the degree of condensation. The flues should be built so that condensate can flow freely to a point where it can be released, preferably into a 25 mm bore lead or copper condensate pipe (see Fig. 7.30).

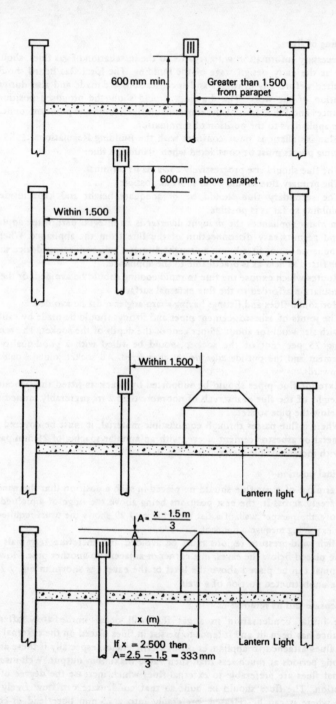

600 mm min.   Greater than 1.500 from parapet

600 mm above parapet.

Within 1.500

Within 1.500

Lantern light

$A = \dfrac{x - 1.5\,m}{3}$

x (m)

If x = 2.500 then $A = \dfrac{2.5 - 1.5}{3} = 333\ mm$

Lantern Light

Fig. 7.29 Flue terminal on flat roof

Large boilers

It is desirable to house large gas-fired boilers in separate boiler rooms, which may be part of the main structure or completely separate. A boiler room sited on the roof of the building requires a very short flue (see Fig. 7.31). Alternatively, the

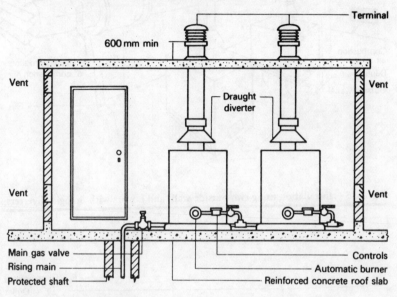

Fig. 7.31   Rooftop boiler room

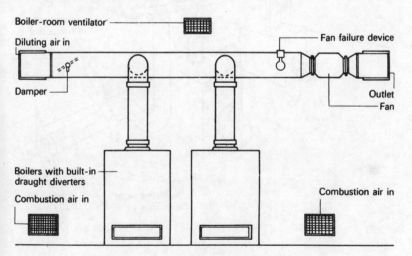

Figs 7.32, 7.33 and 7.34   Fan-diluted flue (Courtesy of the British Gas Corporation)

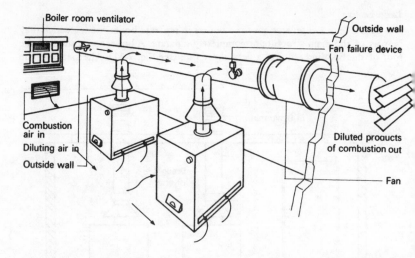

Fig. 7.33 Installation using two outside walls and boilers with draught diverters

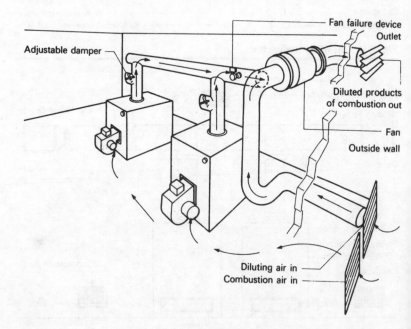

Fig. 7.34 Installation using one outside wall and boilers with automatic gas burners

148

boiler may be installed at ground level and a fan-diluting flue used (see Figs. 7.32, 7.33 and 7.34). With this type of flue, a fan draws in fresh air which is mixed with the products of combustion from the appliance and discharged to the outside air.

It is essential to provide permanent air inlets to the boiler room to ensure a sufficient supply of air for the efficient operation of the boilers and these inlets should be:

1. At least twice as great in free area as the area of the primary flue pipe.
2. Located at least 300 mm above ground level and fitted with a grill.
3. Constructed of durable material.

Note: The provision of combustion air to gas appliances, is covered by the Building Regulations, 1985.

Shared flues

Gas appliances in multi-storey buildings may be connected to a shared flue in the form of a SE-duct, U duct or shunt duct. The use of a shared flue in a multi-storey building, saves considerably in space and installation costs over the use of individual flues. Both the SE-duct and the U duct require room-sealed, balanced-flue appliances, and the shunt duct requires a conventional flue appliance which has the advantage of ventilating the room in which the appliance is installed. For safety reasons, all appliances connected to shared flues must be provided with flame-failure devices.

The degree of dilution of the products of combustion in a shared flue is sufficient to ensure the satisfactory operation of all gas appliances connected to the system.

Calculation of gas consumption

The gas requirement from appliance may be found from the following formula:

$$\frac{power}{calorific\ value} = m^3/s$$

The calorific or heating value of natural gas is approximately 37 000 kJ/m^3 and town gas approximately 19 000 kJ/m^3.

Example 7.1. *Calculate the gas consumed in cubic metres per hour by a 20 kW boiler when natural gas is used.*

$$Consumption = \frac{20 \times 3600}{37\ 000} = 1.946\ m^3/h$$

Note: 1 kW   = 3.6 MJ/h

             1 Therm = 105.5 MJ

Chapter 8

Drainage below ground

Principles of drainage below ground

The efficient disposal of foul and surface water from a building is of great importance to public health and is an essential part of the construction of a building. If a drain is unsound and leaks, the escaping water may contaminate the water supply or air. The escaping water may also wash away the soil below the foundation and cause a risk of settlement of part of the building. The Building Regulations 1985 deals with drainage below ground and the student is strongly advised to become familiar with the various requirements.

Terms used

The following definitions are laid down by section 343 of the Public Health Act 1936:

Drain

Means a drain used for the drainage of one building, or of any buildings or yards, appurtenant to buildings within the same curtilage.

Sewer

Does not include a drain as defined in this section but, save as aforesaid, includes all sewers and drains used for the drainage of buildings and yard appurtenant to buildings.

Private sewer

Means a sewer which is not a public sewer. In general terms, drain, sewer and private sewer may be described as follows:

Drain: a system of pipes used for the drainage of one or more buildings within a private boundary. The owner of the building, or buildings, is responsible for the maintenance of a drain.

Private sewer: a system of pipes used for the drainage of two or more buildings belonging to separate owners. The pipes are inside a private boundary and their maintenance is shared jointly by the separate owners of the buildings.

Public sewer: a system of pipes belonging to the local authority and maintained by the authority. The pipes are outside the private boundary, usually under the roadway. It is the duty of every local authority to provide public sewers and the provision, by means of sewage disposal works, for the effectual disposal of the contents of public sewers. If the public sewer is within 30 m of a building site, the local authority may require the building drainage to connect to the public sewer.

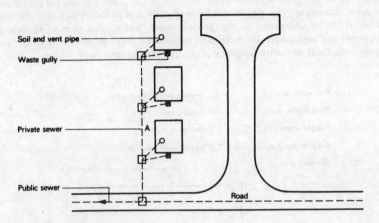

Fig. 8.1   Use of private sewer

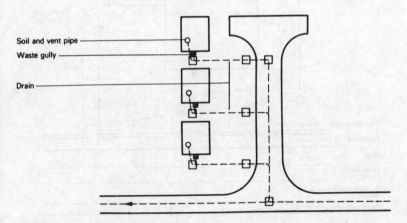

Fig. 8.2   Use of individual drains

Figure 8.1 shows a drainage system for three houses having separate owners, with each house connected to the public sewer by means of a private sewer, which may be run either at the back or front of the houses. Figure 8.2 shows how the houses may be connected to the public sewer by an individual drain from each house.

The first method has the advantage of reducing the number of connections required to the public sewer in the roadway and also the reduction in pipe length and number of manholes. The second method has the advantage of preventing a dispute in the event of a repair or blockage. If, for example, a blockage occurred in the private sewer at A, the owner of the house nearest to the public sewer may refuse to pay towards the work of clearing the blockage because he is not affected. The shared responsibility of maintenance of the private sewer is often included in the title deeds of each house, but this does not always prevent a dispute occurring. The owner will be eventually compelled to pay towards the cost of the maintenance of the private sewer, but a good deal of ill-feeling between the neighbours will have been caused. If a blockage occurs in the public sewer, the local authority would be responsible for its clearance.

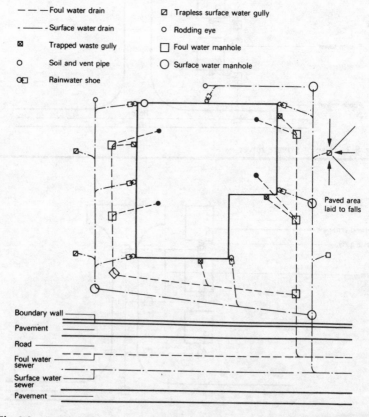

Fig. 8.3 Separate system of drainage for a medium-sized building

Systems of drainage

The type of system used depends upon the local authority regulation. There are three types:

Separate system: in which the foul water discharges from W.C.s, basins, sinks, baths, etc., are conveyed by foul water drains to a foul water sewer, or private sewage disposal plant; the rainwater or surface water from roofs and paved areas are conveyed by surface water drains to a public surface water sewer or soakaway. Figure 8.3 shows a separate system for a medium-sized building.

Combined system: in which the foul water from sanitary appliances and surface water from roofs and paved areas are conveyed by a single drain to a combined sewer. The system saves on drainage costs, but the cost of sewage disposal is increased. Figure 8.4 shows a combined system for the same medium-sized building.

Partially separate system: in which most of the surface water is conveyed by a

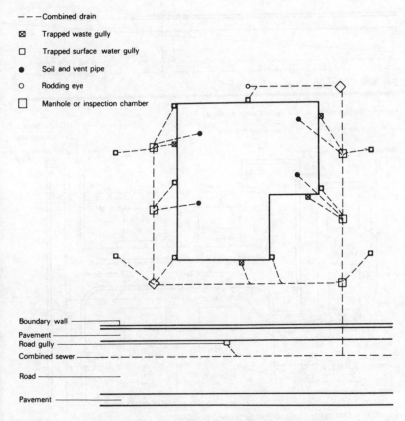

Fig. 8.4   Combined system of drainage for a medium-sized building

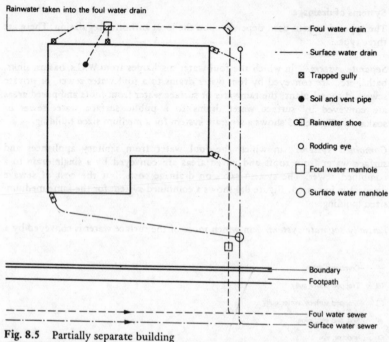

Rainwater taken into the foul water drain

- - - Foul water drain
- · - Surface water drain
⊠ Trapped gully
● Soil and vent pipe
Œ Rainwater shoe
○ Rodding eye
□ Foul water manhole
○ Surface water manhole

Boundary
Footpath

Foul water sewer
Surface water sewer

Fig. 8.5 Partially separate building

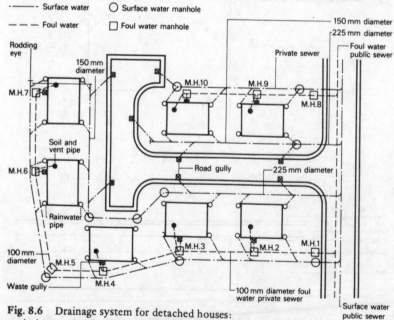

- · - Surface water   ○ Surface water manhole
- - - Foul water   □ Foul water manhole

Rodding eye

150 mm diameter

M.H.7

Soil and vent pipe

M.H.6

Rainwater pipe

100 mm diameter

M.H.5

Waste gully

M.H.4

Road gully

M.H.10   M.H.9

Private sewer

M.H.8

225 mm diameter

M.H.3   M.H.2   M.H.1

100 mm diameter foul water private sewer

150 mm diameter
225 mm diameter
Foul water public sewer

Surface water public sewer

Fig. 8.6 Drainage system for detached houses: typical example of separate system by use of private sewers

154

surface water drain to a surface water sewer or soakaway, but some of the rainwater is connected to the foul water drain. This is done when the rainwater can be conveniently connected to the foul water drain, usually at the rear of the building.

This arrangement, when compared to the separate system, saves on drainage costs and the rainwater will also flush the foul water drain. Figure 8.5 shows a partially separate system for a detached house and Fig. 8.6 shows a drainage scheme for a small private development of detached houses. Table 8.1 gives a comparison of the separate and combined systems.

Table 8.1 Summary of the comparisons between the separate and combined drainage system

Separate system	Combined system
1. Two sets of drains; increases the cost of building drainage	1. Only one drain for both foul and surface water; reduces the cost of building drainage
2. There is a risk of a wrong connection, e.g., a foul water branch drain may be wrongly connected to a surface water drain	2. There is no risk of making a wrong connection
3. The foul water drain is not thoroughly flushed by rainwater	3. Foul water is flushed through the drain by the surface water
4. There is no risk of foul air passing through an unsealed rainwater gully trap	4. The loss of a trap seal in a rainwater gully allows the foul gas from the drain to pass into the open air around the building
5. The size of the sewage disposal plant is much smaller	5. The size of the sewage disposal plant is greater
6. The cost of sewage purification is less	6. The cost of the sewage disposal is greater
7. If the sewage is pumped to the sewage disposal works there is a reduction in the cost of pumping. The surface water may flow by gravity to a nearby river	7. Possibly greater pumping costs, due to both surface water and foul water to have to reach the sewage disposal works

The following points should be considered in the design of drainage systems.

1. The layout of the system should be as simple and direct as possible and the number of bends, traps and manholes kept to a minimum.
2. The pipes should be laid in straight lines, from point to point.
3. The pipes should be non-absorbent, durable, smooth in bore and of adequate strength.
4. The pipes should be adequately supported without restricting movement.
5. Foul water drains should be well ventilated, to prevent the accumulation of foul gases and fluctuation of air pressure within the pipe, which could lead to the unsealing of gully or W.C. traps.
6. All the parts of the drainage system should be accessible for inspection and cleaning.
7. The pipes should be laid to a self-cleansing gradient, that will prevent the

settlement of solid matter, which might lead to a blockage. The minimum gradients are 1 in 80 for a 100 mm diameter pipe serving 5–20 housing units and 1 in 150 for a 150 mm diameter pipe serving 10–150 housing units. For smaller flows and short lengths of drainage, a gradient of 1 in 40 may be used for a 100 mm diameter drain. Flatter gradients are possible when a high standard of workmanship and supervision can be assured. These are 1 in 130 for a 100 mm diameter pipe serving 5–20 housing units and 1 in 200 for a 150 mm diameter pipe serving 10–150 housing units. These flatter gradients save a great deal on excavation costs.

8. The velocity of flow should not be less than 0.8 m/s which will prevent the stranding of solid matter. A maximum velocity of 2 m/s is acceptable, but the upper limit is not considered important and on sloping sites the drain may be allowed to follow the fall of the land. Large diameter sewers, however, require ramps to restrict the fall on sloping sites, to permit workmen to make necessary inspections and repairs.

9. A foul water drain should never run at more than 90 per cent of its capacity. This is equivalent to running at a depth of flow equal to three-quarters of the bore. This maximum discharge, together with adequate ventilation, will prevent the possibility of compression of air in the drain, which could cause unsealing of traps. Surface water drains may be designed to run at full bore.

10. Pipes should not pass under a building unless absolutely necessary and pipes should not be laid close to building foundations.

11. Pipes should not pass near trees because of the possibility of damage by the roots.

12. Where possible, flexible joints should be used and the Code of Practice on drainage recommends that pipes under buildings should have flexible joints and means of access.

13. Where pipes pass through walls, a relieving arch or lintel should be provided in the wall above the pipes to prevent the wall load bearing on the pipe.

14. Bends in pipes should have a large radius of between 215 and 750 mm for 100 mm diameter pipes and between 225 and 900 mm for 150 mm diameter pipes.

15. Branch connections should be swept in the direction of flow.

16. Drain pipes should be at least 900 mm below roads and at least 600 mm below fields and gardens.

17. Clay pipes under roads should have their strength increased by surrounding them with 150 mm thickness of *in situ* concrete. Flexible joints should be used and a 25 mm gap should be left at the joint to give flexibility at this point (see Fig. 8.7). Alternatively, ductile iron pipes may be used with flexible joints.

Note: The BS Code of Practice 2005, 1968, 'Sewerage', recommends a minimum cover of not less than 1.2 m for sewers under roads or footpaths.

18. Where pipes are not under a road and the depth below ground is less than 600 mm, two pre-cast concrete slabs should be laid over the pipes, so that the load transmitted to the pipe walls is at points of about 22.30 hr and 13.30 hr. There should be a minimum thickness of 150 mm of soil, free from large stones, building rubbish, tree roots, vegetable matter and large lumps of clay. Alternatively, broken stone or gravel 10 mm nominal single size may be placed between the concrete slabs and the top of the pipe.

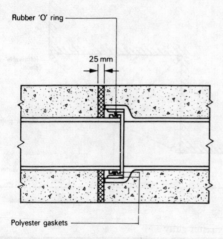

Compressible board such as expanded polystyrene cut to profile of pipe and concrete and inserted to maintain flexibility of pipe line

Rubber 'O' ring

25 mm

Polyester gaskets

Fig. 8.7   Concrete surround for vitrified clay drain pipe passing under road

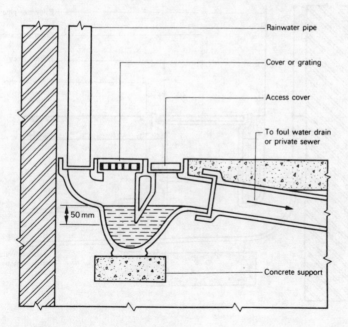

Rainwater pipe

Cover or grating

Access cover

To foul water drain or private sewer

50 mm

Concrete support

Fig. 8.8   Use of back inlet trapped gully

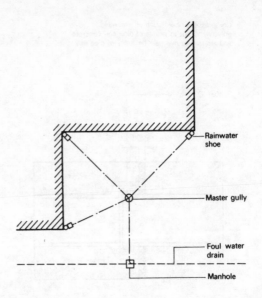

Rainwater shoe

Master gully

Foul water drain

Manhole

Fig. 8.9 Use of master gully

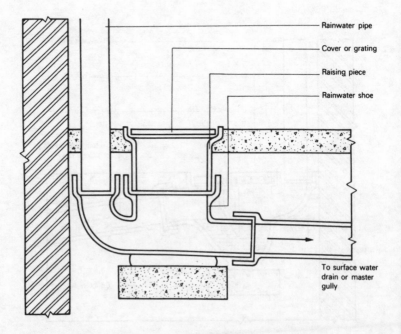

Rainwater pipe

Cover or grating

Raising piece

Rainwater shoe

To surface water drain or master gully

Fig. 8.10 Use of rainwater shoe

Connections to drains

The provision of a water-sealed trap to each connection to foul water drainage is essential and the seal should be maintained under working conditions. The trap prevents the entry of foul air into the building, or into the open air. Soil, vent and waste stacks do not require traps at their bases, because the sanitary fittings connected to the stacks are provided with traps. Other connections to foul water drains such as rainwater pipes in a combined system should be provided with gully traps, as shown in Fig. 8.8.

In order to reduce the number of gully traps from rainwater connections in a combined system, a master gully trap may be used, as shown in Fig. 8.9. Each rainwater pipe is then connected to a rainwater shoe, before discharging into the master gully. This method also reduces the length of drainage and the number of connections to the inspection chamber. Figure 8.10 shows a detail of a rainwater shoe and Fig. 8.11 shows a detail of a master gully trap.

Use of intercepting traps

In the past, intercepting traps were fitted between the drain and a sewer, with the object of preventing sewer gases entering the drainage system (see Fig. 8.12). Modern drainage systems do not include an interceptor and this has led to better ventilation of the sewer, fewer blockages and saving in costs (see Fig. 8.13). The local authority, however, may require in interceptor trap where a new connection is to be made to an old sewer in poor condition, or in a district where the trap has been fitted to each drainage system. Figure 8.14 shows a section through various types of intercepting traps.

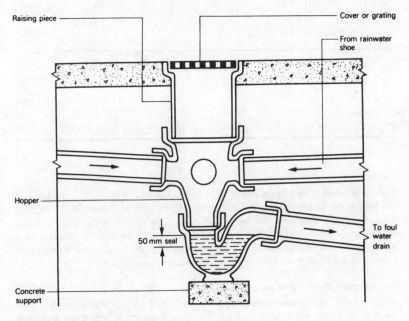

Fig. 8.11   Detail of master gully

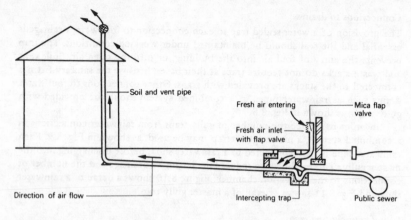

Fig. 8.12 Ventilation of drain with use of interceptor trap

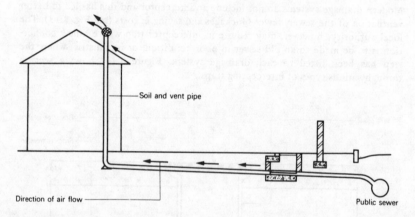

Fig. 8.13 Ventilation of drain without use of interceptor trap

Ventilation

The ventilation of the drain is provided by means of a vent stack at the head of the foul water drain. A soil or waste stack may be used as a vent pipe, providing it is of suitable diameter. The vent stack should be terminated at least 900 mm above any window, within a horizontal distance of 3 m from the stack and a wire balloon should be fitted to the top of the pipe. Foul water drain pipes exceeding 6.4 m long are usually required to be vented.

Surface water from paved areas

When a combined system is used a yard gully having a water seal of not less than 50 mm in depth must be fitted on the surface water branch drain before it connects to the combined foul water drain (see Fig. 8.15).

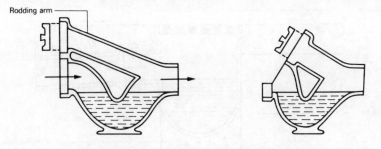

Rodding arm

Vitrified clay interceptor traps with inlet and outlet level

Stopper

Cascade

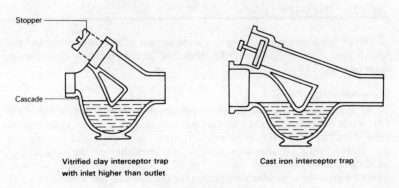

**Vitrified clay interceptor trap
with inlet higher than outlet**

Cast iron interceptor trap

Depth of trap water seals

100 mm diameter	64 mm deep
150 mm diameter	76 mm deep
225 mm diameter	76 mm deep

Fig. 8.14 Types of interceptor traps

Grating

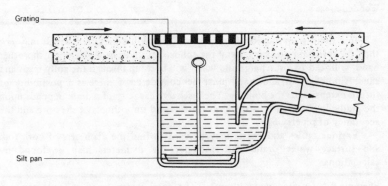

Silt pan

Fig. 8.15 Trapped yard gully

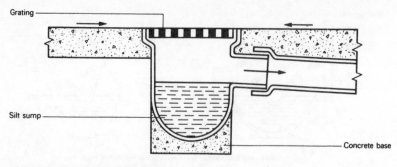

Fig. 8.16 Trapless yard gully

When a separate system is used, a trapless yard gully may be fitted and the branch pipe from the gully may be connected directly into the surface water drain (see Fig. 8.16).

Drain diameters

Under the Building Regulations, the minimum diameters of surface water and foul water drains are 75 and 100 mm respectively. The size of a surface water drain should be sufficient to carry away the usual maximum rainfall intensity for the district, with an allowance for the impermeability of the surface. For building drainage, a rainfall intensity of 50 mm per hour is usually allowed. Table 8.2 gives the impermeability factors for the various types of surfaces.

Table 8.2

Type of surface	Impermeable factor
Watertight roof surfaces	0.70 to 0.95
Asphalt pavements in good order	0.85 to 0.90
Closely jointed wood and stone pavements	0.80 to 0.85
Macadam roadways	0.25 to 0.45
Black pavements with wide joints	0.50 to 0.70
Lawns and gardens	0.05 to 0.25
Wooded areas	0.01 to 0.20

If a drain is oversized, the depth of water will be reduced which may not then be sufficient to carry away the solids. An undersized drain, on the other hand, will lead to a surcharge and water will back up through the gully traps and cause flooding. An allowance must be considered if there is a possibility of future extension to the building. The discharge capacity of a drain depends upon the gradient at which it is laid, the diameter and smoothness of the bore and the accurancy of pipelaying.

Various tables and charts may be used to find the diameters of both foul and surface water drains. Alternatively, the diameters may be found by calculations.

Example 8.1 (surface water drain). *The total surface area of footpaths and roadways of a building development scheme is found to be 4000 m². Calculate*

162

the diameter of the main surface water drain, using the following data:

1. Rainfall intensity 50 mm/hr
2. Impermeable factor of surface 0.9
3. Full bore discharge
4. Velocity of flow required 0.8 m/s

Using the formula

$Q = V.A.$

Where

Q = Volume of flow m^3/s

V = Velocity of flow m/s

A = Area of pipe m^2

$$Q = \frac{\text{Area to be drained (m}^2\text{)} \times \text{Rainfall intensity in (m/hr)} \times \text{Impermeable factor}}{60 \text{ (to bring to minutes)} \times 60 \text{ (to bring to seconds)}}$$

$$Q = \frac{4000 \times 0.05 \times 0.9}{60 \times 60}$$

$Q = 0.05$ m^3/s

$$A = \frac{\Pi D^2}{4}$$

therefore

$$Q = \frac{V \Pi D^2}{4}$$

$$D = \sqrt{\frac{4 Q}{V \Pi}}$$

$$D = \sqrt{\frac{4 \times 0.05}{0.8 \times 3.142}}$$

$$D = \sqrt{\frac{0.2}{2.514}}$$

$D = 0.282$ m

$D = 282$ m

Nearest pipe size = <u>300 mm diameter</u>

The diameter of a foul water drain will depend upon the discharge from the sanitary fittings during the peak demand period. The amount of water used in the building will have to be discharged to the drain and the drain must be sized, therefore, to carry away this discharge.

The following stages may be followed:

1. Establish the possible maximum number of occupants in the building.
2. Establish the consumption of water per day by the occupants.
3. From 1 and 2 find the average flow of water passing into the drain, during a 6 hour period (it may be assumed that half the daily flow will take place during a 6 hour period).

4. Find the average flow rate m^3/s.
5. Find the maximum flow rate m^3/s (it may be assumed that the maximum flow rate will be between four to six times the average flow rate).
6. Calculate the pipe diameter, using the formula $Q = V.A$.

Example 8.2 (foul water sewer).   *Calculate the diameter of a foul water private sewer suitable for fifty houses. The average number of occupants is assumed to be four per house and the water consumption 225 litres per head, per day. The sewer is to be sized, so as to run half-full bore, at a velocity of 0.8 m/s during the peak demand period.*

Flow rate per day	$= 225 \times 50 \times 4$
Flow rate per day	$= 45\ 000$ litre
Average flow rate during a 6-hour period, assumed half the daily flow	$= 22\ 500$ litre
Average flow rate per hour	$= \dfrac{22\ 500}{6}$
Average flow rate per hour	$= 3750$ litre
Average flow rate per second	$= \dfrac{3750}{60 \times 60}$
Average flow rate per second	$= 1.041$ litre
Maximum flow rate per second assumed four times the average	$= 1.041 \times 4$
Therefore maximum flow rate per second	$= 4.164$ litre
Maximum flow rate per second	$= 0.004$ m^3/s

$Q = V.A.$

where

Q = Volume of flow m^3/s

V = Velocity of flow m/s

A = Area of pipe m^2

Area of pipe for half-full bore $= \dfrac{\Pi D^2}{8}$

$$Q = \dfrac{V \Pi D^2}{8}$$

therefore

$$D = \sqrt{\dfrac{8\ Q}{V\ \Pi}}$$

$$D = \sqrt{\dfrac{8 \times 0.004}{0.8 \times 3.142}}$$

$$D = \sqrt{\dfrac{0.032}{2.514}}$$

$D = 0.1128$ m

$D = 113$ mm

Nearest pipe size = 125 mm diameter

When the number and type of sanitary appliances are known, the diameter and gradient of a foul water drain may be found by a discharge unit method. Each sanitary appliance is given a discharge unit value, which represents the rate of discharge, capacity and frequency of use of the appliance. The sum of all the discharge units of the sanitary appliances connected to the drain is found and the British Standard 5572, 1978, gives a list of discharge units and the number that may be connected to 100, 125 and 150 mm nominal bore foul water drains, laid at gradients of 1 in 96, 1 in 48 and 1 in 24. Table 8.3 gives the discharge unit values and Table 8.4 the number of discharge units allowed on vertical stacks and horizontal branches or drains.

Table 8.3 Discharge unit values B.S. 5572 1978

Type of appliance	Frequency of use (minutes)		Discharge unit value
Spray tap (basin)	Add 0.06 litres per second per tap		–
W.C. (9-litre cistern)	20		7
	10		14
	5		28
Sink	20		6
	10		14
	5		27
Wash basin	20		1
	10		3
	5		6
Bath	75	(domestic)	7
	30	(commercial and congested)	18
Shower (per head)	Add 0.1 litre per second per spray		–
Urinal (per stall or bowl)	20	(commercial and congested)	0.3
One group consisting of one WC one bath and 1 or 2 basins, sink			14
Washing machine (automatic)	250		4

Table 8.4(a) Maximum number of discharge units to be allowed on vertical stacks

Nominal internal diameter (mm)	Discharge units
50	10
65	60
75	200 (not more
90	350 than 1 W.C.)
100	750
125	2500
150	5500

Table 8.4(b) Maximum number of discharge units to be allowed on horizontal branches

Internal diameter of pipe (mm)	Gradient		
	½° 9 mm/m	1¼° 22 mm/m	2½° 45 mm/m
32	—	1	1
40	—	2	8
50	—	10	26
65	—	35	95
75	—	100	230
90	120	230	460
100	230	430	1050
125	780	1500	3000
150	2000	3500	7500

Example 8.3. *By the use of the discharge unit value method, find the diameter and gradient of a drain to serve a factory containing 20 W.C.s, 25 wash basins and 4 sinks. The W.C.s are to be provided with 9 litre flushing cisterns.*

W.C.s	20 x 28 DUs	=	560
Basins	25 x 6 DUs	=	150
Sinks	4 x 27 DUs	=	108
Total			818

With reference to Table 8.4, a 150 mm diameter drain having a gradient of 9 mm/m or a 125 mm diameter drain having a gradient of 22 mm/m would be suitable.

Gradient

Various formulae and tables may be used to find the gradient or fall of a drain. One of the best known formulae which may be used for pipes and channels, is known as 'Chezy's' expressed as follows:

$V = C\sqrt{(mi)}$

where

C = Chezy constant

V = velocity of flow in m/s

m = hydraulic mean depth

i = inclination or fall

Chezy constant may be found from the following formula:

$$C = \sqrt{\left(\frac{2g}{f}\right)}$$

where

166

g = acceleration due to gravity (9.81)

f = coefficient of friction

The average coefficient of friction may be taken as 0.0064 and therefore C would be given by:

$$C = \sqrt{\frac{2 \times 9.81}{0.0064}}$$

$C = 55$

The hydraulic mean depth is found from:

$$m = \frac{\text{wetted area}}{\text{wetted perimeter}}$$

For half or full bore discharge, the hydraulic mean depth is equal to $D/4$ which can be shown as follows:

Full bore

$$m = \frac{\dfrac{\Pi D^2}{4}}{\Pi D}$$

$$m = \frac{1}{4} \times \frac{D^2}{1} \times \frac{1}{\Pi} \times \frac{1}{D}$$

by cancellation

$$m = \frac{D}{4}$$

Half-full bore

$$m = \frac{\dfrac{\Pi D^2}{8}}{\dfrac{\Pi D}{2}}$$

$$m = \frac{1}{8} \times \frac{D^2}{1} \times \frac{2}{1} \times \frac{1}{\Pi} \times \frac{1}{D}$$

$$m = \frac{D}{4}$$

The inclination or fall is equal to H/L, where (L) is the length of drain in metres with a head (H) of 1 m.

Example 8.4. *Calculate the gradient required for a private sewer flowing half-full bore at a velocity of 0.8 m/s (Chezy constant = 55).*

Putting the above values into the formula as follows:

$$V = C \sqrt{\left(\frac{D}{4} \times \frac{1}{L} \right)}$$

By transposition

$$\left[\frac{V}{C} \right]^2 = \frac{D}{4} \times \frac{1}{L}$$

$$\frac{1}{L} = \left[\frac{V}{C} \right]^2 \times \frac{4}{D}$$

$$L = \left[\frac{C}{V} \right]^2 \times \frac{D}{4}$$

$$L = \left[\frac{55}{0.8} \right]^2 \times \frac{0.150}{4}$$

$$L = 68.75^2 \times 0.375$$

$$L = 177 \text{ (approx.)}$$

Gradient = 1 in 177

Means of access

The Building Regulations 1985 requires an access point at the following positions on a drain.

1. At each change of direction or gradient, as would prevent any part of the drain being readily cleansed without such a chamber (see Fig. 8.17A, B); and

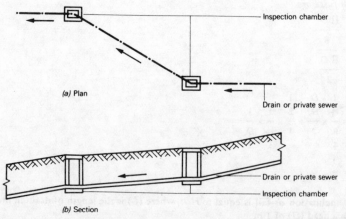

Fig. 8.17 Manholes at change of direction or gradient

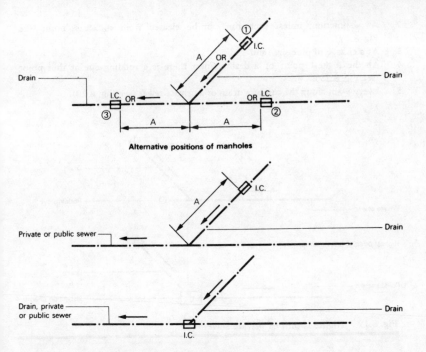

Alternative positions of manholes

Fig. 8.18   Junctions between drains and sewers

Note: The distances marked A will depend upon the type of access (see Table 8.5).

From	To	Access fitting		Junction	Inspection Chamber	Manhole
		Small	Large			
Start of external drain*		12	12	—	22	45
Rodding eye		22	22	22	45	45
Access fitting: small 150 diam.						
150 × 100		—	—	12	22	22
large 225 × 100		—	—	22	45	45
Inspection chamber		22	45	22	45	45
Manhole		22	45	45	45	90

Note: Distances in metres
*Connection from ground-floor appliances or stack

Table 8.5   Maximum spacing of access points for drains up to and including 300 mm diameter (Building Regulations 1985)

2. At a junction, unless each run can be cleared from an access point (see Fig. 8.17).
3. At a change of pipe size; and
4. At the highest point of a drain, unless there is a rodding eye at that point (see Fig. 8.19).
5. Every 90 m along the run of a drain or a private sewer (see Fig. 8.20).

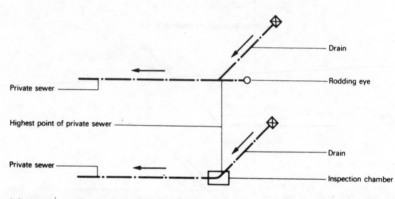

Fig. 8.19 Highest point of private sewer

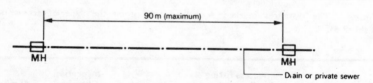

Fig. 8.20 Manholes in run of drain or private sewer

Inspection chamber

The Building Regulations state that an inspection chamber shall be capable of sustaining the loads which may be imposed on it, exclude subsoil water and be watertight. The size of the chamber should be sufficient to permit ready access to the drain or private sewer for inspection, cleansing and rodding and have a removable and non-ventilating cover of adequate strength, constructed of suitable and durable material. Where the depth of the chamber so requires step irons, ladders or other fittings, should be provided to ensure safe access to the level of the drain or private sewer. If the inspection chamber contains an open channel, benching should be provided having a smooth finish and formed so as to allow the foul matter to flow towards the pipe and also to ensure a safe foothold.

An inspection chamber or manhole may be constructed of engineering brick or well-burnt common brick, bedded in cement mortar. The brickwork should

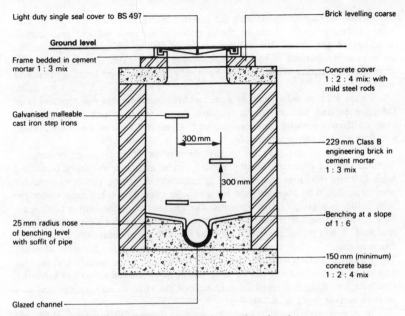

Light duty single seal cover to BS 497

Brick levelling coarse

Ground level

Frame bedded in cement mortar 1 : 3 mix

Concrete cover 1 : 2 : 4 mix: with mild steel rods

Galvanised malleable cast iron step irons

300 mm

300 mm

229 mm Class B engineering brick in cement mortar 1 : 3 mix

Benching at a slope of 1 : 6

25 mm radius nose of benching level with soffit of pipe

150 mm (minimum) concrete base 1 : 2 : 4 mix

Glazed channel

Fig. 8.21 Section through shallow brick inspection chamber

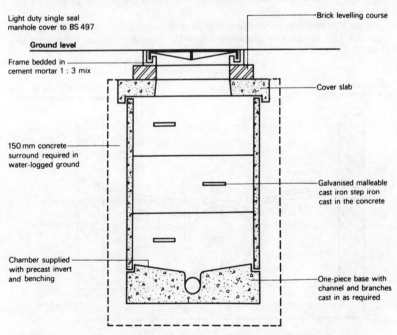

Light duty single seal manhole cover to BS 497

Brick levelling course

Ground level

Frame bedded in cement mortar 1 : 3 mix

Cover slab

150 mm concrete surround required in water-logged ground

Galvanised malleable cast iron step iron cast in the concrete

Chamber supplied with precast invert and benching

One-piece base with channel and branches cast in as required

Fig. 8.22 Section through shallow precast concrete inspection chamber

171

be finished in English bond, with the internal joints finished flush. Cement and sand rendering to the inside of the chamber is not required and may lead to blockage of the drain, due to the rendering flaking off and falling into the channel at the bottom of the chamber. Where a high water table is evident, the chamber will require waterproofing externally, to prevent infiltration of ground water.

Figure 8.21 shows a detail of a shallow brick manhole. Pre-cast concrete manholes are formed with successive sections, jointed together with cement mortar, built up from a pre-cast concrete base unit. Figure 8.22 shows a section through a shallow pre-cast concrete manhole.

The vertical sections are usually circular in plan, although rectangular sections may be obtained. Deep pre-cast concrete manholes should be backfilled with 150 mm thickness of concrete. For chambers exceeding 1 m deep malleable iron steps should be provided, and for manholes exceeding 4.5 m deep a wrought iron ladder is preferable to step irons. The channel at the base of a brick manhole is formed with vitrified clay, which may also be used for a pre-cast concrete manhole. A half round channel is used for through the chamber and a half round channel may also be used for the branch connections to the main channel. Three-quarter section channel bends may be used for the branch connections and these will prevent any risk of solid matter being washed up on the benching. Concrete benching is formed on each side of the channel and is trowelled to a smooth surface (see Fig. 8.23).

If a cast iron drain is used, a cast iron inspection junction which has branches cast on at an angle of 135° is fitted at the bottom of the manhole. The inspection junction has a bolted cover, jointed with a greased felt gasket (see Fig. 8.24).

Unplasticised polyvinyl chloride (upvc) access units are obtainable and one type (Marscar system), manufactured by IMI Yorkshire Imperial Plastics Ltd.,

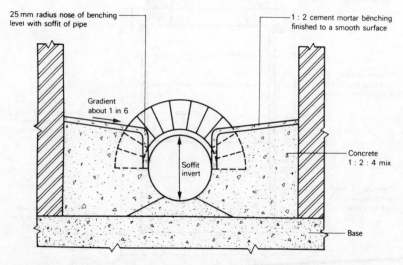

Fig. 8.23   Detail of benching

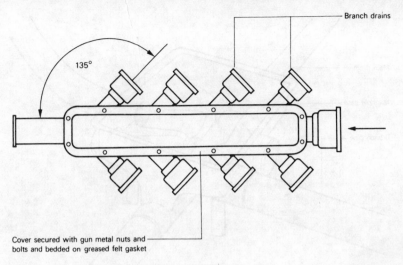

Fig. 8.24 Plan of cast iron inspection chamber

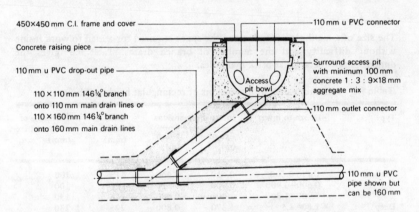

Fig. 8.25 Section through Marscar system of access to main drain

consists of a bowl measuring 114 mm to 485 mm in diameter. The bowl has an outlet at its base and side entries for the branch drains. The outlet pipe and branch pipes are of unplasticised polyvinyl chloride, which are connected to the bowl by means of solvent cement joints. The bowl replaces the traditional brick or concrete manhole and has the advantage of reducing the excavation, drainage costs and the drain is accessible from ground level. Figure 8.25 shows a section through the 'Marscar' system.

A plastic manhole base unit manufactured by Osma Plastics Limited has four branch inlets swept into the main channel and most types of brickwork may be connected to the base unit. The unit obviates conventional channel laying and also provides smooth contours (see Fig. 8.26).

173

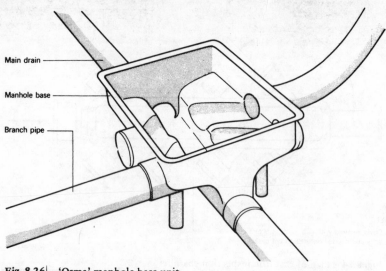

Fig. 8.26 'Osma' manhole base unit

Manhole sizes

The size of a manhole depends upon the space required for a man to work inside without difficulty and the number of branch drains. Table 8.6 gives the dimensions of rectangular brick manholes.

Table 8.6 Minimum sizes of dimensions of rectangular brick manholes

Type	Depth to invert (m)	Internal dimensions		Wall thickness (mm)	Thickness of concrete base (mm)
		Length (m)	Width (m)		
Shallow	Up to 0.600	0.610	0.460	113	100
	0.600–0.900	0.800	0.570	113	100
	0.900–1.80	1.000	0.680	225	150
Deep	1.80–4.5	1.370	0.800	225	230
Extra deep	over 4.5	1.370	1.140	225–337.5	230–450

Subject to the minimum sizes given in Table 8.6 the internal dimensions for manholes with a number of branch drains may be found for straight inverts from the following:

Length	Width
Allow 300 mm for each 100 mm branch and 375 mm for each 150 mm branch, plus adequate allowance on the downstream side, for the angle of entry	Allow 300 mm for each benching with branches, or 150 mm for benching without branches, plus 150 mm, or the diameter of the main drain, whichever is the greater

Manhole covers

Manhole covers and frames are generally made of cast iron. Covers are also made of steel which are unbreakable and therefore safer. Concrete covers may be used when a complete airtight seal is not required between the cover and the frame. BS 497 specifies three grades of manhole cover and frame.

Grade C. Light duty: which are suitable for housing, or in situations where they will not have to withstand wheeled traffic.

Grade B. Medium duty: which are suitable for footpaths, carriage drives and cycle tracks.

Grade A. Heavy duty: for roadways where they must be capable of withstanding constant vehicle traffic.

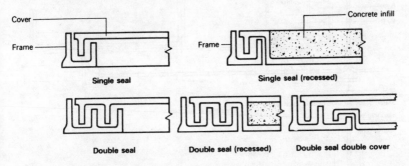

Fig. 8.27 Types of manhole cover seals

Light and medium duty covers are available with single and double seals, whilst heavy duty covers are single seal type only. A double seal cover is required over an open channel type manhole inside a building. Figure 8.28 shows single and double seals for manhole covers. Covers may be rectangular, triangular or circular on plan. Triangular and circular covers have three points of support and have the advantage of being non-rocking. Frames are solidly bedded in 1 in 3 cement and sand mortar on top of the manhole. Covers are bedded in the frames with grease to ensure an airtight joint.

Rodding points

A rodding point may be used in the following systems:

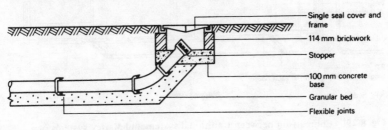

Fig. 8.28 Detail of rodding eye

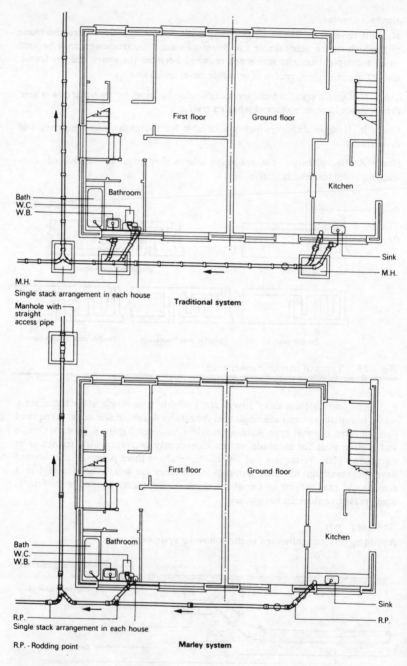

Bath
W.C.
W.B.

Bathroom

First floor

Ground floor

Kitchen

Sink

M.H.

M.H.

Single stack arrangement in each house

Traditional system

Manhole with
straight
access pipe

Bath
W.C.
W.B.

Bathroom

First floor

Ground floor

Kitchen

Sink

R.P.

R.P.

Single stack arrangement in each house

R.P. - Rodding point

Marley system

Fig. 8.29 Comparison between traditional system and Marley systems of drainage

1. In a traditional system, where manholes are used at the various positions required under the Building Regulations and the rodding point is permitted at the head of a private sewer. Figure 8.28 shows a detail of a rodding point at the head of a private sewer, or drain.

2. In a closed drainage system, known as the Marley Rodding Point system, which considerably reduces the number of manholes required for the traditional drainage systems, and there is, therefore, a reduction in the cost of drain laying. The local authority however will have to relax the Building Regulations before the system is adopted. The system is covered by Agreement Certificates Nos 70/72 and 71/99 and consists of unplasticised poly-

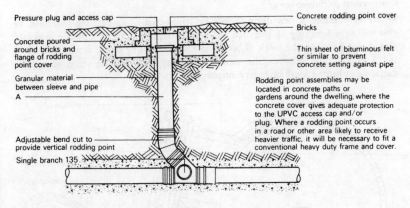

Fig. 8.30 Marley vertical rodding point

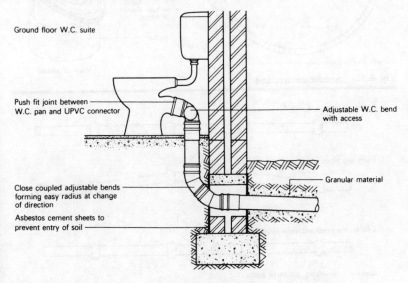

Fig. 8.31 Marley method of connecting ground floor W.C. to drain

177

vinyl chloride pipes and fittings. A full range of fittings is available in 82.4, 110 and 160 mm outside diameter sizes.

One of the most important items is a patented adjustable bend, which may be adopted on site to meet the various angles as they occur at changes of direction in the drainage pipework. The bend is also used in combination with a basic 135° junction, to form vertical rodding points.

Figure 8.29 shows a drainage system for housing, using the Marley system, and Fig. 8.30 shows a vertical rodding point used in the system. Figure 8.31 shows the Marley method of connecting a ground floor W.C. to the drain.

Connection to public sewer

Wherever possible, a new drain should be connected to an existing manhole, as this will save breaking up the road and connecting the drain to a public sewer. If this is not possible, the work of breaking into an existing public sewer and forming a connection between the new drainage system and the sewer is usually carried out by the local authority employees.

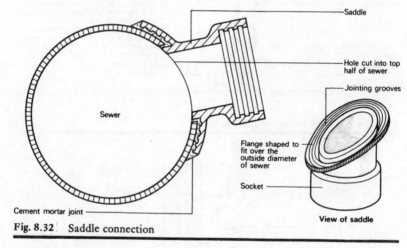

Fig. 8.32 Saddle connection

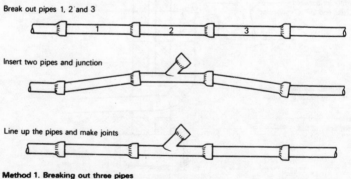

Method 1. Breaking out three pipes

Fig. 8.33 Method of inserting junction in sewer

With a vitrified clay sewer of large diameter, breaking into the sewer should be affected by the continuous enlargement of a small hole made into the sewer. The connection is made by a suitable saddle, bedded on to the sewer by cement mortar and completely surrounding the joint with 1 : 2 : 4 concrete 150 mm thick. Every precaution should be taken to prevent any jointing or excavating material entering the sewer. After the completion of a new connection, the excavation around the joint requires careful reinstatement. Figure 8.32 shows a saddle connection to a sewer.

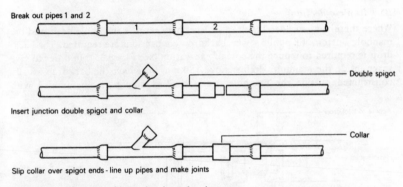

Fig. 8.34   Method of inserting junction in sewer

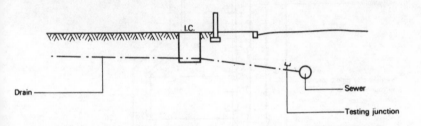

Connection to sewer when there is little difference in level between the drain and the sewer

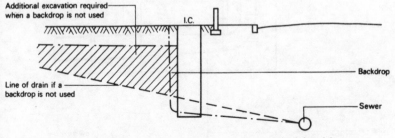

Connection to sewer when there is a large difference in level between the drain and the sewer

Fig. 8.35   Use of backdrop

When the sewer is too small for the opening to use a saddle, it is necessary to insert a 135° junction by one of the following methods:

1. Three pipes are taken out of the sewer line and 135° junction and two plain pipes are inserted, as shown in Fig. 8.33
2. Two pipes are taken out of the sewer line and a collar slipped over the end of the spigot end of the sewer pipeline. A 135° junction and a double spigot pipe are inserted and the collar then slipped into position over the two spigot ends of the pipeline, as shown in Fig. 8.34.

Backdrop connections

Where there is a considerable drop in level between the incoming drain and the manhole bottom, or public sewer, backdrop connections are required. The backdrop is required to reduce the cost of excavation (see Fig. 8.35). In order to save space inside the manhole, drains above 150 mm bore have the backdrop usually constructed outside the manhole, using vitrified clay pipe, surrounded with

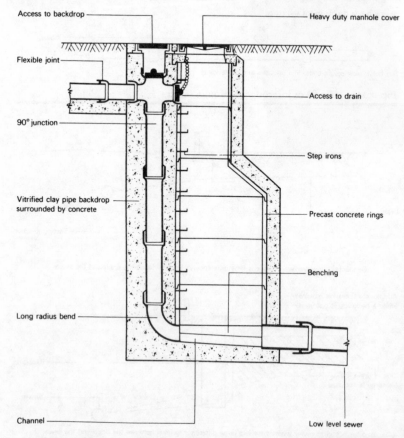

Fig. 8.36 Vitrified clay pipe backdrop outside a deep-precast concrete inspection chamber

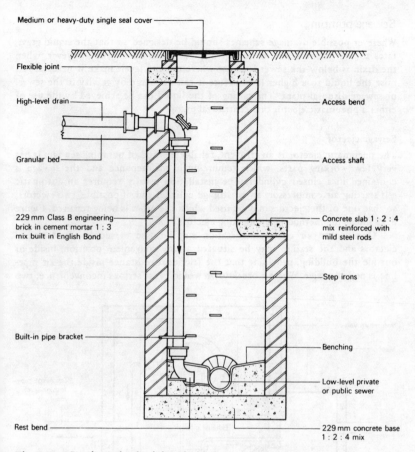

Medium or heavy-duty single seal cover

Flexible joint

High-level drain

Granular bed

229 mm Class B engineering
brick in cement mortar 1 : 3
mix built in English Bond

Built-in pipe bracket

Rest bend

Access bend

Access shaft

Concrete slab 1 : 2 : 4
mix reinforced with
mild steel rods

Step irons

Benching

Low-level private
or public sewer

229 mm concrete base
1 : 2 : 4 mix

Fig. 8.37 Cast-iron pipe backdrop inside a deep-brick inspection chamber

150 mm of 1:2:4 concrete. Figure 8.36 shows a backdrop in vitrified clay pipe outside a pre-cast concrete manhole. For drains up to 150 mm bore, the backdrop may be constructed inside the manhole, providing there is sufficient space left for access. The backdrop may be made by using cast iron, pitch fibre or unplasticised polyvinyl chloride pipe and the pipe should be secured to the manhole face by means of pipe brackets. Figure 8.38 shows a backdrop in cast iron pipe, inside a deep brick manhole. At one time backdrops were used to reduce the gradient of a drain laid below sloping sites, but in modern drainage practice the drain is laid at the same slope of the ground and this method saves a great deal of drainage costs. It has been found that with steeper gradients the tendency for solids to remain behind due to the water running away from the solids does not occur in practice and a steeper gradient, in fact, reduces the risk of blockages. It was also thought that with high velocities grit would cause abrasion to the inside of the pipe, but the high velocity of flow actually reduces scour by carrying the solids in suspension, which at low velocities would travel in contact with the surface of the pipe.

Sewage pumping

Wherever possible drainage schemes should be designed so that the liquid gravitates to the public sewer, or sewage-disposal plant. Cases arise, however, when the drain is below the sewer level, or where the site levels make it necessary to raise the liquid to a higher level before it can discharge by gravity to the sewer, or sewage-disposal plant. The raising of the liquid can be achieved by the use of either a pneumatic ejector or a centrifugal pump.

Sewage ejectors

The pneumatic ejector is an efficient, reliable method of pumping sewage. It has very few working parts, which require little maintenance and the sewage is contained in a closed cylinder. The installation usually requires an automatic self-starting air compressor, an air-storage cylinder and, if possible, two ejectors, so that one of the ejectors may be used whilst the other is being repaired. Figure 8.39 shows the method of duplicating ejectors.

One central air compressor station may be used to supply air to several ejectors and the station may be situated at any convenient position, inside or outside the building, providing that the frictional resistance inside the air pipeline is not excessive. Where a breakdown would cause serious inconvenience, two

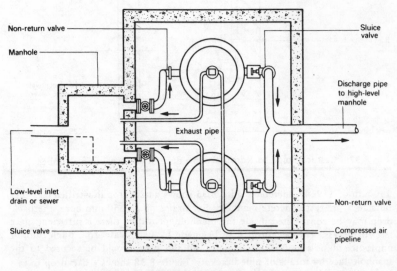

Sizes of ejector chambers

Discharge in litres per second

	1.13	2.3	4.5	6.8	9.5	15
Length (m)	2.1	2.4	2.4	2.4	2.8	3.0
Width (m)	2.1	2.4	2.4	2.4	2.8	3.0

Fig. 8.38 Plan of ejector chamber showing method of duplication of the ejectors

182

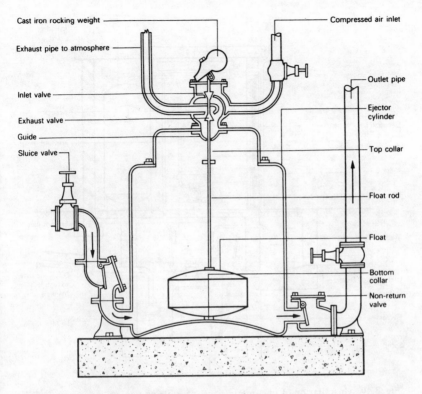

Cast iron rocking weight

Exhaust pipe to atmosphere

Compressed air inlet

Inlet valve

Exhaust valve

Guide

Sluice valve

Outlet pipe

Ejector cylinder

Top collar

Float rod

Float

Bottom collar

Non-return valve

Fig. 8.39   Section through an Adams sewage ejector

air compressors should be installed, so that one can be used for standby purposes.

The size of the ejector depends upon the flow rate entering the cylinder. Cylinder sizes are between 500 and 900 mm inside diameter and between 1 and 1.30 m in height. The discharge from an ejector is from 1.13 litre/s to 15 litre/s. Figure 8.39 shows a section through an ejector, which operates as follows:

1. The liquid to be raised gravitates through the inlet pipe into the cylinder and the non-return valve prevents the liquid from flowing back.
2. The liquid gradually fills the cylinder and as the level of the liquid rises the float slides along the float rod until it reaches to top collar.
3. The float rod is then raised, which lifts the rocking weight, and when the weight passes the vertical position it suddenly falls by gravity, allowing the valve to close and the compressed air inlet valve to open.
4. Compressed air enters the cylinder and forces out the liquid through the outlet pipe until the cylinder is empty.
5. The float falls, thereby actuating the automatic valve which cuts off the compressed air supply and opens the exhaust valve, and the ejector is again ready for the next operation. Figure 8.40 shows the installation of the ejector below ground.

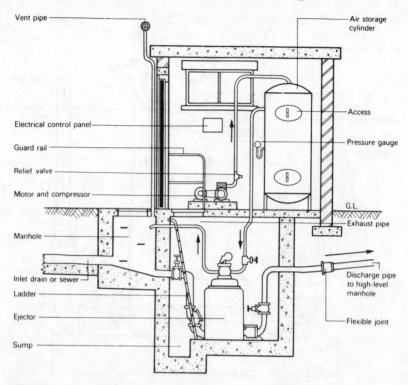

Fig. 8.40 Installation of pneumatic ejector for lifting sewage

Unit ejector

A self-contained unit ejector is operated by means of a small electric motor and compressor, mounted directly on top of the ejector, which eliminates the need for a compressor room, air-receiving cylinder and pipelines.

It operates as follows:

1. Sewage enters through the inlet non-return valve and gradually fills the cylinder, until the liquid reaches the tip of a short electrode.
2. The electric current is switches on, which brings the motor and air compressor into operation.
3. Compressed air enters the ejector and forces out the liquid through the outlet pipe, until the level of liquid falls below a second, longer electrode.
4. The compressor is switched off and the compressed air is exhausted to the atmosphere through an automatic valve.

Figure 8.41 shows the installation of the Simplex self-contained unit ejector. In order to save the cost of excavation and the construction of an injector chamber below ground, a lift and force ejector may be installed. With this type of ejector the whole of the mechanical and electrical equipment is housed above ground, thus providing easy access. Figure 8.42 shows a detail of the installation of the lift and force ejector.

184

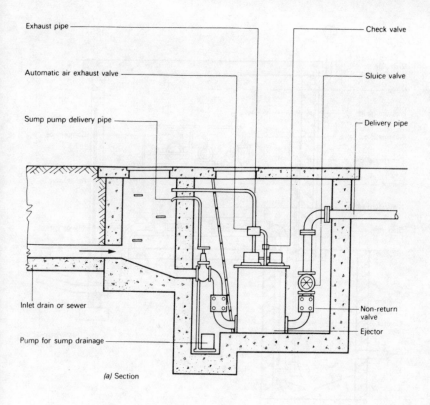

Exhaust pipe

Automatic air exhaust valve

Sump pump delivery pipe

Inlet drain or sewer

Pump for sump drainage

(a) Section

Check valve

Sluice valve

Delivery pipe

Non-return valve

Ejector

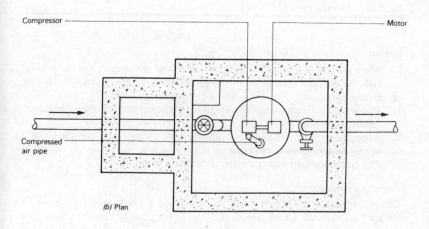

Compressor

Compressed air pipe

Motor

(b) Plan

Fig. 8.41 Installation of the Simplex self-contained ejector

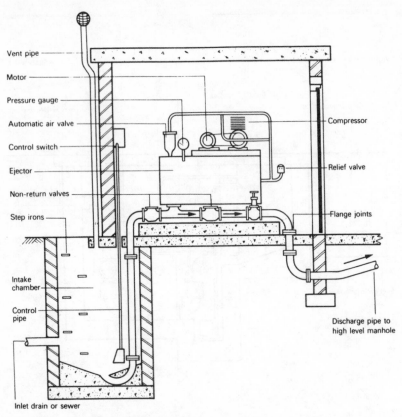

Vent pipe
Motor
Pressure gauge
Automatic air valve
Control switch
Ejector
Non-return valves
Step irons
Intake chamber
Control pipe
Inlet drain or sewer

Compressor
Relief valve
Flange joints
Discharge pipe to high level manhole

Fig. 8.42 Installation of lift and force sewage ejector

Operation

1. When the liquid reaches the high level, the float switches on the compressor and the suction created at its outlet creates a partial vacuum inside the ejector.
2. The sewage is forced into the ejector by the atmospheric pressure acting on top of the liquid.
3. When the ejector is full the automatic valve closes the suction valve and opens the compressed air valve.
4. The compressed air enters the ejector and forces out the liquid.

Connection to sewer

Before the liquid discharged from an ejector or a pump enters the sewer it should pass through a manhole so that the liquid gravitates to the sewer. This method prevents a surcharge in the sewer, backflooding of the drain and provides access for inspection and rodding of the drain. Figure 8.43 shows the type of manhole for connecting the discharge from an ejector, or pump to the sewer.

186

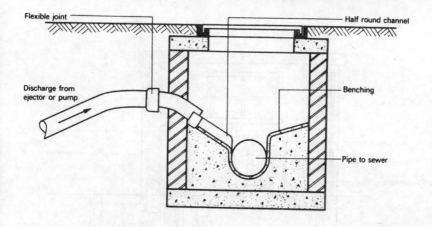

Fig. 8.43   Detail of high-level manhole

Centrifugal pumps

A centrifugal pump can lift a large volume of liquid at a greater speed than the ejector and is therefore suitable for the pumping of sewage or surface water discharges from large building schemes. The pump should be wear resisting and sited so that it is accessible for easy maintenance and, wherever possible, two pumps should be installed, so that one pump can be repaired whilst the other is in use. In cases where a failure of the electrical supply would cause serious inconvenience, such as hospitals, consideration must be given to the installation of a standby petrol or diesel electric generator, so that this may be used to provide electrical power for pumping in the event of the electrical supply from the mains failing due to a power cut or a fault.

Sewage pumps used for building drainage are usually of the following types:

1. Vertical spindle centrifugal.
2. Horizontal spindle centrifugal.
3. Self-priming centrifugal.

The vertical and horizontal centrifugal pumps have full-way impellers, made from special grade cast iron, to ensure maximum life and the impellers are designed to give minimum resistance to the flow of liquid, whilst enabling any solids entering the suction pipe to pass freely through the pump.

Vertical spindle pump

The vertical spindle pump is usually designed for installation in a dry well, constructed below the level of the incoming drain or sewer, discharging into a wet well adjacent to the dry well. In this position the pump is primed under the gravitational head from the liquid inside the wet well and thus avoids the necessity of providing automatic self-starting apparatus. Figure 8.44 shows the installation of a vertical spindle pump. The power required to drive the pump is provided from a vertical spindle electric motor installed in a motor room above the pump chamber. Figure 8.45 shows a section through a vertical centrifugal

187

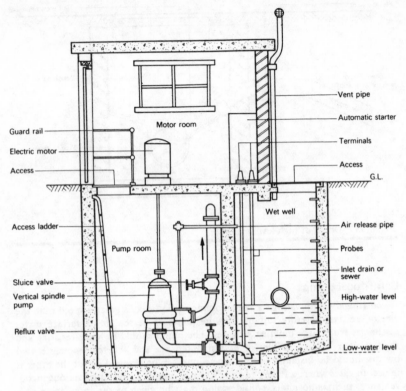

Fig. 8.44 Installation of centrifugal sewage pump with motor room above ground level

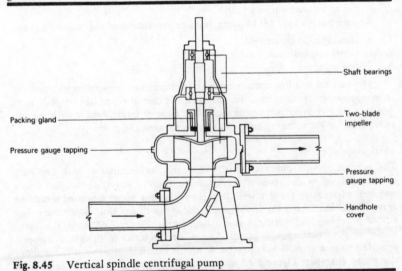

Fig. 8.45 Vertical spindle centrifugal pump

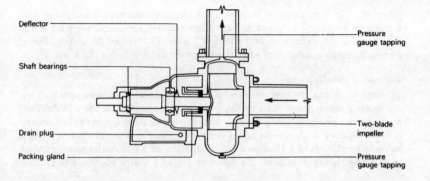

Fig. 8.46 Horizontal spindle centrifugal pump

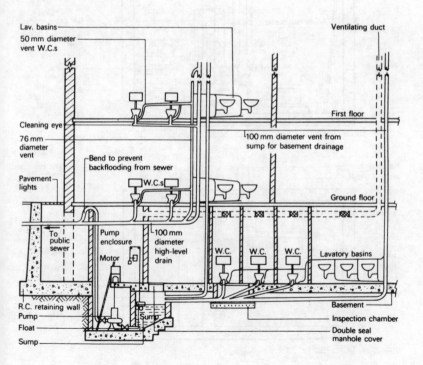

Fig. 8.47 Pumping of drainage from a basement

189

pump and Fig. 8.46 a section through a horizontal spindle centrifugal pump. It is sometimes necessary to pump sewage from sanitary appliances installed in the basement or sub-basements of buildings. Figure 8.47 shows the installation of pumping equipment required when the basement drain is below the sewer.

Horizontal spindle pumps

In order to reduce the cost of installation, a horizontal spindle pump which has the electric motor fixed close to the pump may be used. This method does not require a motor room above ground, but the electrical equipment below ground is more exposed to dampness and is not as accessible as when the motor room is above ground. Figure 8.48 shows the installation of a horizontal spindle centrifugal pump, which eliminates the construction of a motor room above ground.

Self-priming centrifugal pump

This type of pump has the advantage of being sited above ground, which provides protection from dampness for the pump and electrical apparatus.

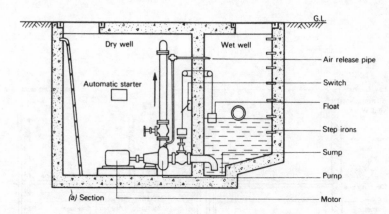

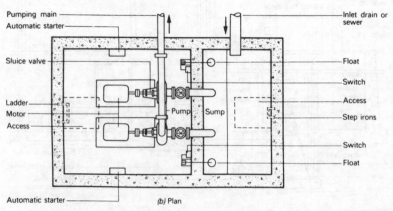

Fig. 8.48   Installation of the horizontal spindle centrifugal pump and method of duplicating pumps

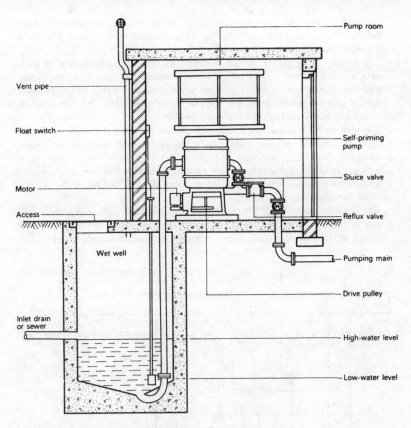

Fig. 8.49   Installation of self-priming centrifugal pump

Figure 8.49 shows the installation of a self-priming centrifugal pump, which operates as follows:

1. When the pump is started, liquid is drawn from the wet well by a partial vacuum, caused by the displacement of a body of water trapped in the lower half of a 'two-storey' priming chamber, to which the suction line is connected.

2. This priming water is delivered by the pump into an upper section of the priming chamber, where it is retained under normal discharge pressure, whilst the liquid from the pump continues to enter the pump and is discharged to the pumping main by centrifugal force in the usual manner.

3. When the pump is stopped by the action of the float switch, the contents of the upper portion of the priming chamber gravitates back through the pump into the lower half, thus repriming the pump ready for the next operation.

The Code of Practice 301, 1971 Building Drainage, gives recommendations for pumping installations, some of which are as follows:

1. The velocity of flow through the pumping main should be between 0.6 m/s and 1.2 m/s. Velocities below 0.6 m/s are likely to permit the accumulation

of solids in the main, whereas velocities above 1.2 m/s are generally considered to be uneconomical due to the resultant high friction head and possible increased surge problems.

2. The layout of pipework should provide for isolating sluice valves on each side of each pump, with a reflux valve between the pump and the sluice valve on the delivery side. The reflux valve should be fitted in a horizontal run of pipe, between the pump and the rising main to avoid sedimentation of solids which occurs in the vertical pipework.

3. The dry well to house vertical spindle pumps or ejectors should be watertight and should provide ample space for easy maintenance of the equipment installed.

4. Pump starters should incorporate in each phase a magnetic over load release, controlled by a hydraulic relay dash pot and they should be of the pattern rated for forty starts per hour.

5. The working capacity of a wet well should be designed in conjunction with the selected pump size to ensure reasonable frequency of operation and reasonable pumping period. On a separate system of drainage and with a

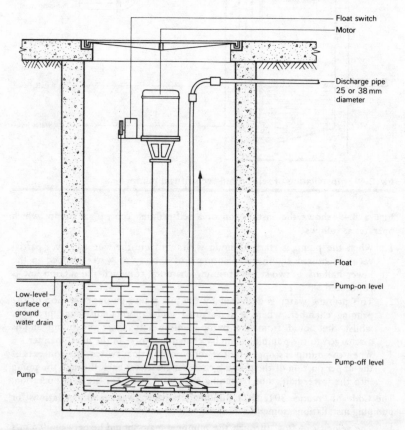

Fig. 8.50   Sump drainage

pump output of six times the 24 hour average, a well capacity of 5 minute pump output may give a reasonable compromise between frequency of starts and duration of pumping periods. To provide against breakdown, the capacity of the wet well below overflow level and above the pump working level, should not be less than 1 hour's average flow, or more if practicable.

Sump drainage

It is sometimes necessary to drain basements and boiler rooms below ground of sub-soil or surface water, which seeps through the structure, or is used for washing down purposes. A concrete or brick sump measuring 460 × 460 mm is constructed and a centrifugal sump pump fitted inside the chamber, as shown in Fig. 8.50. The sump pump shown is fully automatic, but non-automatic sets may also be obtained. Sump pumps are not designed for sewage and a suction strainer is fitted to prevent the entry of large particles which would affect the pump operation. The electric motor is totally enclosed, but if the pump units are required to operate in hazardous atmospheres a flameproof motor should be fitted. The pump will usually lift water to a height of up to 11 m and discharge about 3.2 litre/s.

Mutrator pump

A small-packaged pumping unit consisting of a glass fibre collecting chamber, macerator and a self-priming centrifugal pump may be installed for the pumping of sewage from small or medium sized buildings. The sewage is macerated and then pumped through a 38 mm diameter pipe to the sewer or small sewage-disposal plant.

Drainage pipe materials

Clay

There are four British Standards.
1. BS 65 and 540:1971, clay drain and sewer pipes, including surface water pipes.
2. BS 539:1968, dimensions of fittings for use with clay drain.
3. BS 1143:1955, salt-glazed pipes with chemically resistant properties.
4. BS 1196:1971, clay field drain pipes.

All pipes covered by these standards are often described as salt glazed, but the use of salt glazing is diminishing and unglazed pipes are no less suitable for usage than the older glazed pipe. Clay pipes are resistant to attack by a wide range of effluents, including acids and alkalis, but some flexible jointing material may be affected by certain substances contained in trade wastes.

There are two classes of pipes, British Standard for foul and or surface water, and British Standard Surface Water, for surface water only. When pipes have been tested in accordance with clause 10 of BS 65 they should bear the marking 'Extra Strength', and when tested hydraulically in accordance with clause 12 they should be marked 'Tested'. Pipes may also be marked with the maker's name. Pipes are available in a wide range of sizes, from 75 mm bore to 900 mm bore, and may be obtained in lengths from 300 mm to 8.5 m, either with or without sockets for use with flexible or rigid joints. Figure 8.51 shows a typical BS 65 clay drain pipe.

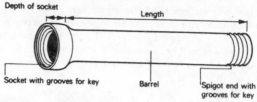

Fig. 8.51 British Standard clay drain pipe

Methods of jointing

The traditional method of jointing of clay pipes is by means of cement and sand mortar, as shown in Fig. 8.52. The joint may still be used for certain trade wastes, but is liable to fracture due to thermal expansion, or ground movement, and in order to prevent fracture various types of flexible telescopic joints are obtainable. These joints are quicker to make, allow up to 5° in lateral movement and allow telescopic movement of up to 18 mm. Figures 8.53 and 8.54 show two types of flexible telescopic joints on clay pipe. With both types of flexible joints shown it is essential that the mating surfaces are clean and that the lubricant supplied by the manufacturer is used.

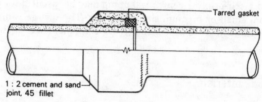

Fig. 8.52 Cement mortar joint on clay pipe

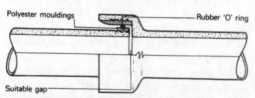

Fig. 8.53 'Hepseal' flexible joint on clay pipe

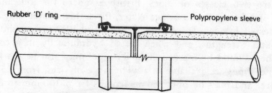

Fig. 8.54 'Hepsleve' flexible joint on clay pipe

With the O-ring joint, the O-ring is placed into the groove on the spigot moulding of one pipe and the socket of the other pipe is lubricated. The spigot is then placed up to the socket of the mating pipe and pushed in with a slight side-to side action. The O-ring is compressed against the polyester moulds, thus making a flexible telescopic watertight joint. The sleeve joint is made by lubricating the end of the pipe and pushing the sleeve on to it. The plain end of the other pipe is then lubricated and pushed into the sleeve.

Unplasticised polyvinyl chloride (upvc)

BS 4660:1971, unplasticised polyvinyl chloride underground drain pipes and fittings, covers the requirements for pipes of nominal 100 mm internal bore, but some manufacturers produce sizes of 89, 110, 160 and 200 mm external diameter pipes, in lengths of 1, 2, 3 and 6 m. BS 4660 pipe is coloured brown, so as to distinguish it from the thinner walled pipe used for drainage above ground. The pipe resists attack by normal domestic wastes and a wide range of acids, alkalis and sulphates. It may be attacked by certain organic solvents, but exposure to small quantities of such substances is unlikely to have significant effect on the pipe. Where large quantities are discharged, however, advice should be sought from the manufacturer.

If the pipe is to be used for prolonged discharges of very hot liquids, there is a risk of distortion of the pipe and it is necessary to cool the liquid before it enters the drain. Before the pipe is to be used for laundries, factories or hospitals, it is essential to ascertain the maximum temperatures to which it is to be subjected and to obtain advice from the manufacturers where necessary. The pipe is light in weight, very quick to lay, permits thermal and ground movement and has a smooth internal bore. Figure 8.55 shows the type of joint used for unplasticised polyvinyl chloride drain pipe.

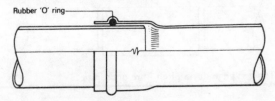

Rubber 'O' ring

Fig. 8.55   Flexible joint on upvc drain pipe

Pitch fibre

Pitch fibre pipe is made by impregnating wood-fibre with pitch. The pipe is suitable for normal drainage use, but is unsuitable for prolonged discharges of very hot liquids and the liquid should be cooled before it is discharged into the drain. Where there is a high concentration of certain trade effluents, such as, oils, fats and organic solvents, the manufacturer's advice should be sought before using pitch fibre pipes.

British Standard 2760:1967 covers pitch fibre pipes and fittings for drainage below and above ground. Standard internal diameters of the pipes are 50, 75, 100, 125, 150 and 200 mm, in lengths of 2.5 and 3 m. When these pipes were first used, they were jointed by means of a coupling, tapered internally at each end at 2° and the pipe ends were machined externally to the same taper.

The couplings were driven on to the pipe and a joint made, without the need of a jointing compound. This type of joint however was inflexible and tended to leak in use due to expansion and contraction of the pipe or ground movement; also sometimes the coupling was over driven and split. A flexible joint is now used, consisting of a polypropylene sleeve containing a rubber 'D' ring, as shown in Fig. 8.56. The joint is made by placing the 'D' ring on the end of the pipe and pushing the end firmly into the socket of the coupling. This movement will cause the 'D' ring to rotate through 360°, snapping into position and creating the seal. Figure 8.57 shows the taper joint for pitch fibre pipe. Connections between pitch fibre and other pipe materials can be made with special adaptors.

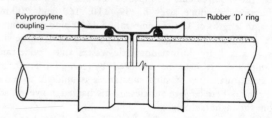

Fig. 8.56   Snap ring flexible joint on pitch fibre joint

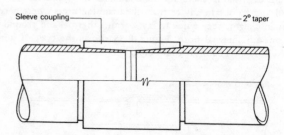

Fig. 8.57   Taper type joint on pitch fibre drain pipe

Cast iron

There are a number of British Standards for cast iron drain pipes:

BS 78 : Part 1, 1961, spigot and socketed pipes, vertically cast, covers pipes for the conveyance of water, gas or sewage. Pipes are available in internal diameters of between 75 and 300 mm and in lengths of 2.74 to 3.66 m.

BS 437 : Part 1, 1970, cast iron pipes are suitable for both surface water and foul water drainage. The pipes are made, socket and spigot, with internal diameters of 48, 74, 100, 150 and 225 mm and in lengths of 1.8, 2.74 and 3.66 m. The pipes are the ones most commonly used for drainage.

BS 1211 : centrifugal spun iron pressure pipes are suitable for water, gas and sewage, where higher internal pipe pressures are expected. They are available in internal diameters from 75 to 900 mm and in lengths of 3.66, 4, 4.88 and 5.5 m. The pipes can be jointed by the traditional caulked lead, or by a flexible joint.

BS 4622 : 1970, grey cast iron pipes and fittings are suitable for drainage and are available with internal diameters of 80 to 700 mm and a variety of lengths. A variety of cast iron drainage fittings are also available. The pipes and fittings are protected from corrosion by a bituminous coating, both inside and outside the pipe, but care should be taken to prevent damage to the coating as it is affected by acidic effluents, or sulphates and acids in the soil. The pipe is very strong and is often used suspended above ground, on brick and concrete piers, under roads and buildings. Figure 8.58 shows a detail of a traditional caulked lead joint in case iron and Figs 8.59 and 8.60 show flexible telescopic joints, for cast iron and spun iron pipes.

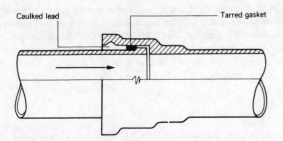

Fig. 8.58 Caulked lead joint on cast iron pipe

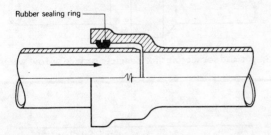

Fig. 8.59 'Tyton' flexible joint on spun iron pipe

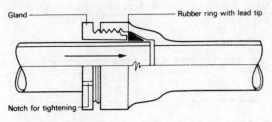

Fig. 8.60 Screwed gland flexible joint in iron pipe

197

Concrete

BS 556:Part 2, 1972, concrete pipes and fittings, lists pipes with internal diameters from 150 mm to 1.8 m, in lengths from 900 mm to 5 m. The pipes are suitable for normal drainage effluents, but may be liable to attack by acids. Pipes of 225 mm diameter and upwards are available with an external wrapping of glass fibre laminate, which reinforces the pipes and protects them from external attack. Various proprietory protective coatings are also available for internal and external application. Pipes may also be obtained manufactured from sulphate-resisting cement, which should be used in soil containing sulphates, but this type of pipe should not be used for acidic effluents, without first consulting the manufacturers. The pipes may be jointed by cement and sand mortar, which is similar to the clay pipe joint, or with a rubber O-ring.

Figure 8.61 shows a rigid spigot and socket joint for concrete surface, or foul water drain or sewer and Figs. 8.62 and 8.63 show ogee and rebated joints for concrete surface water, drain or sewer. The flexible O-ring joint for concrete surface, or foul water drain, or sewer (shown in Fig. 8.64) is made by placing the O-ring on the spigot and then, by means of a ratchet pulling mechanism, forcing the pipe into the socket of the mating pipe, which allows the O-ring to roll into the position shown.

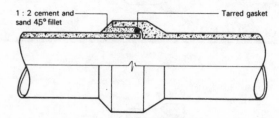

Fig. 8.61 Spigot and socket joint for concrete surface or foul water drain or sewer

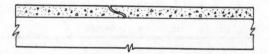

Fig. 8.62 Ogee joint for concrete surface water drain or sewer

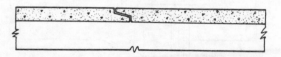

Fig. 8.63 Rebated joint for concrete surface or foul water drain or sewer

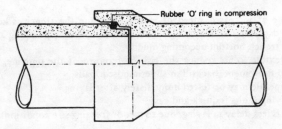

Fig. 8.64 Flexible joint for concrete surface or foul water drain or sewer

Asbestos-cement

BS 3656:1963, asbestos-cement pipes and fittings for sewage and drainage, covers pipes and fittings from 100 to 900 mm internal diameters, in lengths from 1 to 5 m. Substances that attack concrete may also attack asbestos-cement and where exposure to these substances is likely the manufacturer's advice should be sought. Bitumen-dipped pipes are available which gives increased resistance to attack, both internally and externally. There are three classes of pipe strength which can be obtained, depending upon the load which the pipe has to carry. The pipes are normally obtained with flexible O-ring joints as shown in Fig. 8.65.

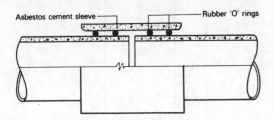

Fig. 8.65 Flexible joint for asbestos cement surface or foul water drain or sewer

Drainlaying

Pipes under roads should be laid with from 900 mm to 1.2 m of cover and pipes under fields and gardens with at least 600 mm of cover. For lesser depths, particularly where there is likelihood of heavy traffic, special protection of the pipes may be necessary. The drain trench should be as narrow as possible, so as to reduce the backfill load on the pipe to the minimum. Local soft spots in the trench bottom should be stabilised by tamping in granular material and large boulders and tree roots should be removed and replaced, by tamped granular material.

The drainage pipeline should be laid so as to provide flexibility and flexible joints are normally preferable to rigid joints, for the following reasons:

1. A minimum of skill is required in laying and is quicker, more reliable and cheaper.

2. Because of increased speed of laying, the time the trench is kept open is reduced to the minimum, with a possible reduction in pumping and less risk of the trench bottom becoming muddy.
3. The flexible joints reduce the risk of fracture of the pipeline, due to the ground movement, backfill or superimposed loads.
4. The pipeline may be tested immediately after laying.
5. Rectifying faults is quick and easy.
6. There is less delay in laying, due to wet or freezing site conditions.

Types of bedding

Class A: this type of bedding is used for rigid pipes such as vitrified clay and asbestos-cement. It is used where additional supporting strength of the pipe is required under roads, or where there is a risk of disturbing the pipeline after laying, such as when excavations have to be made alongside it at a later date. Figure 8.66 shows class A bedding, which is carried out as follows:

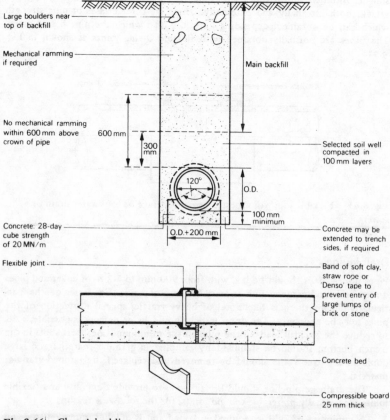

Fig. 8.66   Class A bedding

Figs. 8.67 and 8.68 embody information from BRE Digest 130 'Drainage pipelines', by permission of the Director, Building Research Establishment

1. A layer of concrete at least 50 mm thick should be spread along the prepared trench bottom.
2. The pipes should be supported clear of this concrete by means of blocks or cradles placed under the pipes and a piece of resilient material about 14 mm thick placed between the pipes and the supporting blocks. The total clearance under the pipes should not be less than 100 mm.
3. The pipes should be tested and a piece of compressed board cut to the profile of the pipe, placed at the face of each pipe joint, as shown in Fig. 8.66.
4. A 1:2:4 concrete, using 14 mm maximum size aggregate, giving a minimum 28 days cube strength of 20 M N/m² should be carefully placed under the pipes between the profiles and extended up to the barrel of the pipes to the required height.
5. The trench should be backfilled by first placing three layers of selected soil, free from hard objects, to a depth of 100 mm each and carefully compacting each layer by hand tamping separately. The trench can now be backfilled, but a mechanical rammer should not be used until there is a minimum cover over the pipe of 600 mm.

Class B: this is the usual method of bedding, of both rigid and flexible pipes. Figure 8.67 shows class B bedding, which is carried out as follows:

1. The trench bottom should be prepared and granular material consisting of broken stone or gravel 5 to 10 mm in size should be spread along the prepared trench bottom, to a depth of at least 100 mm; after compacting, the top should be levelled off.
2. Socket holes should be formed where necessary to allow the pipeline to rest uniformly on top of the granular material.

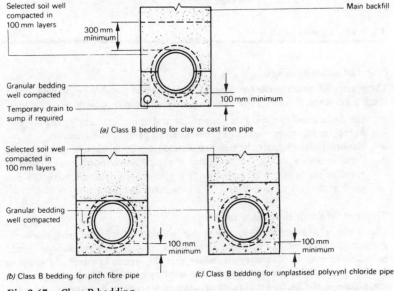

Fig. 8.67   Class B bedding

201

3. The pipeline should be laid and tested and granular material placed at either side of rigid pipes, to a depth of half the diameter of the pipe. For pitch fibre pipes the granular material should be brought up to the top of the pipe, and for unplasticised polyvinyl chloride pipe the granular material should be carried up to a minimum height of 100 mm above the crown of the pipe. For all types of pipes the granular material should be carefully compacted by hand tamping and the main backfill should be placed as described for class A bedding.

Class D: where the soil is reasonably dry, soft and fine grained, the pipes may be laid directly on the trench bottom. Figure 8.68 shows class D bedding, which is carried out as follows:

1. The trench bottom should be prepared by accurately trimming by hand and socket holes cut out, so that the soil will be in contact with the pipe barrel over the whole length of the pipeline. If too much soil is removed, it must be replaced to the correct level and thoroughly rammed.
2. The pipes should be laid and tested and the trench backfilled in 100 mm layers up to a level of 300 mm above the pipes. The main backfill should then be placed as described for class A bedding.

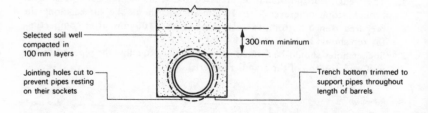

Fig. 8.68 Class D bedding

Pipes laid under buildings

The placing of drains under buildings should wherever possible be avoided, but if there is no other alternative the following points should be observed:

1. The drain should be laid in a straight line and at one gradient.
2. Access for cleansing should be provided to all parts of the drain.
3. Manholes placed inside the building should have double-sealed covers.
4. Flexible joints should be used and the pipe surrounded by 150 mm of granular material, or concrete, with a piece of compressed board 25 mm thick at the face of each pipe joint to maintain flexibility.

Trenches for drains and private sewers

The Building Regulations 1985 states that where any drain or private sewer is constructed adjacent to a loadbearing part of a building such precautions should be taken as may be necessary to ensure that the trench in which the drain or private sewer is laid in no way impairs the stability of the building. Except where the nature of the ground makes it unnecessary, where any drain or private sewer is adjacent to a wall and the bottom of the trench is lower than the foundation of the wall, the trench should be filled in with concrete, to a level which is not lower than the bottom of the foundation of the wall, by more than the distance from the foundation to the near side of the trench, less 150 mm. Provided that where the trench is within 1 m of the foundation of the wall the trench should be filled in with concrete to the level of the underside of the foundation. The concrete filling required by the foregoing paragraph should have such expansion joints as are necessary to ensure that no continuous length of filling exceeds 9 m. Figure 8.69 shows the method of ensuring that the drain or sewer trench is prevented from weakening the stability of the building.

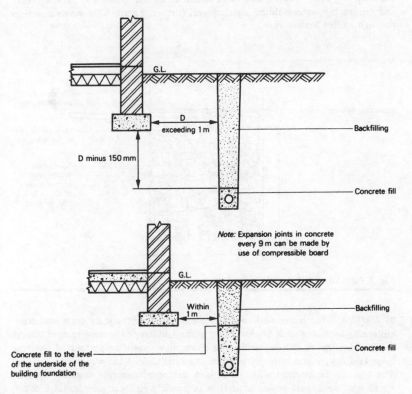

Fig. 8.69   Trenches for drains or private sewers adjacent to building

Use of soakaways

In the absence of a surface water sewer and if it is unnecessary to store rainwater, it is often advantageous to dispose of surface water from impermeable areas to an underground soakaway. The use of a soakaway will reduce the flow of rainwater to a river or stream and thus help to prevent flooding of land during a storm or continuous heavy rainfall. It may also be used to dispose of the final effluent from a small sewage purification plant.

Types of soakaways

A soakaway consists of a pit dug into impermeable sub-soil, from which the water may percolate into the surrounding ground.

There are two types:

1. *Filled:* for small soakaways, the pit can be filled with coarse granular material such as broken bricks, crushed sound stone or river gravel, with a size range of 10 to 150 mm. The end of the inlet pipe should be surrounded with large pieces, to ensure that the rainwater can flow freely into the granular material. This type of soakaway is cheap to construct, but its water-holding capacity is greatly reduced and there is also a risk that leaves and silt may enter and reduce the water-holding capacity still further. Figure 8.70 shows a section through a filled soakaway.

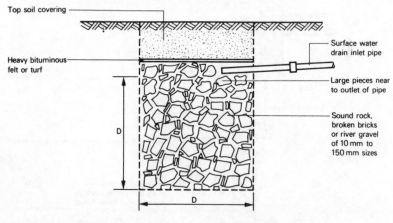

Fig. 8.70 Small filled soakaway

2. *Unfilled:* for larger soakaways, the excavated pit may be prevented from collapsing by lining with brickwork or stone laid dry, or cement-jointed honeycombed brickwork. Alternatively, the lining may consist of perforated concrete rings laid dry, surrounded by granular material to lead the water into the soil. The top can be covered with a standard reinforced concrete manhole top and fitted with an access cover, so that it is possible to clean out leaves and silt. Figures 8.71 and 8.72 show large and small unfilled soakaways.

Design

A soakaway can only be used in pervious subsoil such as gravel, sand, chalk or fissured rock and its base must be above the ground water table. In order to design a soakaway, the following points must be taken into account:

1. The local authority drainage regulations.
2. Area of impermeable surface, such as, roofs and paved areas.
3. Type of subsoil.
4. The rainfall intensity for the district during a storm, or continuous heavy rainfall.

204

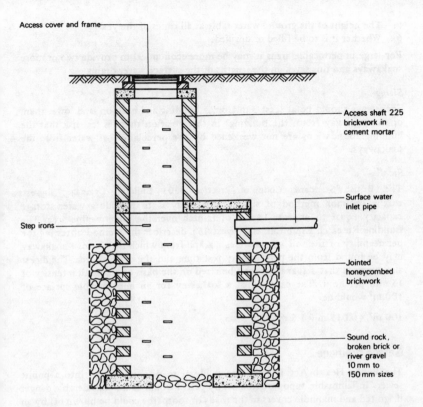

Fig. 8.71 Large honeycombed brickwork unfilled soakaway

Labels for Fig. 8.71:
- Access cover and frame
- Access shaft 225 brickwork in cement mortar
- Surface water inlet pipe
- Step irons
- Jointed honeycombed brickwork
- Sound rock, broken brick or river gravel 10 mm to 150 mm sizes

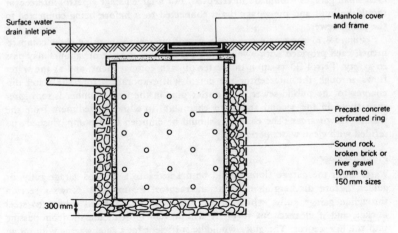

Fig. 8.72 Small precast concrete unfilled soakaway

Labels for Fig. 8.72:
- Surface water drain inlet pipe
- Manhole cover and frame
- Precast concrete perforated ring
- Sound rock, broken brick or river gravel 10 mm to 150 mm sizes
- 300 mm

5. The height of the ground water table at all times of the year.
6. Whether it is to be filled or unfilled.

For large impermeable areas it may be more economical to provide two or more soakaways and this saves on the lengths of the surface water drains.

Siting

Soakaways should be at least 3 m from a building and built on land lower than, or sloping away from, the building. In this position there is less risk that the building foundations are not weakened by the percolation of water from the soakaways.

Size

The British Standard, Code of Practice 8301 Building Drainage, suggests that a common method of sizing a soakaway is to provide a water storage capacity equal to at least 13 mm of rainfall over the impermeable area. The Building Research Establishment Digest 151 describes the method of testing the permeability of the soil and provides a graph from which the size of a soakaway may be found from the permeability test time and the drained area. The digest also suggests that a soakaway may be sized on the basis of a rainfall intensity of 15 mm per hour. The capacity of a soakaway for an impermeable surface of 100 m² would be:

$$100 \text{ m}^2 \times 0.015 \text{ m} = 1.5 \text{ m}^3$$

Garage drainage

The Public Health Act 1936 makes it illegal to discharge spirit into a public sewer. Inflammable vapours given off by petrol would cause considerable danger if ignited and manhole covers in the roads or footpaths could be blown off by an explosion, thus endangering the public. These vapours may also cause danger to workmen carrying out maintenance work in the sewers. To prevent the entry of petrol into the sewer, the floor washings of large garages, petrol stations and even small garages should be intercepted. For a large garage a petrol interceptor should be built and the garage drain connected to it before being connected to the public sewer.

Figure 8.73 shows a section of a petrol interceptor housing three compartments, each provided with a ventilating pipe so that the petrol vapours may pass to safety. Petrol floats upon the water of each compartment, and as the water flows through the interceptor the petrol will evaporate before the water discharges to the public sewer. The outlet pipe in the first chamber is set higher than those in the second and third chambers, to allow for sediment from the washing-down areas. The chambers should be emptied by a pump, flushed and refilled with clean water periodically.

Floor drainage

Water from the garage floor should be drained into a trapped garage gully, or gullies, before discharging into the interceptor. Figure 8.74 shows a section through a garage gully, which is provided with a perforated galvanised steel bucket, and if cleaned out regularly will prevent most of the silt from passing into the interceptor. The gully would be sufficient for a small garage without an interceptor.

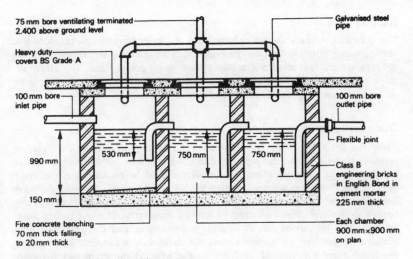

75 mm bore ventilating terminated 2.400 above ground level

Galvanised steel pipe

Heavy duty covers BS Grade A

100 mm bore inlet pipe

100 mm bore outlet pipe

Flexible joint

990 mm

530 mm   750 mm   750 mm

150 mm

Class B engineering bricks in English Bond in cement mortar 225 mm thick

Fine concrete benching 70 mm thick falling to 20 mm thick

Each chamber 900 mm × 900 mm on plan

Fig. 8.73   Detail of petrol interceptor

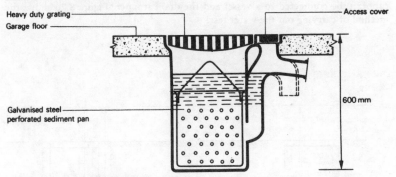

Heavy duty grating
Garage floor

Access cover

Galvanised steel perforated sediment pan

600 mm

Fig. 8.74   Section through garage gully

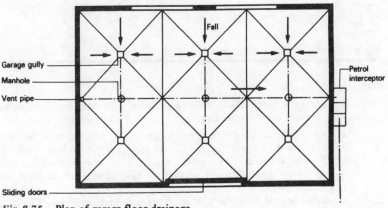

Fall

Garage gully
Manhole
Vent pipe

Petrol interceptor

Sliding doors

Fig. 8.75   Plan of garage floor drainage

Drainage layout

The petrol interceptor should only be used for water from the garage floor and surface water from the roof and external paved areas should be excluded. Figure 8.75 shows the layout of a drainage system for a garage floor. The minimum slope of the floor to each gully should be 1 in 80 and the area of surface to be drained by each gully should be about 50 m².

Drain testing and inspection

After the drain has been laid and before backfilling, or placing concrete, or granular material round the pipes, it should be tested by either water or air. If any leak occurs, the defective pipe or joint should be rectified and the drain again tested. Wherever possible, testing should be carried out between the manholes and short branch drains tested along with the main drainage system. Long branch drains and manholes should be tested separately. The test before backfilling should be carried out as soon as is practicable and the pipe should be strutted, to prevent any movement of the drain during the test. A temporary bend and stand pipe should be fitted at the head of the drain and a stopper fitted at the lower end. Alternatively, the test may be applied by means of a rubber tube connected to a vessel and the drain stopper. Figure 8.76 shows the method of carrying out the water test.

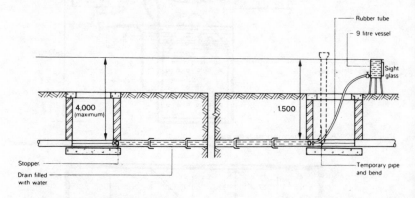

Fig. 8.76 Water test on drainage

The Code of Practice 8301, Building Drainage, recommends the following procedure in carrying out the water test:

1. The drain should be filled with water, to give a test pressure equal to 1.5 m of water above the soffit of the drain at the high end, but not more than 4 m head of water above the soffit of the drain at the low end. Steeply graded drains should be tested in stages, so that the head of water at the lower end does not exceed 4 m.

2. The pipeline should be allowed to stand for two hours and topped up with water.

3. After two hours the loss of water from the pipeline should be measured by noting the quantity of water needed to maintain the test head for 30 minutes. The fall of water in the vessel or stand pipe may be due to one or more of the following causes:

(a) Absorption by pipes or joints
The initial absorption may be of the order of 5 per cent of the total weight of the pipeline.

(b) Trapped air
This usually occurs at the joints and the amount will vary with the type of joint, diameter of pipe, number of joints and the gradient. Eventually the air is absorbed by the water, but this can take some time.

(c) Sweating of pipes and joints
Occasionally pipes and joints under water pressure may sweat slightly, but this should not be considered a cause for rejection of the pipeline.

(d) Leakage from defective pipes or joints
The defective pipe or joint should be taken out and replaced and the pipeline re-tested.

(e) Leakage from stoppers
These should be tightened, but if the leakage continues a new plug should be inserted. Sometimes a leakage can occur on the threaded portion of the plug. All equipment used for testing should be thoroughly checked before being used and the rubber surfaces of plugs should be free from grit.

Final water test
The rate of water loss should not exceed 1 litre/hour per metre diameter, per metre run of pipe. For various pipe sizes the rate of loss per metre run during the 30-minute period is 0.05 litre for 100 mm pipe, 0.08 litre for 150 mm pipe, and 0.12 litre for a 225 mm pipe.

Air test
The length of drain to be tested should be effectively plugged and air pumped into the pipe until a pressure equal to 100 mm head of water is indicated by a U-tube connected to the testing equipment. The air pressure should not fall to less than 75 mm head of water during a test period of 5 minutes without pumping. Air expands or contracts by about 1/273 of its normal volume of each 1 °C change of temperature and if there is a drop in temperature of the pipeline during the test the air inside will contract, causing a drop in the water level in the U-gauge. Figure 8.78 shows the method of carrying out an air test. The test is carried out by fixing a stopper, sealed with a cap, at one end of the drain and pumping in air at the other end until the U-gauge shows a pressure equal to 100 mm water gauge.

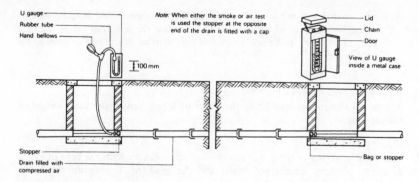

Fig. 8.77 | Air test on drainage

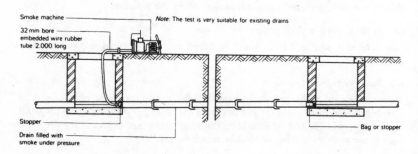

Fig. 8.78 | Smoke test on drainage

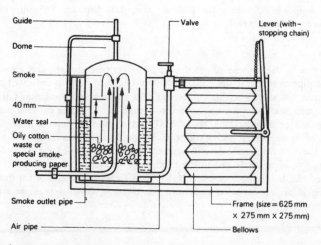

Fig. 8.79 | Smoke machine during test

Smoke test

The use of smoke cartridges for this test is not to be recommended, due to the possibility of the build up of high pressure inside the drain. The test by use of a smoke machine is usually applied to existing drains with the purpose of locating a leak. In order to ensure that the drain is filled with smoke, a rubber tube should be passed through the water seal of gully traps, so that air contained inside the drain may escape. Figure 8.78 shows the method of carrying out a smoke test. The test is carried out by placing a stopper, sealed with a cap, at one end of the drain and pumping in smoke at the other. The dome rises with the action of the bellows and if the drain is sound is maintained in this elevated position. Figure 8.80 shows the smoke machine during a test.

Types of stoppers

The drain is plugged or stopped by either an expanding drain plug (shown in Fig. 8.80) or by an inflatable bag (shown in Fig. 8.81).

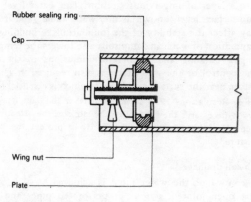

Fig. 8.80   Expanding drain plug

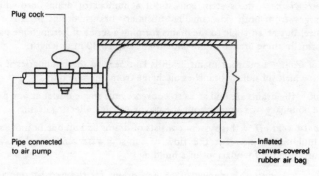

Fig. 8.81   Inflatable bag drain stopper

Tests for straightness and obstruction

This can be carried out by placing an electric torch at one end of the drain and looking through a mirror at the other end of the drain. Any fault in alignment or obstruction will be seen through the mirror.

Testing manholes

A drain plug should be inserted in the drain in the inlet pipe of the manhole at a lower level than the manhole to be tested. The manhole to be tested and the length of drain should be filled with water and after 30 minutes the water level checked. After the initial drop of water, due to absorption into the cement joints, the level should remain stationary.

Sub-soil drainage

Some of the water which reaches the ground either as snow or rain flows to streams and rivers or into the surface water drainage system. Some of the water also enters the ground and at some point below ground is prevented from flowing, due to a layer of impervious stratum. The water level thus rises and reaches the sub-surface level, known as the 'water table', and if this level rises too high it may affect the stability of the foundations of buildings, roads or car parks. The evaporation of water in damp soils also lowers the temperature of the air surrounding a building and is therefore injurious to the health of the occupants. The control of the water table is also required in agriculture, since excessive moisture near the surface excludes air which is essential to plant life.

The Building Regulations 1985 states: 'Wherever the dampness or position of the site renders it necessary, the sub-soil of the site shall be effectively drained, or such other steps shall be taken as will effectively protect the building against damage by moisture.'

Systems of sub-soil drainage

The artificial control of the water table is achieved by a system of sub-soil drainage, using open jointed, porous or perforated pipes and the following systems may be used (see Fig. 8.82).

1. *Natural:* the pipes are laid to follow the natural depressions or valleys of the site; branches discharge into the main as tributaries do into a river.

2. *Herringbone:* the system consists of a number of drains into which discharges from both sides smaller subsidiary branch drains parallel to each other, but at an angle to the mains forming a series of herringbone patterns. Normally these branch drains should not exceed 30 m in length.

3. *Grid iron:* a main or mains drain is laid near to the boundaries if the site into which subsidiary branches discharge from one side only.

4. *Fan:* the drains are laid so as to converge on a single outlet at one point on the boundary of a site without the use of a main collecting drain.

5. *Moat or cut off:* this system consists of drains laid on one or more sides of a building to intercept the flow of sub-soil water and carry it away, so protecting the foundations of a building.

Table 8.7 gives the spacing of branch drains for the herringbone and grid iron systems.

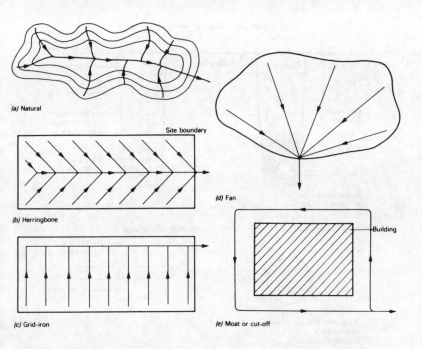

Fig. 8.82   Subsoil drainage

Table 8.7   Spacing of branch drains, British Standard Code of Practice BS 8301: 1985 *Building Drainage*

Soil	Distance between groundwater drains for various depths to invert of main drains	
	Mains 0.8 to 1.0 m deep	**Mains 1.0 to 1.5 m deep**
	(m)	(m)
Sand	–	45–90
Sandy loam	–	30–45
Loam	18–20	20–30
Clay loam	12–16	15–20
Sandy clay	6–12	–
Clay	2–6	–

Pipe laying

The main pipes should be either 75 or 100 mm nominal bore and the branch pipes 65 or 75 mm nominal bore. The pipes should be laid at between 600 and 900 mm in heavy soils, and deeper in light soils and the gradients rather by the fall of land than by consideration of self-cleansing velocity. Figure 8.83 shows the methods of laying the pipes.

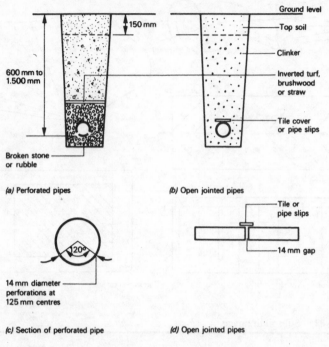

Trench width just sufficient to permit pipe laying

150 mm

Ground level

Top soil

Clinker

600 mm to
1.500 mm

Inverted turf,
brushwood
or straw

Tile cover
or pipe slips

Broken stone
or rubble

(a) Perforated pipes

(b) Open jointed pipes

120°

Tile or
pipe slips

14 mm gap

14 mm diameter
perforations at
125 mm centres

(c) Section of perforated pipe

(d) Open jointed pipes

Fig. 8.83   Methods of pipe laying

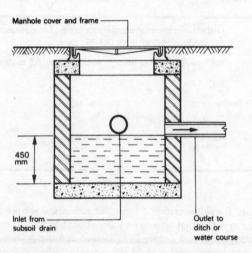

Manhole cover and frame

450
mm

Inlet from
subsoil drain

Outlet to
ditch or
water course

Fig. 8.84   Detail of catchpit

214

Discharge of water

The ground water may discharge into a soakaway, or through a catch pit into the nearest ditch or water course (see Fig. 8.84). Alternatively, the water may discharge into a surface water drain, through either a silt trap or a reverse action intercepting trap (see Figs. 8.85 and 8.86).

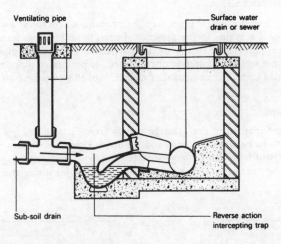

Fig. 8.85   Reverse action interceptor

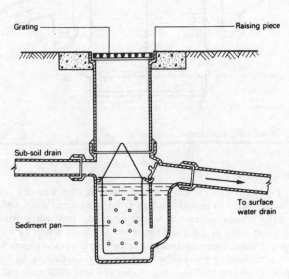

Fig. 8.86   Detail of silt trap

Types of pipes

1. Clayware field drain pipes BS 1196.
2. Concrete pipes BS 4101.
3. Perforated clay pipes BS 65 and 540.
4. Perforated pitch fibre pipes BS 2760.
5. Porous concrete pipes BS 1194.
6. Surface water clay pipes BS 65 and 540.
7. Plastic pipes BS 3506.

Note: The use of concrete pipes may be unsuitable where sub-soil water carries sulphates, or is acid due to the presence of peat. In other circumstances, porous concrete pipes prevent the entry of fine particles of silt into the pipes. In order to prevent the soil from entering open jointed, or perforated pipes, they should be surrounded by a filter composed of clinker, broken stone or rubble.

Grease traps

Where grease may enter the drainage system from canteen sinks, a grease trap should be fixed between the sinks and the drain. Figure 8.87 shows a detail of a grease trap which contains a large volume of water. Grease entering the trap is congealed by the water and is periodically removed by lifting the perforated tray.

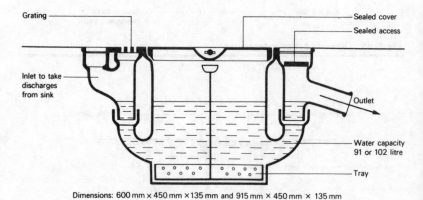

Dimensions: 600 mm × 450 mm × 135 mm and 915 mm × 450 mm × 135 mm

Fig. 8.87   Detail of grease trap

Anti-flooding devices

On a drainage system which is liable to back flooding from a surcharged sewer, it is sometimes necessary to provide an anti-flooding device. Figure 8.88 shows an anti-flood gully which contains a copper or plastic ball. When back-flooding occurs, the water rising in the gully forces the ball float against a rubber seating and so prevents water escaping through the top of the gully. Figure 8.89 shows the 'Eureka' anti-flooding trunk valve. Under normal conditions the hinged valve remains open, but when back-flooding occurs the cork float rises and closes the valve against the rubber seating.

216

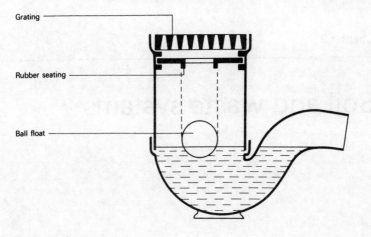

Fig. 8.88   Anti-flood gully

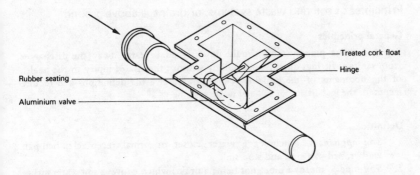

Fig. 8.89   The 'Eureka' anti-flood trunk valve with the cover removed

Chapter 9

Soil and waste systems

Principles of soil and waste systems, or drainage above ground

General principles

Soil and waste pipe systems should be designed to carry away the discharges from sanitary fittings quickly and quietly without the risk of injury to the health of the occupants of the building. The following give the definitions and requirements for the installation of soil and waste systems:

Definitions

1. *Soil appliances:* includes a water closet or urinal receptacle, bed-pan washer, bed-pan sink and slop sink.
2. *Soil pipe:* means a pipe (not being a drain) which conveys soil water either alone or together only with waste water, or rainwater, or both.
3. *Ventilating pipe:* means a pipe (not being a drain) open to the external air at its highest point, which ventilates a drainage system, either by connection to a drain, or to a soil pipe, or waste pipe and does not convey any soil water, waste water or rainwater.
4. *Waste appliance:* includes a slipper bath, lavatory basin, bidet, domestic sink, cleaner's bucket sink, drinking fountain, shower tray, wash fountain, washing trough and wash-tub.
5. *Waste pipe:* means a pipe (not being a drain, or overflow pipe) which conveys waste water, either alone or together only with rainwater.
6. *Waste water:* means used water not contaminated by soil water or trade effluent.

Requirements

1. *Water seals in traps*

Such provision shall be made in the drainage system of a building, either above or below the ground as may be necessary to prevent the destruction under working conditions of the water seal in any trap in the system, or in any appliance which discharges into the system.

2. *Sizes of pipes*

The internal diameter of any soil, waste pipe or ventilating pipe shall not be less than the internal diameter of any pipe, or the outlet of any appliance which discharges into it. The internal diameter of a soil pipe shall not be less than: (*a*) 50 mm, if it exclusively serves one or more urinals, or (*b*) 75 mm, in any other case. The internal diameter of a waste pipe shall not be less than 32 mm if it serves a lavatory basin.

3. *Materials, fixing and joints*

Any soil pipe, waste pipe or ventilating pipe shall be composed of suitable materials of adequate strength and durability. Bends in pipes should have the largest practicable radius of curvature and there should be no change in the cross-section of the pipe throughout the bend. Pipes should be adequately supported throughout their lengths, without restricting thermal movement, and any fitting which gives such support should be securely attached to the building.

A soil or waste pipe should be fixed inside the building, except a waste pipe from a waste fitting fixed on the ground floor, providing that the pipe discharges into a trap fitted with a suitable grating, so that the water may discharge below the grating and above the level of water in the trap (see Fig. 9.1). All pipes should be placed so that they are reasonably accessible for maintenance and repair, and be provided with such means of access for internal cleansing. Joints should be made so that they remain air-tight and any dissimilar materials used for jointing should not cause electrolytic corrosion. *Note:* The Building Regulations 1985 permit a soil and vent stack sited externally for buildings up to three storey in height.

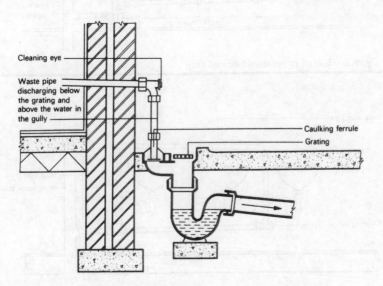

Fig. 9.1   Waste pipe from an appliance situated on the ground floor

4. *Traps*

A trap should be fitted close to a waste or soil appliance, unless the appliance has an integral trap. Alternatively:

(a) a waste pipe serving two or more baths, or lavatory basins, may discharge into a semi-circular and accessible open channel of glazed stoneware, or equally suitable material formed or fixed in or above the floor immediately below the baths, or lavatory basins and discharging over or into a suitable trap (see Fig. 9.2);

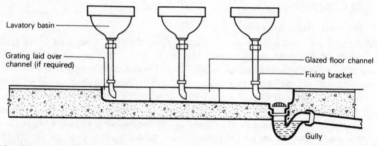

Fig. 9.2 Use of glazed channel

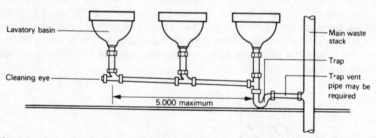

Fig. 9.3 Use of common waste and trap

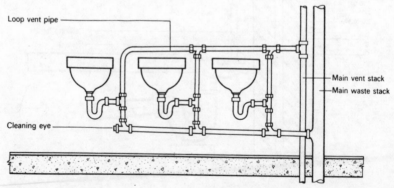

Fig. 9.4 Individual traps connected to a common waste pipe

(b) a waste pipe serving a number of lavatory basins, or shower trays, or both fixed in a range, may have one trap fitted at the end of the pipe, providing the length of the pipe does not exceed 5 m in length (see Fig. 9.3). A trap should have an adequate diameter water seal and means of access for internal cleansing. Figure 9.4 shows three basins having individual traps, connected to a common waste pipe.

5. *Tests*

A soil and waste system should be capable of withstanding a smoke or air test for a minimum period of 3 minutes, at a pressure equivalent to a head not less than 38 mm head of water (see Fig. 9.5). During the test every trap should maintain a minimum water seal of 25 mm.

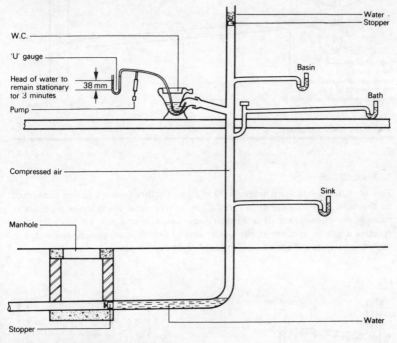

Fig. 9.5 Air test on soil and waste pipes

Loss of water seal in traps

1. *Self-siphonage*

This is usually greater in wash basins and other small appliances, due to their curved shape, and is caused by a moving plug of water in the waste pipe. A partial vacuum is created at the outlet of the trap, thus causing siphonage of the water. Air bubbles are drawn through the trap during discharge of the water, which assist the siphonage by their pumping action.

The diameter, length and slope of the waste pipe affect the hydraulic behaviour of the plug of water. Experimental work at the Building Research

Establishment has set limiting values within which it is safe to say that the seal of a trap will not be lost by self-siphonage. If the diameter, length and slope of the waste pipe fall outside these limits set for unvented wastes, then either a vent pipe must be provided, or a resealing trap used. Figure 9.6 shows how self-siphonage occurs.

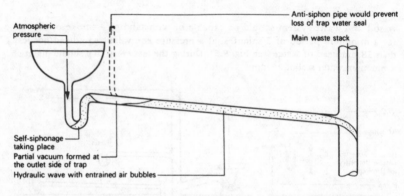

Fig. 9.6   Self siphonage

2. Induced siphonage

This is caused by the discharge of water from another sanitary fitting connected to the same pipe. In either a vertical, or a horizontal main waste pipe, water passing the connection of a branch waste pipe may draw air from it, thus creating a partial vacuum at the outlet side of the trap and causing siphonage of the water. Figure 9.7 shows how induced siphonage occurs.

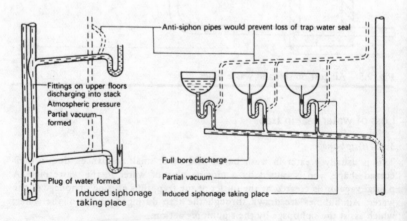

Fig. 9.7   Induced siphonages

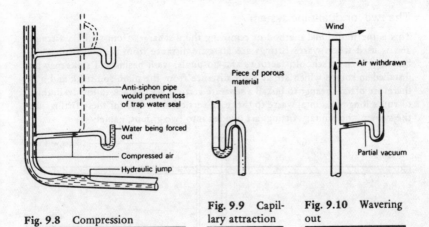

Fig. 9.8 Compression

Fig. 9.9 Capillary attraction

Fig. 9.10 Wavering out

3. *Compression or back pressure*

This is caused by a build up of air pressure near the bend at the foot of the stack. A waste pipe connected to the stack in the pressure zone may have the seal of the trap lost by the compressed air forcing out the water. Detergent foam increases the risk of compression. Figure 9.8 shows the loss of the seal of a trap by compression.

4. *Capillary attraction*

This is caused by a piece of porous material being caught at the outlet of the trap, so that one end is in the water and the other end is hanging over the outlet. The water may be drawn out of the trap by capillary attraction (see Fig. 9.9).

5. *Wavering out*

This is caused by high-velocity gusts of wind passing over the vent pipe, which draw some of the air out of the pipe, thus creating a partial vacuum on the outlet side of the trap. The gusts of wind cause the water in the trap to oscillate, until the water seal in the trap is broken (see Fig. 9.10).

6. *Evaporation*

When the trap is not in use, the rate of evaporation of the water will depend upon the relative humidity of the air in the room. The rate is approximately 2.5 mm per week, so a 25 mm seal would last 10 weeks.

7. *Momentum*

This is caused by a sudden discharge of water into a fitting and the force of the water may be sufficient to unseal the trap. The discharge of a bucket-full of water into a W.C. is the most usual cause.

8. *Leakage*

This is usually due to a faulty joint on the cleaning eye, or a crack in the trap due to expansion and contraction of the material.

The two- or dual-pipe system

This is the traditional method of removing the discharges from sanitary fittings and is used when waste fittings are at some distance from the soil fittings. In buildings such as schools, factories and hospitals, wash basins and sinks may be installed in rooms which are at some distance from the main soil stack and it is therefore often cheaper to install a separate vertical waste stack to the drain than to run a long horizontal waste to the main vertical soil stack for these fittings. In the system, the sanitary fittings are divided into two groups, namely:

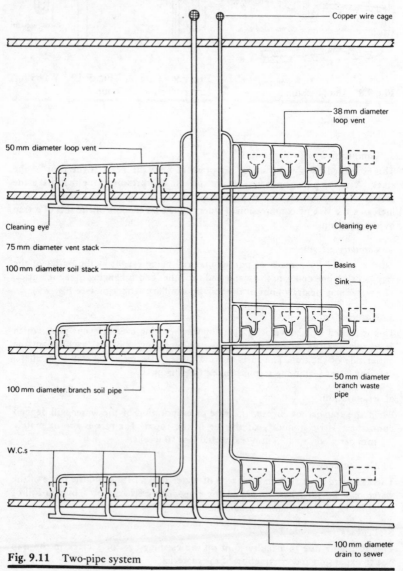

Fig. 9.11   Two-pipe system

1. Soil fittings

These are for the disposal of foul matter and include W.C.s, urinals, slop sinks and bed-pan washers. These fittings are connected to a vertical soil stack, which is connected to the drain by means of a rest bend at the foot of the vertical stack.

2. Waste or ablution fittings

These are for the disposal of mainly soapy water and include wash basins, showers, baths, sinks, bidets, wash-tubs, drinking fountains and island washing fountains. These fittings are connected to a vertical waste stack, which is connected to the drains by means of a rest bend at its base.

Note: Some local authorities may require a back inlet gully at the foot of the waste stack. This was the traditional method of connecting the vertical waste stack to the underground drain.

Depth of trap water-seals

If the internal diameter of the trap is 64 mm or more it should have a 50 mm water-seal. If the trap has an internal diameter less than 64 mm it should have a 38 mm water-seal.

Soil stack

The internal diameter should not be less than the internal diameter of any soil fitting discharging into it and in any case not less than 75 mm.

Waste stack

The internal diameter will depend upon the type and number of fittings discharging into it, but should not be less than 50 mm.

Figure 9.11 shows a two-pipe system for a three-storey building having three W.C.s, three wash basins and one sink on each floor. It will be noted that anti-siphonage or vent pipes are provided to all the traps, which is a high-class method of installation. A cheaper method is the fitting of resealing traps to the waste fittings, but some local authorities object to this method, due to the possibility of these traps becoming inoperative by fouling with waste matter.

The one-pipe system

This system was introduced into this country from the USA in the 1930s, but due to the regulations existing at that time, which did not permit the connection of a waste pipe to a soil pipe, it was some time before this country amended the regulations and approved the use of the system. In the system, all soil and waste fittings discharge into common waste and soil stack and all the trap ventilating or anti-siphon pipes connect into one ventilating stack. This ventilating stack is extended down to the horizontal drainage system, to relieve any compressed air which might exist at the base of the waste and soil stack. Alternatively, the relief vent may be connected to the waste and soil stack, near the lowest branch connection. Where the planning of the building provides for close grouping of the waste and soil fittings, the elemination of the waste and waste ventilating stacks required for the two-pipe system results in a saving in installation costs and duct space.

The system is used in hospitals, large offices, schools and factories where there are ranges of fittings on one or several floors of the building. Figure 9.12 shows a fully vented one-pipe system for a three-storey office, or similar type of

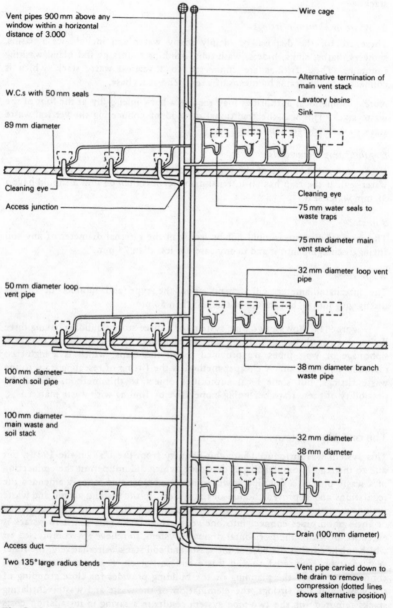

Vent pipes 900 mm above any window within a horizontal distance of 3.000

Wire cage

Alternative termination of main vent stack

W.C.s with 50 mm seals

Lavatory basins

Sink

89 mm diameter

Cleaning eye

Access junction

Cleaning eye

75 mm water seals to waste traps

75 mm diameter main vent stack

32 mm diameter loop vent pipe

50 mm diameter loop vent pipe

100 mm diameter branch soil pipe

38 mm diameter branch waste pipe

100 mm diameter main waste and soil stack

32 mm diameter

38 mm diameter

Access duct

Two 135° large radius bends

Drain (100 mm diameter)

Vent pipe carried down to the drain to remove compression (dotted lines shows alternative position)

Fig. 9.12 Fully vented one-pipe system

building. It will be noted that each fitting is provided with a trap and a trap ventilating or anti-siphon pipe.

The Building Research Establishment has carried out extensive research on the one-pipe system, which has resulted in the reduction in the amount of ventilating or anti-siphon pipes. The design is based upon the experience that some loss of trap seal is acceptable and that the soil and waste stack may be designed to restrict air pressure fluctuations to $\pm$ 375 N/m^2. A negative pressure of this magnitude corresponds to about 25 mm loss of seal from a washdown W.C. This loss of trap seal would be acceptable in practice, but the local authority would have to be consulted in order to ensure that the regulations would not be contravened.

Ranges of W.C.s

The research has shown that branch pipes from a range of W.C.s which are normally 100 mm diameter do not run full bore and thus there is no risk of induced siphonage; therefore branch ventilating or anti-siphon pipes may be omitted. It is possible that up to eight W.C.s may be installed in a range, with a straight branch pipe at an angle of ½° to 5°, without the need for anti-siphon pipes. The angle is not critical, but where there are bends in the branch pipe it may be necessary to fit a ventilating pipe to the fitting furthest from the waste and soil stack.

Ranges of lavatory basins

There is a greater risk of the branch pipe from lavatory basins flowing full than a branch soil pipe from W.C.s, and therefore more risk of induced siphonage of the traps. With normal taps where the basin is filled with water, it may be necessary to provide trap ventilating or anti-siphon pipes, but if spray taps are used which allows hand washing under the spray the branch waste pipe will run only partly filled. Experiments have shown that where spray taps are used, a 32 mm internal diameter branch waste pipe may serve up to eight lavatory basins without the need of trap ventilating or anti-siphon pipes. The use of spray taps, however, results in the formation of sediment in the waste pipe and regular cleaning is usually necessary. Other methods of avoiding the installation of anti-siphon pipes in ranges of basins are: (a) the use of special resealing traps to each basin,

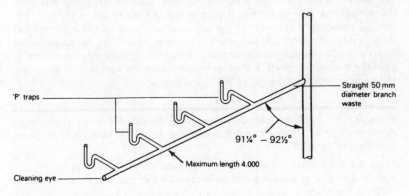

'P' traps

Straight 50 mm diameter branch waste

91¼° − 92½°

Maximum length 4.000

Cleaning eye

Fig. 9.13   Range of up to four basins without vent pipes

227

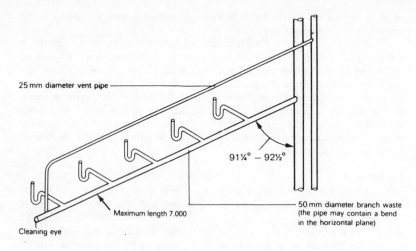

25 mm diameter vent pipe

91¼° − 92½°

50 mm diameter branch waste
(the pipe may contain a bend
in the horizontal plane)

Maximum length 7.000

Cleaning eye

Fig. 9.14 Range of up to five basins with vent pipe

(b) the use of a single running trap at the end of the branch waste pipe, (c) the use of P traps for up to four basins discharging into a 50 mm diameter branch waste pipe, installed at an angle of between 1¼ to 1½° (see Fig. 9.13). Figure 9.14 shows the method used to reduce the amount of trap ventilating pipework for up to five basins.

Ranges of urinals

Trap ventilating pipes are not normally necessary from the consideration of flow of water, but they are available in order to obtain a flow of air through the soil pipe, which helps to reduce the build up of sediment inside the pipe.

Diameters of stacks

The internal diameters of the main soil and waste and vent stacks depends upon the number and type of fittings, pattern of use and the height of the building. Internal diameters of 100 and 150 mm are commonly used for the waste and soil stack. Table 9.1 covers 100 mm internal diameter stacks used for up to twelve floors and 150 mm internal diameter stacks used for up to twenty-four floors. It gives the minimum vent stack sizes recommended for use with vertical waste and soil stacks, serving equal ranges of W.C.s, and basins.

Example 9.1. *Find the internal diameters of the soil and waste stack for an eight-storey office, having five W.C.s, and five basins on each floor, assuming public use of fittings.*

Table 9.1 shows that a 100 mm diameter soil and waste stack with a 40 mm internal diameter vent stack would be suitable with a cross vent on each floor, as shown in Fig. 9.15.

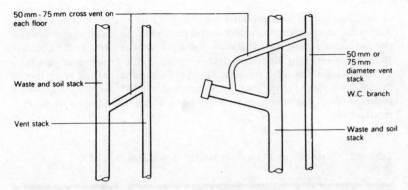

50 mm - 75 mm cross vent on each floor

Waste and soil stack

Vent stack

50 mm or 75 mm diameter vent stack

W.C. branch

Waste and soil stack

Fig. 9.15 Cross vents to prevent air pressure fluctuations in waste and soil stacks

Table 9.1 Vent stack sizes (diameter in mm) for office buildings. (From the *Building Research Establishment Digest*, p. 115.)

Diameter of drainage stack	100 mm			150 mm				
Number of floors	4	8	12	8	12	16	20	24
W.C.s and basins								
(a) 10-min. interval								
'Public' use — 1 + 1	0	0	30	0	0	0	0	0
2 + 2	0	0	30	0	0	0	0	0
3 + 3	0	30	40	0	0	0	0	0
4 + 4	0	40	40	0	see note			
5 + 5	0	40	see note	0				
(b) 5-min. interval								
'Peak' use — 1 + 1	0	0	30	0	0	0	0	0
2 + 2	0	50	50	0	0	0	0	0
3 + 3	0	50		0	0	0	50	65
4 + 4	30	see note		0	*Note:* for situations outside the range of the table, refer to B.S. 5572.			
5 + 5	30			0				

Main assumptions: 0 means no vent stack needed; Cast iron drainage stack and fittings BS 416; Washdown W.C. to BS 1213 with 9-litre flush; No offset in 'wet' part of drainage stack; Large-radius bend at foot of stack.

Note: The 'public' use (10 min.) table should be sufficient for most purposes and the 'peak' use (5 min.) table is included to cover special situations where concentrated peak use may be expected. The table does not cover offsets in the 'wet' part of the waste and soil stack, nor a series of changes of direction between the lowest point of connection to the stack and the public sewer, which may increase back pressure above that likely in a simpler situation. In cases where above-normal back pressures are likely to arise as a result of downstream conditions, a relief vent connected to the stack near the lowest branch connection is recommended, especially when Table 9.1 shows no vent stack needed. A 50 mm diameter vent pipe for a 100 mm stack and a 75 mm vent pipe for a 150 mm stack are usually sufficient. The use of a large-radius bend at the foot of the stack is required to the root of 150 mm, but two 135° large-radius bends are preferred. With a 100 mm stack, a bend and a drain of 150 mm diameter is recommended.

Table 9.2 Discharge unit values for sanitary appliances, B.S. 5572 *1978*

Type of appliance	Frequency of use (minutes)		Discharge unit value
Spray tap (basin)	Add 0.06 litre per second per tap		—
9 litre water closet	20		7
	10		14
	5		28
Sink	20		6
	10		14
	5		27
Wash basin	20		1
	10		3
	5		6
Bath	75	(domestic)	7
	30	(commercial and congested)	18
	—		—
Shower (per head)	Add 0.1 litre per second per spray		—
Urinal (per stall or bowl)	20	(commercial and congested)	0.3
One group consisting of one W.C. one bath, 1 or 2 basins, sink			14
Washing machine (automatic)	250		4

20 min corresponds to peak domestic use
10 min corresponds to peak commercial use
 5 min corresponds to congested use in schools etc

Example 9.2. *Find the internal diameter of the soil and waste stack for a four-storey office having four W.C.s, and four basins on each floor, assuming public use of fittings.*

Table 9.1 shows that a 100 mm diameter stack may be used without the need of a vent stack. For other types of buildings and design considerations, the Code of Practice 304, 1968, Sanitary Pipework Above Ground, provides tables for the sizing of vertical stacks based on the discharge unit values for sanitary appliances. Table 9.2 gives the discharge unit table, which is used in conjunction with Table 9.3 to find the diameter of the stack.

Example 9.3. *Determine the diameter of the main waste and soil stack for a five-storey hotel, having 6 W.C.s, 8 wash basins, 3 urinals and 2 sinks on each floor.*

From Table 9.2

30 W.C.s, × 14	=	420·0	Discharge units
40 basins × 3	=	120·0	Discharge units
15 urinals × 0·3	=	4.5	Discharge units
10 sinks × 14	=	140.0	Discharge units
Total	=	684·5	

From Table 9.3 it can be seen that a 100 mm diameter stack will be satisfactory.

Table 9.3. Maximum number of discharge units to be allowed on vertical stacks (see note) B.S. 5572 1978

Nominal internal diameter of pipe (mm)	Discharge units
50	10
63	60
76	200 (not more than 1 W.C.)
89	350
100	750
125	2500
150	5500

Note: Discharge pipes sized by this method give the minimum size necessary to carry the expected flow load. Separate ventilating pipes may be required. It may be worthwhile to consider oversizing the discharge pipes to reduce the ventilating pipework required.

Trap water seals

1. Traps up to 64 mm internal diameter not provided with a ventilating or anti-siphon pipe should have a 75 mm seal.
2. Traps up to 64 mm internal diameter provided with a ventilating or anti-siphon pipe may have a 38 mm seal (depending upon the local authority approval).
3. Traps from 75 to 100 mm internal diameter should have a 50 mm seal, whether or not they are provided with a ventilating or anti-siphon pipe.

Diameter of traps

Table 9.4 gives the minimum internal diameters of traps for sanitary fittings.

Table 9.4 Minimum internal diameter of traps

Domestic type of fitting	Diameter (mm)	Non-domestic type of fitting	Diameter (mm)
Wash basin	32	Drinking fountain	19
Bidet	32	Bar well	32
Sink	40	Hotel and canteen sink	40
Bath	40	Urinal bowl	40
Shower	40	Urinal stall (1 or 2)	50
Wash-tub	50	Urinal stall (3 or 4)	65
Kitchen waste disposal		Urinal stall (5 or 6)	75
unit	40	Waste disposal unit	50

Connection of anti-siphon pipe

Figures 9.16 and 9.17 show the methods of connecting the anti-siphon pipe to the branch waste pipe. The connection should be away from the crown of the trap and at an angle in the direction of flow of water to prevent the anti-siphon pipe being blocked by grease or soap.

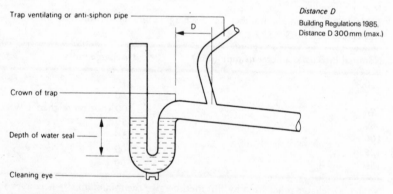

Distance D
Building Regulations 1985.
Distance D 300 mm (max.)

Fig. 9.16 Anti-siphon pipe connected to 'P' trap

Terminal velocity in stacks

In the past many designers were concerned that the velocity of the flow of water in high waste and soil stacks would be excessive, with the consequent noise, damage to the pipework and unsealing of traps. In some buildings stacks have been offset to reduce the velocity of flow, but this is unnecessary, because the forces of gravity soon balance when the flow of water takes place and a maximum speed of flow called the 'terminal velocity' is quickly reached. The height of the stack necessary for terminal velocity to be achieved depends upon the diameter of the pipe, amount of flow and the smoothness of the internal bore.

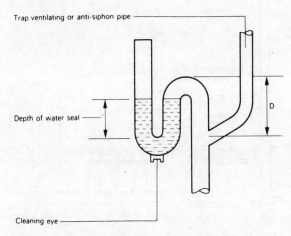

Note: The diameter of the anti-siphon pipe to be two-thirds the diameter of the waste pipe

Trap ventilating or anti-siphon pipe

Distance D

Building Regulations 1985.
Distance D 300 mm (max.)

Depth of water seal

D

Cleaning eye

Fig. 9.17 Anti-siphon pipe connected to 'S' trap

The height is only likely to be equal to one-storey and therefore offsets in stacks should be avoided, as these may cause a pressure build-up in the stack, add to the cost of installations and may cause blockages.

The single-stack system

In order to reduce the installation costs of soil and waste systems the Building Research Establishment carried out a great deal of experimental work and as a result the single-stack system was evolved, which has dispensed with the need for almost all the ventilating pipework. The single-stack system is a simplification of the one-pipe system, with the trap ventilating or anti-siphon pipes being either completely omitted or including only in special circumstances. In order to prevent the loss of water seals in the traps due to siphonage or back pressure, a high degree of planning and installation work is required.

Figure 9.18 shows a single-stack system for a two-storey block of flats, Fig. 9.19 a single-stack system for a ten-storey block of flats and Fig. 9.20 shows a view of the pipework on each floor.

The main requirements of the system are as follows:

1. Sanitary fittings must be grouped close to the stack, so that the branch waste and soil pipes are as short as possible.
2. All the sanitary fittings must be individually connected to the main stack. This will prevent the loss of trap water seal by induced siphonage.
3. An offset should not occur below the highest branch, in what is known as the 'wet' part of the stack. This is to prevent compression of air in the stack.
4. The foot of the stack should be connected to the drain with a large radius (150 mm root radius) or, preferably, two large radius 130° bends. This is to prevent compression of air at the base of the stack.

233

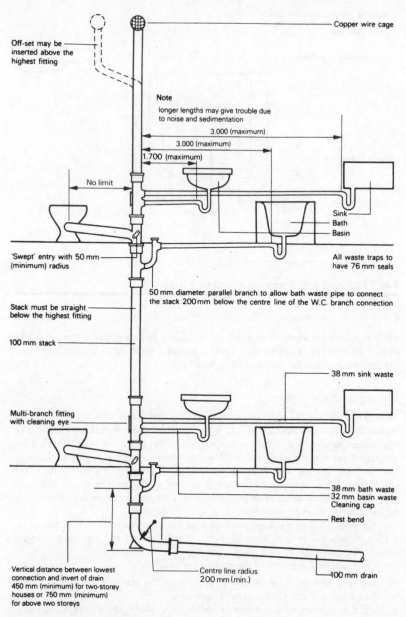

Fig. 9.18 Single stack system

5. The vertical distance between the lowest branch connection to the stack and the invert of the drain should be at least 450 mm for two-storey housing and at least 750 mm for above two storeys. Where this cannot be achieved,

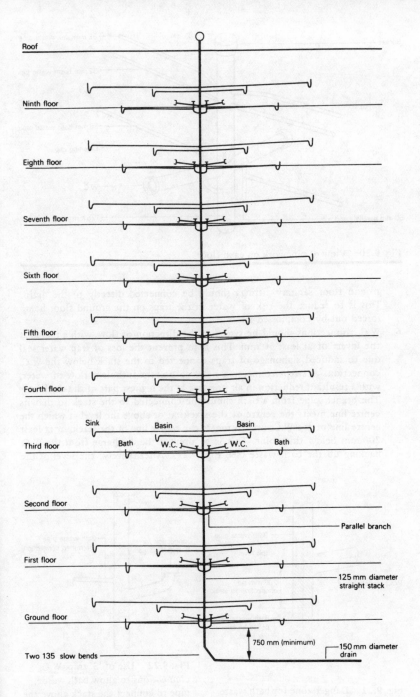

Roof

Ninth floor

Eighth floor

Seventh floor

Sixth floor

Fifth floor

Fourth floor

Third floor

Sink   Basin   Basin

Bath   W.C.   W.C.   Bath

Second floor

Parallel branch

First floor

125 mm diameter
straight stack

Ground floor

750 mm (minimum)

Two 135 slow bends

150 mm diameter
drain

Fig. 9.19   Single stack for a ten-storey block of flats

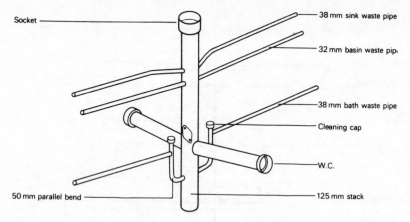

Fig. 9.20 View of pipework on each floor

ground floor sanitary fittings should be connected directly to the drain. This is to reduce the risk of water in the traps on the ground floor being forced out by compressed air.

6.   W.C. connections should be swept in the direction of flow, with a radius at the invert of at least 50 mm. This is to prevent the loss of trap water seal due to induced siphonage of traps connected to the stack below the W.C. connection. A swept connection helps to prevent turbulent flow of water, with a resultant reduction in air pressure at the highest part of the stack.

7.   The branch pipe from a bath should be connected to the stack so that its centre line meets the centre of the stack, at or above the level at which the centre line of the W.C. branch meets the centre line of the stack, or at least 200 mm below this point. This is to prevent the discharge from the W.C. backing up the bath waste (see Fig. 9.21). Alternatively, the level of the

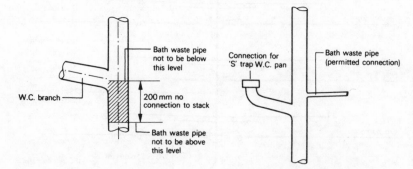

Fig. 9.21 Danger zone for bath waste connection

Fig. 9.22 Use of 'S' trap. W.C. connections to allow bath waste pipe to connect the stack above the W.C. branch

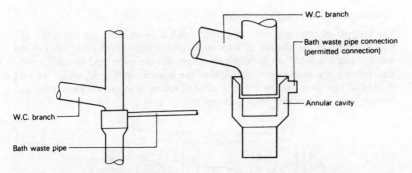

Fig. 9.23 Use of special 'Marley' collar boss fitting to prevent the W.C. discharge from backing up the bath waste pipe

W.C. branch connection can be lowered by use of an 'S' trap, W.C. pan (see Fig. 9.22) or a special collar boss may be used (see Fig. 9.23). These methods will prevent the discharges from the W.C. backing up the bath waste.

8. The Building Regulations 1985 state the following maximum lengths of branch waste and soil pipes: Wash basin, 1.7 m for 32 mm diameter and 3 m for 40 mm diameter; Sink and bath 3 mm for 40 mm diameter and 4 m for 50 mm diameter; WC no limit.

9. The slopes of the branch pipes are: Wash basin, 20–120 mm/m; Sink and bath, 18–90 mm/m; WC, 18 mm/m (minimum).

Use of multi-branch fittings

These are obtainable to suit most installations and are available in plastic, cast iron, copper, galvanised steel and pitch fibre materials. In blocks of flats the bath, basin and sink may be connected to a multi-branch fitting, thus saving in labour and materials. The slope and position of the pipes are set in these fittings and helps to ensure correct installation.

Stack diameter

(a) 76 or 89 mm diameters are suitable for up to two-storey housing (providing the W.C. outlet is 76 mm diameter for a 76 mm stack and 89 mm diameter for an 89 mm stack).

(b) 100 mm diameter is suitable for flats up to five storeys, with two groups of fittings on each floor.

(c) 125 mm diameter is suitable for flats up to twelve storeys with one group of fittings on each floor, or for flats up to ten storeys with two groups of fittings on each floor.

(d) 150 mm diameter is suitable for flats up to at least twenty storeys, with two groups of fittings on each floor.

Note: One group of fittings consists of one or two W.C.s, with a 9 litre flushing cistern, bath, sink and one or two lavatory basins.

Resealing and anti-siphon traps

The purpose of resealing and anti-siphon traps is to maintain the water seal of a trap without the installation of trap ventilating or anti-siphon pipe. The soil and waste systems is therefore cheaper and neater, but the traps tend to be noisy and also prevent the thorough ventilation of the branch waste pipe, which on long lengths of pipe may lead to the formation of sediment inside the pipe. They also require more maintenance than ordinary traps.

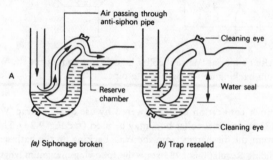

(a) Siphonage broken   *(b)* Trap resealed

Fig. 9.24   The 'Grevak' resealing trap

Figure 9.24 shows the 'Grevak' trap, which works as follows:

(*a*) Siphonage of the water in the trap takes place and the water level is lowered to point A of the anti-siphon pipe.

(*b*) Air passes through the anti-siphon pipe and equalises the air pressures on the inlet and outlet sides of the trap, thus breaking the siphonic action.

(*c*) Water gravitates back from the reserve chamber into the U of the trap and maintains the water seal.

Figure 9.25 shows the 'McAlpine' trap, which works as follows:

(*a*) Siphonage of water in the trap takes place and the water level is lowered to point A.

(*b*) Air passes through the pipe thus breaking the siphonic action and also causes water to be retained in the reserve chamber.

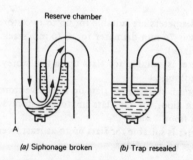

(a) Siphonage broken   *(b)* Trap resealed

Fig. 9.25   The 'McAlpine' resealing trap

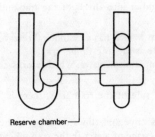

Fig. 9.26 'Econa' resealing trap

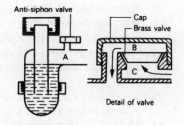

Fig. 9.27 Bottle trap with anti-siphon valve

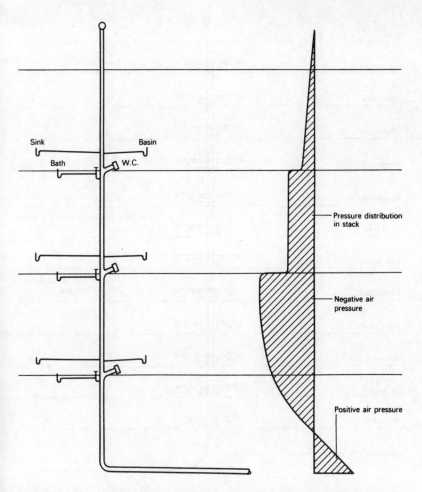

Fig. 9.28 Air pressure distribution with water flowing down the stack

(c) Water gravitates back from the reserve chamber into the U of the trap and maintains the water seal.

Figure 9.26 shows the 'Econa' resealing trap, which has a cylindrical reserve chamber. The trap operates on the same principle as the 'McAlpine' trap.

Figure 9.27 shows a bottle trap with an anti-siphon valve, which works as follows:

(a) If a partial vacuum is formed at the outlet side of the trap at A, there is a reduction of air pressure inside chamber B.
(b) The greater air pressure at C lifts the brass valve and flows through to the outlet side of the trap, thus preventing siphonage of water in the trap taking place and the seal is maintained.

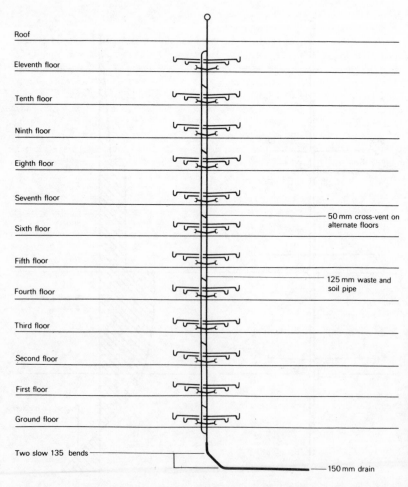

Fig. 9.29 Modified one-pipe vented stack system for a twelve-storey building

Modified one-pipe system

The modified one-pipe system is basically similar to the one-pipe and single-stack systems, but unlike a one-pipe system, the trap ventilating or anti-siphon pipes are omitted. In the system a main vent stack is installed which prevents fluctuations of air pressure inside the main waste and soil stack. A cross vent pipe is connected between the vent stack and waste soil stack, or, alternatively, a loop vent pipe may be connected from the W.C. branch pipe to the vent stack. These cross vent or loop pipes are usually installed on each floor and air may be drawn through them on the upper floors, to prevent a negative pressure from being created inside the waste and soil stack. The vent stack is terminated below the lowest waste or soil branch pipe and the vent stack at this point removes any compressed air at the lowest part of the waste and soil stack.

Figure 9.28 shows a typical air pressure distribution diagram, with water flowing down the stack.

If the negative or positive air pressures in the stack are above or below 373 N/m^2 a modified one-pipe system would be necessary, or a larger diameter waste and soil stack installed. A 150 mm diameter waste and soil stack is satisfactory without venting for up to twenty storeys, with the equivalent loading of two W.C.s, two sinks, two basins and two baths on each floor, or up to twenty-five storeys with one W.C. bath, basins and sink on each floor. Since a 150 mm diameter stack is the maximum size obtainable, a building above twenty or twenty-five storeys having the same number of fittings on each floor will require a modified one-pipe system.

Figure 9.29 shows a modified one-pipe vented stack system for a twelve-storey building. Table 9.5 gives the recommendations of the Building Research Establishment for the installation of vented stacks, or modified one-pipe systems.

Table 9.5 Minimum stack sizes and vents required for various loading conditions

Type of building	Stack diameter (mm)	Requirements
Flats	Stack serving one group on each floor	
6 to 10 storeys	100	50 mm vent stack with one cross connection on alternate floors
11 to 15 storeys	100	50 mm vent stack with one cross connection on each or alternate floors
16 to 20 storeys	100	64 mm vent stack with one cross connection on each or alternate floors
12 to 15 storeys	125	50 mm vent stack with one cross connection on alternate floors
Maisonettes	Stack serving one group on alternate floors	
11 to 15 storeys	100	50 mm vent stack with one cross connection on alternate bathroom floors
16 to 20 storeys	100	64 or 50 mm vent stack with one cross connection on alternate bathroom floors

Materials used for soil and waste systems

Lead

This is the traditional material for soil and waste systems and was sometimes used for the entire installation. Lead is now used for short branch pipes to the main case iron stacks and has the advantage of adaptability, especially in restricted duct spaces. It has a smooth internal bore and is resistant to acid attack, but it can be attacked by Portland cement, lime, plaster, brickwork and magnesite and therefore where lead pipes pass through floors or walls they should be protected by Denso tape, or waterproof paper wrapping, or coated

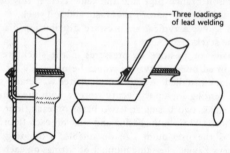

Fig. 9.30 Lead welded pipe joints

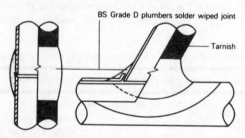

Fig. 9.31 Wiped soldered joints

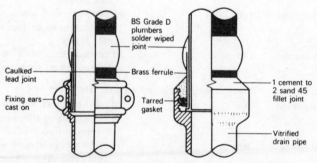

Fig. 9.32 Lead pipe to cast iron and clay pipe joints

with bitumen. Lead is heavy and easily damaged and is liable to thermal movement. The pipes require frequent or event continuous support and allowance must be made for expansion and contraction.

Jointing: pipes are jointed by either lead welding or soldered joints, as shown in Figs 9.30 and 9.31. Figure 9.32 shows the method of jointing lead to cast iron and clay pipes.

Cast iron

The metal is widely used for soil and waste systems and has the advantage of resisting mechanical damage better than most other materials. The pipes are heavy and require good support, but they do not expand and contract as much as lead, copper and unplasticised polyvinyl chloride pipes. If caulked lead joints are used, however, they may require recaulking periodically, due to the pipeline receiving discharges of hot water. The pipes are protected from corrosion by a coating both inside and outside with pitch. A wide range of fittings are available, especially various types of multi-branch junctions.

Jointing: pipes are jointed by caulked lead, or by a proprietary cold caulking compound as shown in Fig. 9.33. A rollring flexible joint may also be used, which is quicker to make and permits thermal movement. Figure 9.34 shows a rollring joint on cast iron pipe, supplied by Burn Brothers (London) Ltd.

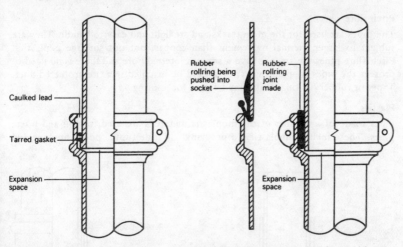

Fig. 9.33 Cast iron to cast iron caulked joint

Fig. 9.34 Cast iron to cast iron rubber rollring joint

Copper

This is an adaptable metal of medium weight and the pipes can be obtained in long lengths, which reduces the number of joints. The thermal expansion of copper is higher than that of cast iron and expansion joints may be required on long runs. The pipe has a smooth internal bore, is strong, rigid and resists attack from most building materials. Where the pipes can be seen, they may be chromium plated or polished.

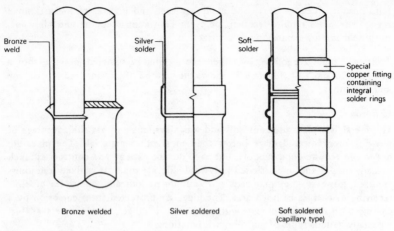

Fig. 9.35 Joints on copper pipes

Jointing: pipes may be jointed by bronze welding, silver or soft soldering (see Fig. 9.35).

Pitch fibre

The pipes are used for the main stacks and are light and easy to handle. They are subject to larger thermal movement than copper, but not so large as plastics. Pitch fibre pipes are strong, have a smooth internal bore and there is no need to protect the pipes by painting. They should be installed in a fire-protected duct. Taper or rubber 'O'-ring joints may be used for jointing.

Plastics

Pipes made of a number of thermoplastic materials are used for soil and waste pipes. These include unplasticised polyvinyl chloride (upvc) polypropylene and

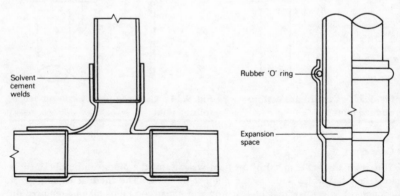

Fig. 9.36 Solvent weld joint for pvc waste pipe

Fig. 9.37 Rubber 'O' ring joint for pvc or copper waste or soil pipe

acylonitrile butadiene styrene (abs). The pipes are light in weight, easy to handle, smooth internal bore and highly resistant to corrosion. Their coefficients of expansion are, however, much higher than those of metals and much more provision for thermal movement is required. Unplasticised polyvinyl chloride is the most commonly used plastic material for larger diameter stacks, but due to the risk of distortion it should not be used where large volumes of water are discharged at temperatures exceeding 60 °C.

Polypropylene and acylonitrile butadiene styrene pipes may be used for conveying water at higher temperatures, but manufacturer's instructions should be consulted where these conditions exist. Plastics should be installed in a fire-protected duct. Jointing may be accomplished by welding techniques, or by a rubber 'O'-ring (see Figs 9.36 and 9.37).

Galvanised steel

This is lighter than cast iron and is extremely strong and resistant to mechanical damage. The pipe is liable to be attacked by lime and plaster and should be coated with bitumen if it is in contact with these materials. Large diameter pipes have spigot and socket caulked joints and smaller diameter pipes have screwed joints (see Figs 9.38 and 9.39).

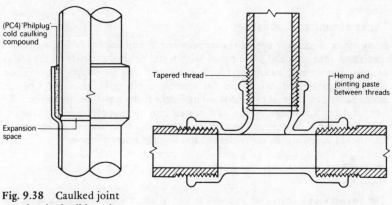

Fig. 9.38 Caulked joint on galvanised mild steel waste or soil pipe

Fig. 9.39 Screwed joint for steel waste pipes

Prefabrication

Wherever possible pipework assemblies should be prefabricated for fixing on site and this will save a good deal of site work and time. A number of manufacturers make soil and waste assemblies and offer a design service to architects and builders.

Chapter 10

Sanitary appliances

Types of sanitary appliances

Many types of sanitary appliances are required in buildings to fulfil a variety of specialised functions and are supplied with water either directly from the main, or from hot or cold storage vessels. It is essential that the supply water is not contaminated by foul water and for this reason in most cases the taps are designed to discharge above the flooding level of the appliance, to prevent the risk of back siphonage of the foul water into the supply pipe. A sanitary appliance should be designed so that its fouling area is reduced to the minimum and should have durable, easily cleaned and non-absorbent surfaces.

Materials

Ceramics

The strength and degree of impermeability of the materials depends upon the composition of the clay mixture and the temperature at which they are fired.

Glazed earthenware: this produces appliances of good colour, lends itself well to the formation of complicated shapes and is relatively cheap. It is used mainly for sinks and W.C. pans.

Glazed fireclay: this produces a tough appliance which is resistant to knocks and hard wear. Fireclay appliances such as urinals, sinks and W.C. pans are often specified for use in schools and factories.

Glazed stoneware: this produces a tough appliance which is resistant to knocks and hard wear, but, unlike earthenware and fireclay, the material is non-absorbent even when it is unglazed. It is mainly used for channels, sinks and urinal stalls.

Vitreous china: this lends itself to fine detail and good finish, but is not as strong as fireclay and is therefore unsuitable for buildings where hard wear is expected, such as schools and factories. It is, however, used extensively in houses and hotels. The material does not absorb water even when the glaze is broken and can be used for the manufacture of almost all types of appliances, in which various colours may be obtained.

Pressed metal

Mild steel, stainless steel and monel metal sheets are moulded in a press to form one-piece units. Mild steel should be galvanised or enamelled to protect the metal from corrosion and it is used for troughs and sinks where cheapness is of paramount importance. Stainless steel is used for sinks, urinals, wash basins, W.C. pans and draining units. It is rather expensive but has a good appearance and is highly resistant to hard wear. Monel metal has many of the properties of stainless steel, but does not have quite as good an appearance. It is used for sinks and is generally cheaper than stainless steel.

Note: Stainless steel and monel metal bar sinks are more resilient and therefore breakages of glass does not occur as frequently as in the case of ceramic sinks.

Acrylic plastic (perspex)

This is produced in many colours, is light in weight and relatively cheap. It takes a hard gloss finish and has an excellent appearance. Hot water, however, tends to soften the material and baths made from it must be supported with metal cradles.

Glass-reinforced polyester

This material is more expensive than acrylic plastic, but is much stronger. A good gel coat finish is essential to protect the reinforcing fibres and various colours may be obtained.

Note: Baths made from acrylic plastic or glass-reinforced polyester have a lower thermal conductivity than baths made from cast iron and therefore tend to feel warmer to the touch.

Cast iron

This is used mainly for large appliances such as baths, which would be too heavy if made in ceramics. The material is strong but heavy and may have either a white or a coloured vitreous enamel finish fired on. It is a very cheap material which is also used extensively for sink and wash basin brackets.

Terrazzo

The manufacture of small sanitary appliances from the material is very difficult and uneconomical, but it is often used for large appliances formed *in situ*. In special circumstances washing fountains, sunken baths and shower trays may be formed on site to the architect's design.

Soil fittings

Water closets

The most widely used pattern is the 'wash-down', in which the contents of the pan are removed by a gravity water flush. These W.C.s, are cheap, simple and efficient and are rarely blocked by misuse. The pan shape has been developed

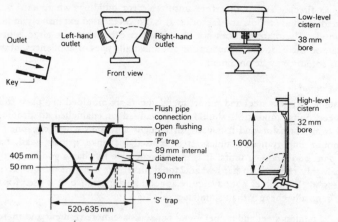

Fig. 10.1 Wash down W.C. pan

from the earlier long and short hopper types, to provide the minimum of fouling area. They are designed to maintain a 50 mm minimum water seal.

Figure 10.1 shows a section through a wash-down W.C. pan. The outlet may be obtained left or right hand and also P or S as shown; it may be flushed from a high- or low-level flushing cistern depending upon the circumstances. The high-level cistern provides a more effective flush, but is not as neat and as modern as the low-level cistern. Siphonic water closets are more silent and positive in action than the wash-down type, but are more prone to blockages.

Figures 10.2 and 10.3 show sections of two types of single trap siphonic W.C.s, which operate as follows:

1. The cistern is flushed and water passes through the pan to the long leg of the siphon, which is shaped to restrict the flow of water.
2. The long leg of the siphon is momentarily filled with water and a siphonic action set up, which empties the water and any contents from the pan.

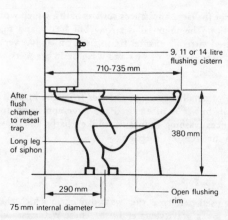

Fig. 10.2 Single-trap type siphonic W.C. (Twyfords Ltd.)

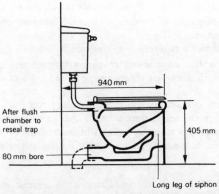

Fig. 10.3 Single-trap type siphonic W.C. (Twyfords Ltd.)

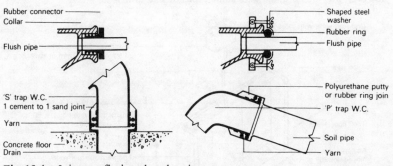

Fig. 10.4 Joints on flush and outlet pipes

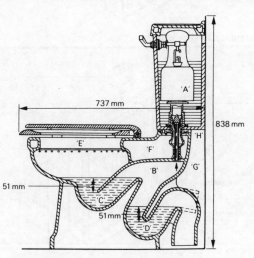

Fig. 10.5 Two-trap siphonic W.C. (Twyfords Ltd.)

3. Water contained in the after flush chamber reseals the trap.

Figure 10.4 shows the method used to joint flush and outlet pipes to both wash-down and siphonic W.C.s.

Figure 10.5 shows a two-trap type siphonic W.C. which operates as follows:

1. The cistern is flushed and water passes through the pressure reducing fitment A, which draws air through pipe G and reduces the air pressure in chamber B.
2. A siphonic action is set up, which empties the water and any contents from the pan through the sealed traps C and D. At the same time, the sides of the pan are thoroughly washed by streams of water from the perforated rim E.
3. Water contained in the after-flush chamber F reseals the trap.

Urinals

Figures 10.6 and 10.7 show the installations of ceramic slab and stall-type urinals respectively. The slab type is cheaper than the stall type, but it does not provide the same degree of privacy. Vertical partitions which increase privacy, however, may be obtained with some types of slab urinals.

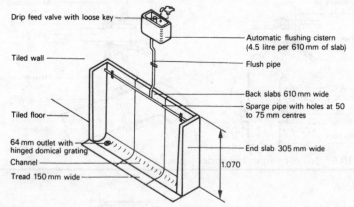

Fig. 10.6   Ceramic slab-type urinal

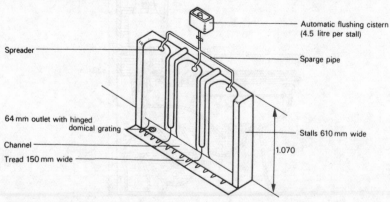

Fig. 10.7   Ceramic stall-type urinal

250

Figure 10.8 shows the installation of ceramic bowl-type urinals, which have less fouling area than the slab and stall urinals. Pipework is also more accessible and there is no problem with traps below the floor level.

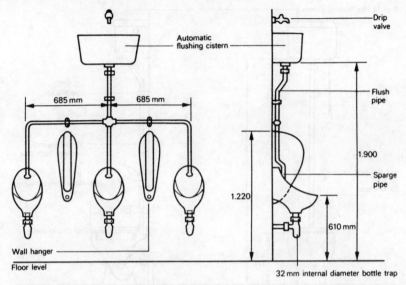

Fig. 10.8 Ceramic bowl-type urinals

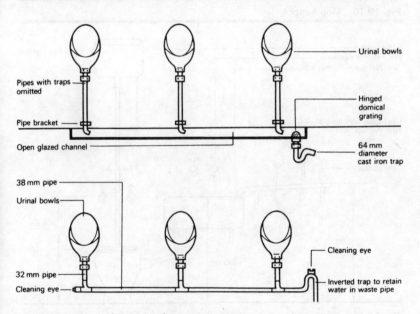

Fig. 10.9 Alternative waste pipe arrangements

Figure 10.9 shows alternative waste pipe arrangement for bowl type urinals.

Note: Before installing the open channel method it will be necessary to seek permission from the local authority.

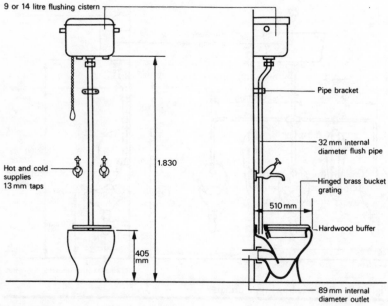

Fig. 10.10   Slop hopper

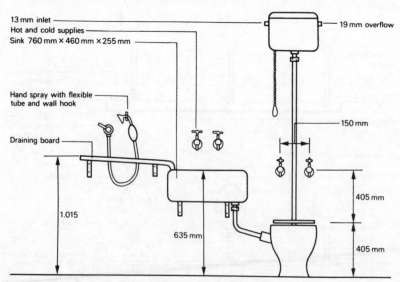

Fig. 10.11   Combined wash-up sink and slop hopper

Slop hopper

This is a very useful appliance for use in hospitals and hotels for the efficient disposal of slops. The hinged brass grating allows for the filling of a bucket from the hot and cold taps. Figure 10.10 shows the installation of a slop hopper and Fig. 10.11 shows a combined washup sink and slop hopper, also for use in hospitals.

Flushing cisterns

The capacity of the cistern is governed by the water supply authority, but the 9 litre capacity is now becoming more popular. Figure 10.12 shows the piston type flushing cistern, which operates as follows:

1. When the lever is depressed sharply, the piston is lifted, which displaces water over the siphon.
2. Water discharging down the flush pipe takes some air with it and creates a partial vacuum in the siphon.
3. The greater air pressure acting upon the water in the cistern forces water through the siphon until air is admitted under the piston, which breaks the siphonic action. A dual flush siphon, which is shown as part of Fig. 10.12, reduces the water consumption.

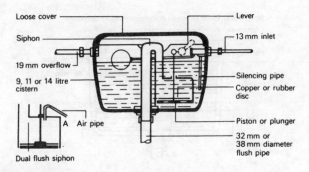

Fig. 10.12 High- or low-level piston-type flushing cistern

Operation

1. When the flush lever is depressed and immediately released, air is drawn through the air pipe at A, which breaks the siphonic action at this level and only 4.5 litres of water is used.
2. When the flush lever is depressed and then held down, the piston closes the air pipe and a normal 9-litre flush takes place.

Figure 10.13 shows a bell-type flushing cistern which operates as follows:

1. The lever is depressed, which lifts the bell inside the cistern.
2. The lever is released, which allows the bell to fall, thus displacing water under the bell down the stand pipe.
3. Water flowing down the stand pipe takes some of the air with it and creates a partial vacuum in the pipe, which starts the siphonic action and the cistern is emptied.

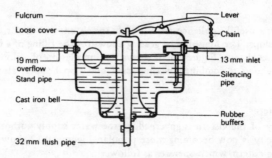

Fig. 10.13 Bell-types flushing cistern (for high-level only)

Automatic flushing cistern

This is used for the automatic flushing of urinals. It is usual to allow a capacity of 4.5 litres of water per stall, or 600 mm of slab and for an interval of 20 minutes between each flush. Some water authorities require the water supply to

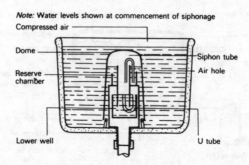

Fig. 10.14 Automatic flushing cistern

automatic flushing cisterns to be metered. Figure 10.14 shows a section through an automatic flushing cistern, which operates as follows:

1. Water rises evenly inside and outside the bell until it reaches the air hole.
2. Air inside the bell is thus trapped and becomes compressed as the water level rises outside the bell.
3. When the water level reaches a certain height above the dome, the compressed air is sufficient to force water out of the U-tube and reduce the air pressure inside the dome.
4. The reduced air pressure inside the dome immediately allows water to flow through the siphon and a siphonic action is set up, which empties the cistern.
5. When the flush is finished, water from the reserve chamber is siphoned through the siphon tube, which refills the lower well and U-tube.

254

Flushing troughs

This may be used as an alternative to separate cisterns, for the flushing of a range of W.C.s. It has the advantage over separate W.C.s of reducing the supply pipework, connections and valves, but if a repair is required to one of the siphons or the trough, the range of W.C.s cannot be used. It is used in schools, factories and public conveniences. Figure 10.15 shows the installation of a flushing trough, which operates as follows:

1. The siphon is operated in the same manner as the individual cistern and as water flows down the long leg of the siphon air is withdrawn from the small diameter air pipe, which allows water in the timing box to be siphoned out.
2. Air is admitted through the top of the timing box and the main siphonic action is broken at a predetermined time.
3. Water flows through the refilling hole and the timing box is refilled with water.

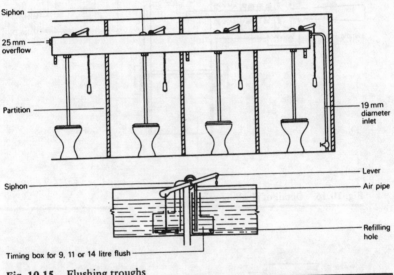

Fig. 10.15 Flushing troughs

Flushing valve

This is an alternative method to the flushing cistern or trough, for the flushing of W.C.s, and is very popular on the Continent and USA. The water authorities in Great Britain, however, are reluctant to allow the use of the valve, due to the possibility of waste of water and also the danger of back siphonage. The valve should be supplied from a storage cistern and no other sanitary fitting should be connected to the supply pipe to the valve.

Figure 10.16 shows a section of a flushing valve, which operates as follows:

1. When the handle is operated, the release spindle A and release valve C are tilted and water escapes from the upper chamber B through to the flush pipe, quicker than water can enter through the bypass.

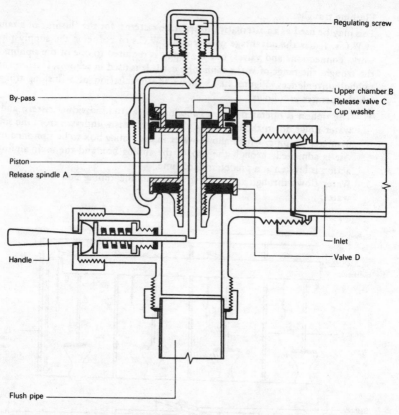

Fig. 10.16 Detail of flushing valve

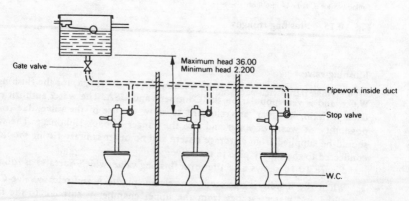

Fig. 10.17 Installation of flushing valves

2. The pressure in the upper chamber B is lowered and the greater upward pressure of water under the piston lifts valve D from its seating.

3. When the piston reaches the top of the upper chamber B, valve D is fully open and water passes down the flush pipe.

4. Water also passes through the bypass and fills the upper chamber B and equalises the upward and downward pressures on the piston, thus permitting the piston to fall gradually under its own weight.

5. The amount of water passing down the flush pipe is determined by the time it takes to fill the upper chamber B with water through the bypass. The regulating screw is used to determine the amount of water discharged by the valve.

Figure 10.17 shows the method of installing the flushing valve for a range of three W.C.s.

Waste appliances

Wash basins: many wash basin designs are available, ranging from surgeon's basins to small hand rinse basins. They can be obtained to fit into a corner of the room and may be supported on brackets, a pedestal or by a 'built in' corbel. Figure 10.18 shows a vertical section and a plan of a typical wash basin supported on a pedestal, which allows the supply pipes to be concealed from view.

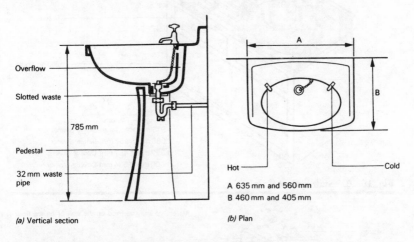

Overflow

Slotted waste

785 mm

Pedestal

32 mm waste pipe

(a) Vertical section

A

B

Hot — — Cold

A 635 mm and 560 mm
B 460 mm and 405 mm

(b) Plan

Fig. 10.18   Wash basin with pedestal

Sinks: Figure 10.19 shows the Belfast, London and combination type glazed fireclay sinks and Fig. 10.20 shows a view of a stainless steel sink having a cupboard with sliding doors below. Figure 10.21 shows a cleaner's bucket sink which is usually installed in a cleaner's cubicle. Figure 10.22 shows an ablution fountain, which may be used as an alternative to a range of eight wash basins in schools and factories. the central chromium plated or stainless steel pillar is fitted with a thermostatically controlled umbrella spray, or, in some fountains,

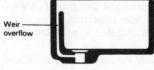

Weir overflow

Sizes

Length	Width	Depth
1. 220 mm	× 610 mm	× 305 mm (outside)
915 mm	× 610 mm	× 305 mm (outside)
915 mm	× 510 mm	× 255 mm (outside)
610 mm	× 510 mm	× 255 mm (outside)

(a) Belfast type sink

Sizes

Length	Width	Depth
610 mm	× 460 mm	× 255 mm (outside)
460 mm	× 380 mm	× 200 mm (outside)

(b) London type sink

Drainer

Sizes

Length	Width	Depth
1.070 mm	× 460 mm	× 240 mm (outside)
915 mm	× 460 mm	× 240 mm (outside)

(c) Combination sink

Fig. 10.19   Glazed fireclay sinks

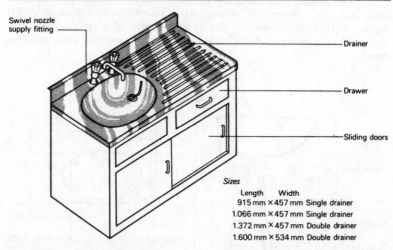

Swivel nozzle supply fitting

Drainer

Drawer

Sliding doors

Sizes

Length	Width	
915 mm	× 457 mm	Single drainer
1.066 mm	× 457 mm	Single drainer
1.372 mm	× 457 mm	Double drainer
1.600 mm	× 534 mm	Double drainer

Fig. 10.20   Stainless steel sink

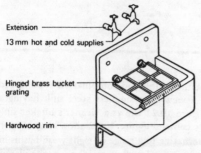

Note: Sink may be fixed on the wall or on the floor

Extension

13 mm hot and cold supplies

Hinged brass bucket grating

Hardwood rim

Sizes

Length	Width	Depth
510 mm	× 380 mm	× 230 mm (outside)
460 mm	× 380 mm	× 200 mm (outside)

Fig. 10.21   Cleaner's bucket sink

258

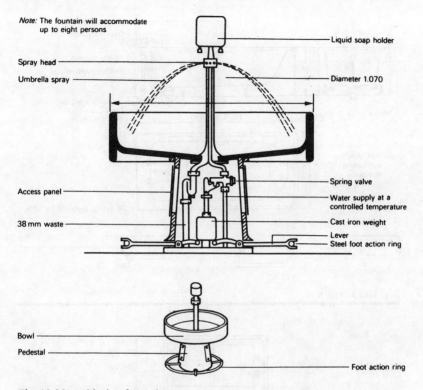

Note: The fountain will accommodate up to eight persons

Liquid soap holder

Spray head

Umbrella spray

Diameter 1.070

Access panel

Spring valve

Water supply at a controlled temperature

38 mm waste

Cast iron weight

Lever

Steel foot action ring

Bowl

Pedestal

Foot action ring

Fig. 10.22 Ablution fountain

spray taps are fitted, fed from hot and cold supply pipes. The minimum head of water above the spray is 3 m and the water supply is usually controlled by foot pedals. A liquid soap dispenser or a soap tray may be fitted at the top of the central pillar.

The fountain is a very hygienic method of washing, but is only economical where several persons wash at the same time.

Baths: although a shower is a more efficient and hygienic means of washing than the bath, most people find a bath more relaxing and it is therefore more popular. Figure 10.23 shows a typical installation of a bath and also various siting arrangements. The water supply may be by pillar taps as shown, or by a special fitting incorporating a diverter and a shower. For domestic installations, the taps and supply pipes are 19 mm internal diameter, but for institutions these are sometimes enlarged to 25 mm, to increase the speed of filling. The trap and waste pipes are 38 mm internal diameter for domestic installations and 50 mm internal diameter for institutions.

Figure 10.24 shows the 'sitz' bath, which is short, deep and incorporates a seat. It may be used where space is limited, but is not conducive to relaxation. It is, however, suitable for old people since the user may maintain a normal sitting position.

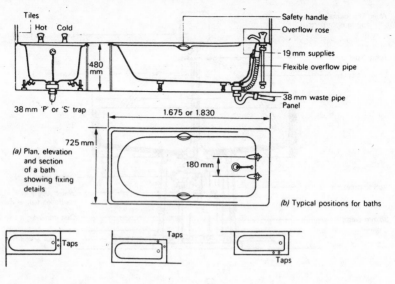

Fig. 10.23 Bath

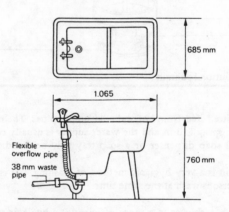

Fig. 10.24 Sitz bath

Showers: these are more hygienic, quicker to use and require less water than the bath. For an efficient shower, a minimum head of water of 1 m above the spray is required. A head of water of 1.5 m is however, preferable.

Two types of spray heads are obtainable.

1. A traditional rose type, which delivers water through a perforated disc fitted at high level.
2. An adjustable umbrella spray, which is usually fitted at chest level. Some people, especially women, find the umbrella spray preferable to the disc, because the shower may be used without wetting the hair.

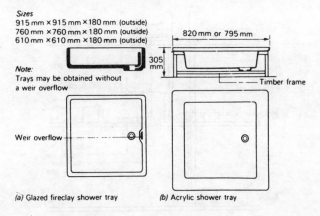

Sizes
915 mm × 915 mm × 180 mm (outside)
760 mm × 760 mm × 180 mm (outside)
610 mm × 610 mm × 180 mm (outside)

Note:
Trays may be obtained without
a weir overflow

305 mm

820 mm or 795 mm

Timber frame

Weir overflow

(a) Glazed fireclay shower tray

(b) Acrylic shower tray

Fig. 10.25 Shower trays

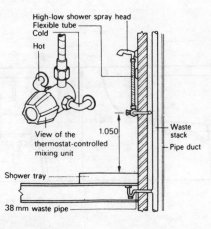

High-low shower spray head
Flexible tube
Cold
Hot

View of the
thermostat-controlled
mixing unit

1.050

Waste
stack
Pipe duct

Shower tray

38 mm waste pipe

Fig. 10.26 Installation of shower

Hot and cold water to the shower should be made through 13 or 19 mm internal diameter pipes and a thermostatically controlled mixing valve is recommended to prevent scalding. The shower tray may be of glazed fireclay, or acrylic plastic as shown in Fig. 10.25. Figure 10.26 shows the installation of the shower, including a view of the thermostat-controlled mixing unit. The modern type of mixing unit does not require non-return or outlet valves. A flexible chromium plated outlet pipe is shown, with two wall brackets for the spray, which allows the spray unit to be used at adult height, or at a lower position for children. The spray unit may also be held in the hand for shampooing the hair. Figure 10.27 shows the hot and cold pipework required for a shower, including the minimum head of water above the spray. Where this minimum head of water is not available a small low-voltage pump may be inserted in the outlet pipe.

261

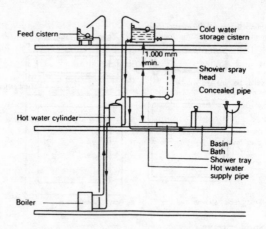

Fig. 10.27 Hot and cold pipework

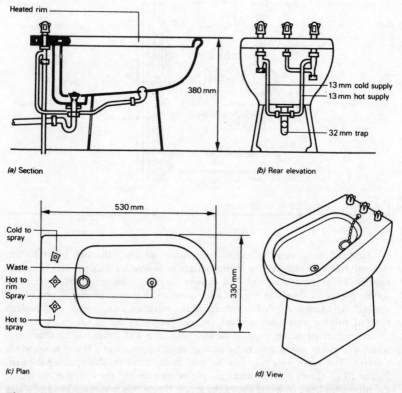

Fig. 10.28 Bidet

Bidet: (pronounced 'beeday': French for little horse) is used for perineal wash-ing and may also be used as a footbath. The hot and cold water supplies are 13 mm internal diameter and hot water may be supplied to the rim. A mixed supply of hot and cold water is also connected to an ascending spray, either through individual control valves or by a thermostatic valve, which eliminates any risk of scalding. Since the spray may be submerged if the waste became blocked, the bidet represents a special risk to the contamination of the water supply by back siphonage; this may be reduced by having the supply pipes at least 2 m above the bidet. Some water authorities may require bidets to be supplied from a separate cold water cistern, or separate hot and cold water supplies.

Figure 10.28 shows details of a bidet, including the water supplies and waste connections.

Drinking fountain: this is used in most business and industrial buildings, as well as in schools and colleges. Several patterns are available in fireclay or stain-less steel. Figure 10.29 shows a fireclay drinking fountain having a hooded jet, which prevents water from the mouth coming into contact with the jet. The water supply should always be directly from the main and a spray-operated, non-concussive self-closing valve is essential. The waste pipe sizes vary from 19 to 32 mm internal diameter.

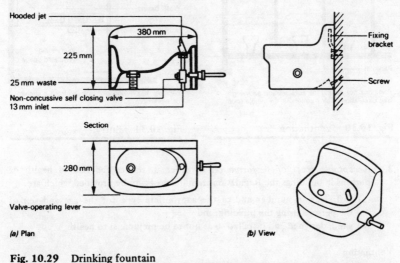

Fig. 10.29   Drinking fountain

Sanitary conveniences

The list of provisions required to comply with the Building Regulations 1985 with regard to entry and performance of sanitary conveniences are as follows:

263

1. Sufficient sanitary conveniences shall be provided which shall be:

   (*a*) in rooms separated from places where food is stored or prepared; and
   (*b*) designed and installed so as to allow effective cleaning.

   Figure 10.30 shows partitions not sealing the cubicles which will allow effective cleaning of the floor and also permit good ventilation. Figure 10.31 shows the method of entering a sanitary convenience from a kitchen or workroom. The ventilated space will separate the convenience from the kitchen or workroom.

   Figure 10.32 shows the entry to a bathroom direct from a bedroom or dressing room. It is good practice however, to separate the bathroom or dressing room by means of an intervening ventilated space, especially if the only WC in the premises is in the bathroom. A landing or corridor will act as a ventilated space (see Fig. 10.33).

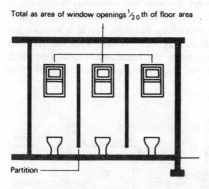

Total as area of window openings $\frac{1}{20}$ th of floor area

Partition

Partitions not sealing the cubicles and allowing free circulation of air throughout the whole room

Flushing trough

W.C.   W.C.   W.C

Kitchen

Wash basins

Drinking fountain

Intervening ventilated space

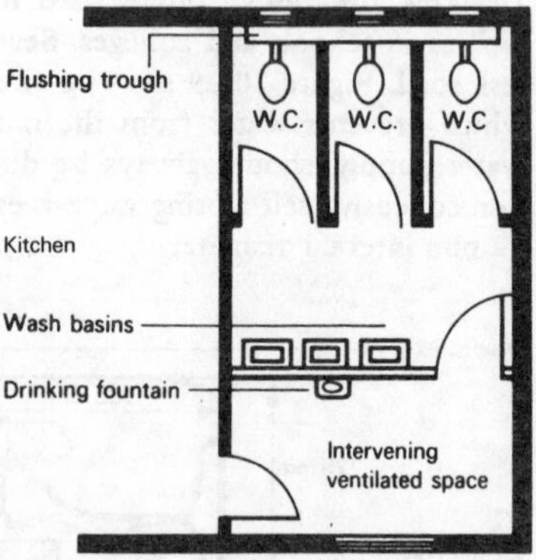

Sanitary accommodation entered from a kitchen or workroom

Fig. 10.30   Ventilation

Fig. 10.31   Entry

2. *Acceptable level of performance.* In order to reduce the risk of health of persons in buildings the Regulations require closets to be provided which are:

   (*a*) sufficient in number and of the appropriate type for the age and sex of the persons using the building; and
   (*b*) sited, designed and installed so as not to be prejudicial to health.

Ventilation

If mechanical ventilation of a sanitary convenience is required, the Building Regulations 1985 require a minimum air change of three per hour. The ventilation may be intermittent but should run for 15 minutes after the convenience has been vacated.

If natural ventilation is used this can be by means of a window, skylight or similar means of ventilation which open directly into the external air.

Planning of sanitary apartments

Legislation such as the Standards for School Premises, Public Health Act,

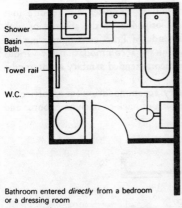

Bathroom entered *directly* from a bedroom or a dressing room

Fig. 10.32 Bathroom containing a W.C. (with another W.C. in the dwelling)

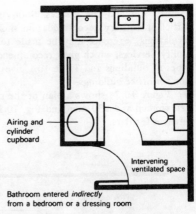

Bathroom entered *indirectly* from a bedroom or a dressing room

Fig. 10.33 Bathroom containing a W.C. (without another W.C. in the dwelling)

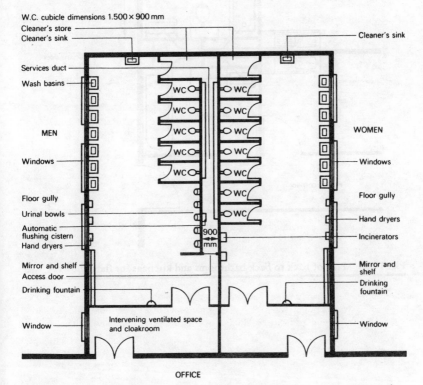

Fig. 10.34 Plan of sanitary accommodation for an office for 120 women and 130 men

Factory Act and the Offices, Shops and Railway Premises Act require that sufficient sanitary accommodation should be provided. In the absence of such regulations, reference may be made to the Code of Practice, Engineering and Utility Services, which gives recommended sanitary accommodation for various types of buildings and Table 10.1 gives the recommended sanitary accommodation for office buildings.

Figure 10.34 shows a plan of the sanitary accommodation for an office for 120 women and 130 men and Fig. 10.35 a plan of back-to-back bathrooms and kitchens for flats.

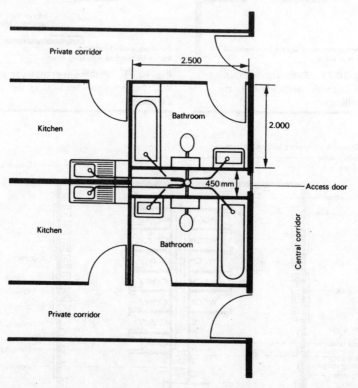

Fig. 10.35 Plan of back to back bathrooms and kitchens for flats

Table 10.1 Office Buildings, British Standards Code of Practice CP 3, Engineering and Utility Services

Fitments	For accommodation other than for principals, etc.	
	Male personnel	Female personnel
W.C.s	1 for 1–15 2 for 16–35 3 for 36–65 4 for 66–100 For over 100 add at the rate of 3 per cent	1 for 1–12 2 for 13–25 3 for 26–40 4 for 41–57 5 for 58–77 6 for 78–100 For over 100 add at the rate of 5 per cent
Urinals	Nil up to 6 1 for 7–20 2 for 21–45 3 for 46–70 4 for 71–100 From 101–200 add at the rate of 3 per cent. For over 200 add at the rate of 2½ per cent	
Lavatory basins	1 for 1–15 2 for 16–35 3 for 36–65 4 for 66–100 For over 100 add at the rate of 3 per cent	1 for 1–12 2 for 13–25 3 for 26–40 4 for 41–57 5 for 58–77 6 for 78–100 For over 100 add at the rate of 5 per cent
Cleaners' sinks	At least 1 per floor, preferably in or adjacent to a sanitary apartment	

Chapter 11

Sprinklers, risers and hose-reel installations

Fire-fighting equipment

Fire-fighting equipment for buildings may be divided into the following categories:

1. Sprinklers and other fixed water sprays.
2. Fixed foam, carbon dioxide and dry powder extinguishers.
3. Fixed wet or dry risers.
4. Portable extinguishers.
5. Fire doors, dampers and fire-resisting forms of construction.

Although fire detectors and alarms are not fire-fighting equipment, their installation will provide a warning of fire and reduce the time taken for the fire to be brought under control and extinguished. They will also reduce the risk of injury or loss of life by providing a warning of a fire.

Sprinkler systems

These are the most important and successful of the fire-fighting systems and fire insurers will allow a rebate of up to 70 per cent when an automatic sprinkler system is installed, which will offset the cost of the installation.

However, a sprinkler installation is a first-aid system for dealing with a fire in its early stages and cannot be relied upon to deal with a large fire which has started in, or spread from, an unprotected part of the building. It is essential, therefore, that a sprinkler installation should cover the whole of the building and not just the parts that are considered to have a high fire risk. Exceptions to full fire protection of a building occurs when the part protected is separated from other parts by efficient fire stops, or rooms used solely for the housing of electrical switchgear, or other electrical apparatus.

Types of pipes

Pipes above ground must be of at least medium-grade steel tube conforming to

BS 1387. Pipes laid below ground must conform to one or the other of the following specifications subject to the local Water Authority Regulations:

BS 78 (Parts 1 and 2): Cast-iron spigot and socket pipes (vertically cast) and fittings.

BS 486: Asbestos-cement pressure pipes.

BS 1211: Centrifugally spun iron pressure pipes.

BS 1387: Steel tubes of heavy grade.

BS 2035: Cast-iron flanged pipes and fittings.

BS 3506: Unplasticised PVC pipes for industrial purposes.

Historical

In 1874 an American, Henry Parmelee, produced the first automatic sprinkler system, and in 1882 the first English installation of the Parmelee system was in a cotton mill in Bolton.

In the next decade many people helped to develop still further the sprinkler system and in 1883 an American, Frederick Grinnell, finally produced a system which achieved outstanding success. The Grinnell system utilises a special sprinkler head which automatically operates in the immediate vicinity of the fire and discharges water to control the fire. Since the invention of the Grinnell automatic system many thousands of fires have been extinguished in buildings protected by the system. Well over 50 per cent of the fires have been extinguished or controlled after the operation of two sprinklers or less, and over 38 per cent of the total number of fires after the operation of just one sprinkler.

Types of systems

Wet system

This is used in heated buildings where temperatures remain above 0 °C and there is therefore no risk of the water in the system freezing. As the name implies the 'wet' system pipework is constantly filled with water. Heat produced by an outbreak of fire causes the nearest sprinkler head or heads to open at their operating temperature. Immediately the water is discharged on to the fire, the flow of water activates a hydraulically operated alarm bell outside the building and arrangements can also be made to alert the local Fire Brigade. Figure 11.1 shows a typical wet sprinkler system where the water supply is taken directly from the water main.

Dry system

This is used in unheated buildings where the temperatures may be below 0 °C and therefore water in the system is liable to freeze. The installation pipework is charged with compressed air at a moderate pressure and the water is held back by a special differential valve which, when a sprinkler head opens and releases air in the pipes, lifts and allows water to enter the pipework.

Alternate wet and dry system

This is used in buildings where freezing is likely during the winter months. During the summer months the system is filled with water and operates as a 'wet' system. When winter approaches the pipework is emptied of water and charged with compressed air and operates as a 'dry' system. Figure 11.2 shows the installation of a dry, or an alternate wet and dry system. A pump has been included which is fitted on all except the smallest of systems. The purpose of the

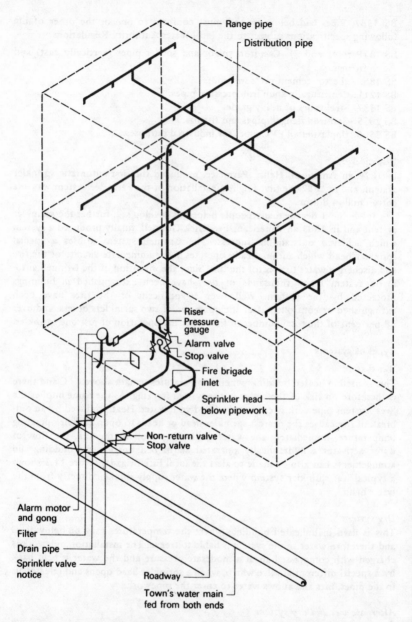

Range pipe

Distribution pipe

Riser
Pressure gauge
Alarm valve
Stop valve
Fire brigade inlet
Sprinkler head below pipework

Non-return valve
Stop valve

Alarm motor and gong
Filter
Drain pipe
Sprinkler valve notice

Roadway
Town's water main fed from both ends

Fig. 11.1 Typical 'wet' sprinkler installation for a two-storey building

pump is to increase the velocity of the flow of water and to speed up the lifting of the differential valve, therefore reducing the time taken for the water to reach the fire after a sprinkler head has opened.

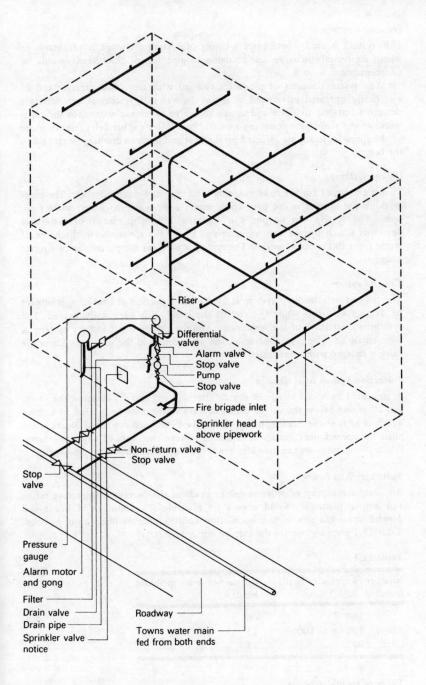

Fig. 11.2 Typical 'dry' or 'alternate wet and dry' sprinkler installation for a two-storey building

Pre-action system

This system is used where prior warning of system discharge is necessary, or where accidental discharge, due to damaged pipes or sprinkler heads, would be unacceptable.

The system consists of pipework charged with air at low pressure and an electrically operated valve used to retain the water. A system of heat-sensitive detectors respond to a fire and signals the valve to release water into the pipework, at the same time sounding an alarm bell. After a short delay, one or more of the sprinkler heads are affected by the heat and open to discharge water on to the fire.

Deluge system

This is employed for fire risks requiring total or zoned water coverage. The pipework in the system is not pressurised and all the water-discharge nozzles are open. The system can be put into operation either by manual or automatic detectors which open a control valve and allows the simultaneous discharge of water from all the open nozzles. The system is used for the protection of aircraft hangars.

Tail-end system

The tail-end or subsidiary system is used when a portion of a building is subject to damage by frost, while the rest of the building is adequately heated. The system is a variation of the wet system and the alternate wet and dry system. A differential air valve is connected to the pipework, and the pipework above the valve is charged with compressed air.

Protection against frost damage

In unheated buildings using the dry or alternate wet and dry systems, the valves and all piping below the valves which contain water must be housed in a room which is kept above freezing-point, or in a frost-insulated cupboard. Drain valves must be opened occasionally in order to remove the pipes of any condensate. For draining purposes the sprinkler heads must be fitted above the pipework.

Spare sprinkler heads

An adequate supply of spare sprinkler heads of the correct temperature rating and orifice diameter should always be available. The number of heads will depend upon the size of the installation and the number likely to be opened. Table 11.1 gives a guide for the average requirements.

Table 11.1

Number of sprinkler heads installed	Number of spare sprinkler heads
300	6
Above 300 up to 1000	12
Over 1000	24

Types of sprinkler heads

There are four types of sprinkler heads:

1. *Quartzoid bulb type*

In this type the head incorporates a quartzoid bulb filled with a highly expansive coloured liquid having different expansion rates (see Table 11.2).

Table 11.2 Bulb temperature rating

Bulb rating (°C)	Colour of bulb liquid
57	Orange
68	Red
79	Yellow
93	Green
141	Blue
182	Mauve
227/288	Black

Operation: When the liquid expands due to receiving heat from the fire, the pressure within the bulb increases rapidly to a point at which the bulb shatters (bulb-temperature rating). The valve assembly falls away from the seat and allows water to flow to the deflector thus causing a water spray over the fire.

Note: The liquid in the bulb shrinks as it cools, so that even if it is exposed to intense cold there is no development of pressure within the bulb; the quartzoid bulb sprinkler heads are therefore suitable for cold as well as hot climates. Figure 11.3 shows a quartzoid bulb-type sprinkler head.

2. *Side-wall types*

These are designed for use at the side of rooms or corridors, so that the water spray will be projected into the centre of the room or corridor protected. They are also used in drying tunnels or hoods over papermaking machines, where con-

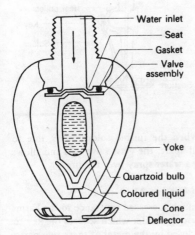

Fig. 11.3 Grinnell-type quartzoid sprinkler

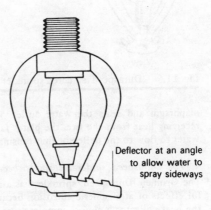

Fig. 11.4 Side-wall sprinkler

densed vapour dripping from the sprinklers and pipework overhead may be troublesome. The only difference between the usual type of sprinkler head and the side-wall sprinkler head is the angle of the deflector (see Fig. 11.4).

3. The soldered-strut sprinkler head (see Fig. 11.5)

A soldered-strut type consists of three bronze plates joined together by a special solder. These plates hold a glass valve in position against an orifice in a flexible

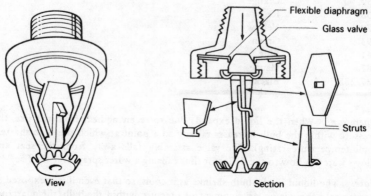

Fig. 11.5 Soldered-strut sprinkler

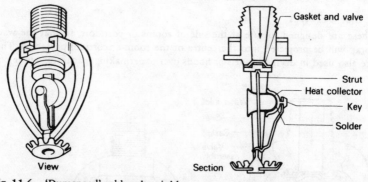

Fig. 11.6 'Duraspeed' soldered sprinkler

diaphragm and seals the water outlet. When the fusible solder melts, due to receiving heat from the fire, the plates fall apart, the glass valve falls and allows water to flow to the deflector thus causing a water spray over the fire.

4. The 'Duraspeed' soldered sprinkler head (see Fig. 11.6)

The Grinnell 'Duraspeed' sprinkler has a much increased resistance to the harmful effects of atmospheric corrosion because the solder which secures the key to the heat collector is almost completely enclosed by the metal of these two parts. A protective film, which has no adverse effect on the sensitivity of the sprinkler, is applied to the thin edge of the solder as a further protection against atmospheric corrosion. In conditions which are likely to produce corrosion, the efficiency of the 'Duraspeed' sprinkler head will remain unimpaired longer than the soldered-strut-type sprinkler. Table 11.3 gives the temperature ratings of 'Duraspeed' sprinklers and the maximum ambient temperatures.

Table 11.3

Rating of sprinkler recommended (°C)	Temperature not to be exceeded where sprinkler is located (°C)
72	38
93	60
141	107
182	149
227	191

Maintenance

Sprinkler heads must be maintained in good condition, be free from corrosion and not covered with paint, distemper, dust or fluff. Where there is a risk of corrosion the heads should be coated with petroleum jelly and those defective — or suspected of being defective — should be replaced.

Cold flow

If the temperature at which a soldered sprinkler head is exposed when stored, in transit or installed, appreciably exceeds the safe value for which it is intended, the solder can be weakened to a point at which it begins to creep or yield under the load it has to support. This yield is at first minute, but once started it continues, owing to the load, even at temperatures which would be too low to initiate it. This yield or stretch of the fusible solder is called 'cold flow' and will continue, but for exactly how long is difficult to predict because it depends upon the extent the safe temperature was exceeded in the first place. If the safe temperature is not greatly exceeded, the continued yield of the solder can be so slow that many years may elapse before the cold flow becomes so advanced as to result in an unwanted operation.

Note: Manufacturers claim that 'cold flow' is a rare happening providing that the correctly rated sprinkler head is chosen and the ambient temperature does not rise abnormally. The temperature rating is engraved on the deflector of every 'Duraspeed' sprinkler head.

Escape from fire

Besides reducing the insurance premiums for the fire cover of a building, a sprinkler system may also provide an improved means of escape in case of a fire.

Operation of alarm gong (Fig. 11.7)

The ringing of the alarm gong should occur after the opening of a sprinkler head. An alarm-clock valve is fitted on the main supply pipe immediately above the stop valve. The valve is closed when the water is static, but when water is discharged from an open sprinkler head the pressure above the valve falls and the greater pressure below lifts the valve, thus allowing the water to flow to the

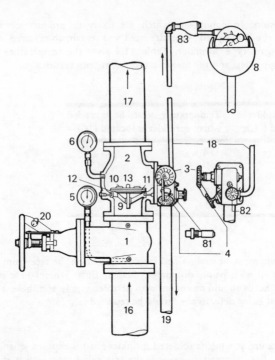

1. Installation stop valve
2. Alarm valve
3. Drain and test valve
4. 13 mm Test valve
5. Water supply pressure gauge
6. Installation pressure gauge
8. Alarm motor and gong
9. Combined valve seating and guide
10. Alarm valve clock
11. Composition disc

12. Annular groove in valve seating
13. Compensator
16. Water supply
17. Main feed to installation
18. Connection to alarm equipment
19. Drain pipe
20. Padlock and strap
81. Drip plug
82. Alarm stop valve
83. Strainer

Fig. 11.7 Installation controlling valves — wet system (Courtesy of Mather and Platt Ltd.)

sprinkler head. At the same time water is admitted to the annular groove in the valve seating and water is allowed to flow to the water turbine causing the alarm gong to be sounded.

Operation of dry and alternate systems (see Fig. 11.8)

Two circular clacks (27) and (31), mounted on a common spindle, rest on the seating (29) and (32) fitted in the valve casing. The area of the upper clack (27), which is fitted with a special quality composition disc (28), is eight times the area of the lower clack (31). Thus, where the pipes of an installation are charged with air at a pressure of 138 kPa, the differential valve would hold back a water supply with a pressure less than 1104 kPa acting on the underside of the lower clack (31).

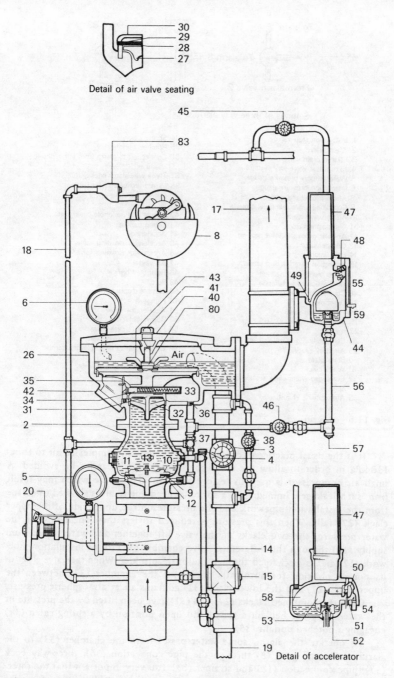

Detail of air valve seating

Air

Detail of accelerator

Fig. 11.8 The installation valve set on the dry system (Courtesy of Mather and Platt Ltd.)

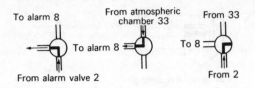

To alarm 8 To alarm 8 From atmospheric chamber 33 From 33 To 8

From alarm valve 2 From 2

Settings of three-way alarm cock

1. Installation stop valve	34 Spring catch
2. Alarm valve	35 Notched upright
3. 50 mm drain valve	36 Connection to alarm from atmospheric
4. 13 mm test valve (dry system)	chamber
5 Water-supply pressure gauge	37 Three way alarm cock
6 Installation pressure gauge	38 13 mm test valve (wet system)
8 Alarm motor and gong	40 Differential valve cover
9 Combined valve seating and guide	41 Plug
10 Alarm valve clack	42 Handle and handhole cover plate
11 Composition disc	43 Lifting handle
12 Annular groove in valve seating	44 Accelerator
13 Compensator	45 Accelerator isolating valve
14 Drip union	46 Accelerator isolating valve
15 Inspection plug for drip union	47 Air vessel
16 Water-supply connection	48 Restricted orifice
17 Connection to installation	49 Port
18 Connection to alarm motor	50 Flexible diaphragm
19 Drain pipe	51 Plunger
20 Padlock and strap	52 Accelerator valve
26 Differential valve	53 Bobweight
27 Air clack	54 Pressure release valve
28 Composition disc on air clack	55 Accelerator cover plate
29 Air clack seating	56 Connection to atmospheric chamber
30 Brass plate	57 Plug
31 Water clack	58 Accelerator valve chamber
32 Combined water clack seating and valve	59 Accelerator test valve
spindle guide	80 Rubber buffer
33 Atmospheric chamber	83 13 mm strainer

Fig. 11.8 – *continued*

It is the usual practice to charge the pipework with compressed air to about 138 kPa in order to allow for the slight leakage which cannot be avoided. A small air compressor is used to restore any loss of pressure which may result from such leakages. Immediately a sprinkler head opens, air is allowed to escape from the installation pipework and the pressure on the upper side of the upper clack (27) falls. When this pressure is reduced to less than one-eighth of the water pressure, the two clacks of the valve lift together and water flows from supply (16) through the differential valve chamber (33) to the installation pipework (17) and is discharged through the open sprinkler. When the valve is set in its normal position for automatic operation, the chamber (33) between the upper clack (27) and the lower clack (31) contains air at atmospheric pressure.

Once the combined clacks (27) and (31) have been lifted by the pressure of the water, they are held in a raised and open position by a spring catch (34) engaging a notched upright (35).

To operate the alarm, some water passes from the chamber (33) to the alarm motor and gong (8) through the pipe connection (36), three-way cock (37), pipe connection (18) and strainer (83). It is very important that the three-way cock (37) should be set in the appropriate position to allow water from the alarm valve (2) to pass via the annular groove (12) and the alarm cock (37) to the alarm motor and gong (8).

The drain valve (3) is provided to drain the installation after a fire and also when the installation is being changed over from the wet to the dry system.

The air compressor used to restore any loss of pressure is arranged to start automatically when the air pressure falls to a minimum value and automatically cut out when it has restored the pressure.

When a sprinkler operates, the air that escapes is very much more than can be provided by the compressor and therefore it has little or no effect on the time for the water to issue from the sprinkler.

Drencher systems

A drencher system provides a discharge of water over the external openings of a building, to prevent the transmission of fire from adjacent buildings. It comprises a system of pipework fitted on the outside of the building with discharge nozzles, known as 'drenchers', fixed at suitable intervals on roofs, under the eaves and over windows and doorways. In theatres, drenchers are fitted above the proscenium arch at the stage side for protection of the safety curtain.

Automatic drenchers are similar in construction to the quartzoid bulb sprinkler head and operate individually on the same principle. Non-automatic drenchers have open nozzles and normally operated valves, which when opened bring them all into operation simultaneously. The location of the valves for both systems should be clearly marked by a suitable notice.

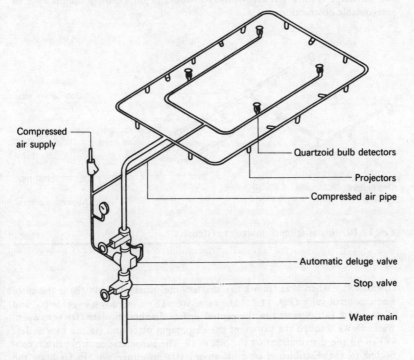

Compressed air supply

Quartzoid bulb detectors

Projectors

Compressed air pipe

Automatic deluge valve

Stop valve

Water main

Fig. 11.9   The Mulsifyre system

The Mulsifyre system (see Fig. 11.9)

Oil fires can be extinguished by droplets of water travelling at high velocity, which bombard the surface of the oil to form an emulsion of oil and water that will not support combustion. The Mulsifyre system applies water on oil or paint fires in the form of a conical spray, consisting of droplets of water travelling at high velocity, thus extinguishing the fire by emulsification, cooling and smothering.

Operation: The conical spray of water, consisting of droplets at high velocity, is discharged through specially designed projector-mounted pipework. Quartzoid bulb detectors, mounted on independent pipework containing compressed air, are positioned so that wherever a fire occurs at least one detector will operate. If a fire occurs, the heat causes the bulb to shatter and the compressed air in the pipework to escape. This causes a rapid fall in air pressure on a diaphragm in the automatic deluge valve, which allows the valve to open and water to discharge through the projectors on to the fire.

An important feature of the system is the automatic alarm equipment: this is usually an alarm gong operated by a water motor which is driven by a small flow of water diverted at the installation control valves, when open.

The multi-jet sprinkler system (Fig. 11.10)

The multi-jet system is designed to provide an even distribution of water where the discharge from a standard sprinkler would be impeded by the presence of unavoidable obstructions.

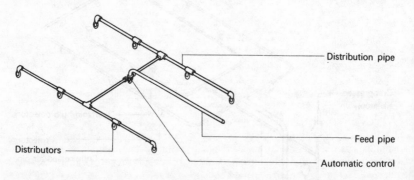

Fig. 11.10   Installation of multi-jet system

Operation: When heat from a fire shatters the quartzoid bulb (B) in the automatic control valve (Fig. 11.11) the valve stem (E) slides down in guide (G) and allows valve (V) − seated in the central orifice diaphragm plate (D) − to open. Water flows through the orifice of the diaphragm plate and via the two outlets (Y) to all the distributions on the pipework. The automatic control valve is connected to the distribution pipe by unions (U) on either side, to facilitate the fitting of a new automatic control valve. The distributor (Fig. 11.12) has an

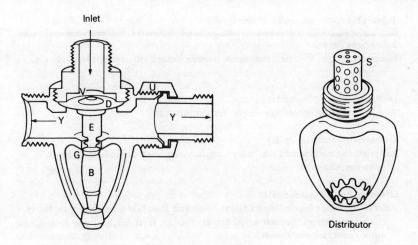

Inlet

S

Y

Y

Distributor

Figs 11.11 and 11.12   The multi-jet sprinkler system

orifice of 6 mm diameter which is normally sealed against the entry of dust and fumes by means of a light waxed-paper disc, which yields instantly to water pressure. A strainer (S) is fitted to prevent the orifice from being choked with foreign matter.

Classes of systems

Three classes of sprinkler systems have been developed to suit the following fire hazard classes of occupancy.

1. *Extra light hazard:*   Non-industrial occupancies where the amount and combustibility of the contents is low.

2. *Ordinary hazard:*   Commercial and industrial occupancies involving the handling, processing and storage of mainly ordinary combustible materials unlikely to develop intensely burning fires in the initial stages. Ordinary hazard occupancies have been divided into four groups according to the degree of fire hazard.

3. *Extra high hazard:*   Commercial and industrial occupancies having abnormal fire loads. There are two types of these as follows:

(*a*)   where the materials handled or processed are mainly of an extra hazardous nature likely to develop rapid and intensely burning fires;
(*b*)   involving high piling of goods.

Note: The Rules of the Fire Offices' Committee for Automatic Sprinkler Installations, 29th edition, gives full details of fire hazard classification and types of occupancy, a summary is however given in Table 11.4.

Table 11.4 Classification of occupancies

Extra light hazard
Hospitals, hotels, libraries, museums, nursing homes, offices, prisons, schools, colleges

Ordinary hazard (Group I)
Butchers, breweries, cement works, restaurants, cafés

Ordinary hazard (Group II)
Bakeries, chemical works (ordinary), engineering works, laundries, garages, potteries, shops

Ordinary hazard (Group III)
Aircraft factories (excluding hangars), boot and shoe factories, carpet factories, clothing factories, departmental stores, plastics factories, printing rooms, saw mills, tanneries, warehouses

Group III (special)
Cotton mills, distilleries, film and television studios, match factories

Extra high hazard
Celluloid works, foam plastics and foam rubber factories, paint and varnish factories, wood wool works, high piled storage risks, oil and flammable liquid hazard

Note: Some hazards in the ordinary hazard group having high fire load areas are placed in the extra high hazard class.

Spacing arrangements

Figure 11.13 shows a standard spacing of sprinkler heads where the distances between the heads is as follows:

S = design spacing of sprinklers on range pipes
D = distance between rows of sprinklers

$\left\{ \begin{array}{l} \text{max. 4.6 m extra light hazard} \\ \text{max. 4.0 m ordinary hazard} \\ \text{max. 3.7 m extra high hazard} \end{array} \right.$

$S \times D = \left\{ \begin{array}{l} 21 \text{ m}^2 \text{ or less, extra light hazard} \\ 12 \text{ m}^2 \text{ or less, ordinary hazard} \\ 9 \text{ m}^2 \text{ or less, extra high hazard} \end{array} \right.$

Figure 11.14 shows the staggered arrangement for ordinary hazard systems where it is desirable to space sprinklers more than 4.0 m apart on the range pipes as follows:

S = design spacing of sprinklers on range pipes = max. 4.6 m

D = distance between adjacent rows of sprinklers = max. 4.0 m

Figures 11.15(a) and (b) show the end side arrangements where there are range pipes on one side only of the distribution pipe. Figures 11.16(a) and (b), show the end centre arrangements where there are range pipes on both sides of the distribution pipe.

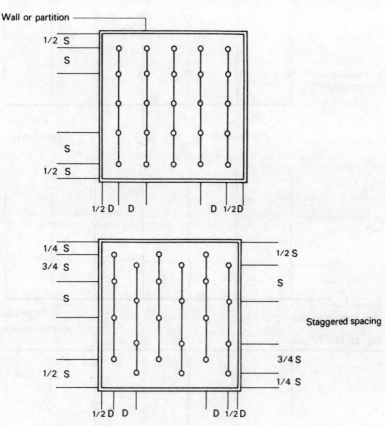

S   Design spacing of sprinklers on range pipes
D   Distance between adjacent rows

Figs 11.13 and 11.14   Spacing arrangements

Positioning of sprinklers

Sprinklers must be placed so that the deflectors are not more than 300 mm from non-fire-resisting ceilings and not more than 450 mm from fire-resisting ceilings. There must be a clear space of 300 mm below the level of a deflector within a radius of 600 mm from each sprinkler. In storage rooms, therefore, goods must not be stored within 300 mm of the level of the deflectors above them. Sprinklers must not be placed within 600 mm of columns or beams.

Water supplies for sprinklers

The efficiency of a sprinkler system depends largely upon the source of water supply, which should be adequate for the size and type of building protected. Acceptable sources of water supply are as follows:

1.   Town main.
2.   Elevated private reservoir.

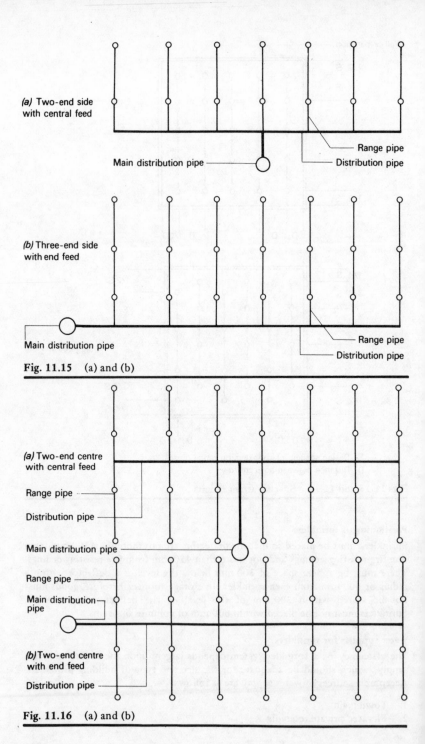

Fig. 11.15   (a) and (b)

Fig. 11.16   (a) and (b)

3. Gravity tank.
4. Town main and automatic pump.
5. Town main, automatic pump, with either a pressure tank, gravity tank or elevated private reservoir.
6. Automatic pump drawing water from river or canal.

Water used for sprinklers must be free from suspension matter liable to cause accumulations in the system. Sea-water or brackish water is not normally allowed.

Town main (Figs 11.1 and 11.2)

This must be capable of providing at all times the minimum pressure and flow rate to the sprinkler heads, specified by the Fire Offices' Committee Rules. Preferably, the main should be fed from both directions and the connection to the building duplicated. In special circumstances a single feed pipe may be used, providing there is a main stop valve on either side of the single feed pipe connection to the main.

Elevated private reservoir (Fig. 11.17)

This is a ground reservoir situated at a higher level than the building to be protected. The reservoir is under the sole control of the owner of the building protected by the sprinkler system. The reservoir must hold between 500 m^3 and 1875 m^3 of water.

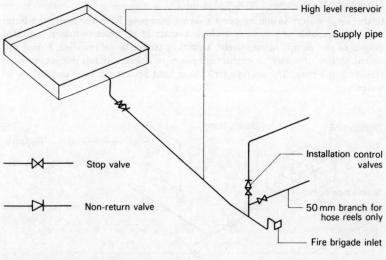

Fig. 11.17   Elevated private reservoir

Gravity tank (Fig. 11.18)

This is a purpose-made water vessel, erected on the site of the protected building, at such a height as to provide the required pressure and flow rate at the

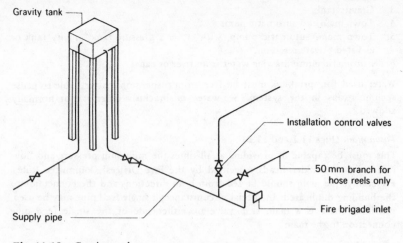

Fig. 11.18   Gravity tank

sprinkler heads. The supply to the tank should be such that it can be refilled in not less than 6 h. The tank must hold between 9 m³ and 875 m³ of water.

Town main and automatic pumps (Fig. 11.19)

If the local Water Authority permit direct pumping from the main, the latter should be capable of providing sufficient water at all times to match the rated output of the pump. Alternatively, a suction tank may be installed, having sufficient inflow of water to enable the pump to operate at full output, without emptying the tank. The suction tank must hold between 2.5 m³ and 585 m³ of water.

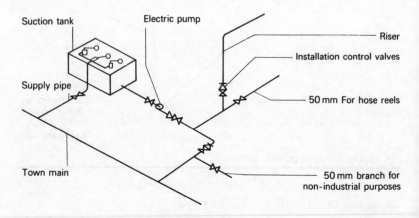

Fig. 11.19   Town main and automatic pump

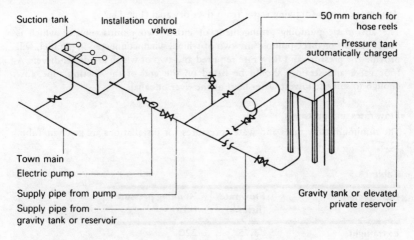

Fig. 11.20 Town main, automatic pump with either a pressure tank, gravity tank or elevated private reservoir

Town main (automatic pump, with either a pressure tank, gravity tank or elevated private reservoir (Fig. 11.20)

This provides a duplicated water supply so that in the event of the main failing and the suction tank emptying, there is another source of water supply from either a pressure tank, gravity tank or an elevated private reservoir.

A pressure tank, when used as the sole source of water supply, is only acceptable for extra light and ordinary (Group I) fire hazards. However, it is acceptable for the remaining groups of ordinary hazards providing it is only as one source of duplicated supply. The tank must hold between 7 m³ and 23 m³ of water.

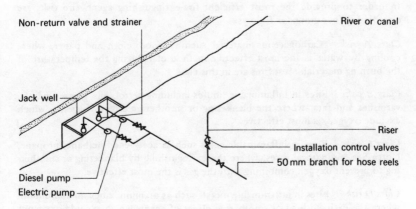

Fig. 11.21 Automatic pump supply drawing water from river or canal

Automatic pump (drawing water from river or canal (Fig. 11.21)

The automatic pumping arrangement of either two pumps (one of which is diesel-driven) or three pumps, any two of which, when connected in parallel, will provide the pressure and flow rate required and two of which are diesel-driven. A foot valve and strainer should be fitted on the end of the suction pipe, low enough to suit the lowest water level of the river or canal.

Flow rates and pressures

The minimum flow rates and water pressures for installations are given in Table 11.5.

Table 11.5

Hazard class	Flow rate (litres/s)	Running pressure (kPa)
Extra light	3.75	220
Ordinary Group I (light)	6.25	100
	9.00	70
Ordinary Group II (medium)	12.10	140
	17.00	100
Ordinary Group III (high)	18.3	170
	22.5	140
Ordinary Group III (special)	30.0	200
	35.0	150
Extra high	Refer to Fire Offices' Committee Rules, which are too involved to include in the table	

Classification of fire risks

In order to provide the most efficient fire-extinguishing agent, fire risks are classified in four groups as follows:

Class A risk: Carbonaceous material such as wood, cloth and paper, where cooling by water is the most effective method of reducing the temperature of the burning material. Most fires are in this class.

Class B risk: Fires in inflammable liquids including petrol, oils, greases, paints, varnishes and fats, where the blanketing or smothering effect of agents, which exclude oxygen, is most effective.

Class C risk: Fires in inflammable gases such as acetylene, methane, propane, North Sea and natural gases, where the extinguishing by blanketing or smothering to prevent oxygen combining with the gas is the most effective.

Class D risk: Fires in inflammable metals such as uranium, zinc and aluminium, where the extinguishing or smothering effect of agents which exclude oxygen is most effective.

Class E risk: This is not a strictly separate classification, but includes all risks where the problem of extinguishing the fire is increased, due to the danger of an electric shock. The fire is in the presence of live electrical equipment or wiring and a non-conducting extinguishing agent is therefore required.

Extinguishing agents

Class A	Water or dry powder
Class B and C	Dry powder, foam, or carbon dioxide
Class D	Dry sand or dry powder
Class E	Dry powder, or carbon dioxide

Testing of sprinkler installations

Weekly tests should be made to ascertain if the alarm apparatus is in order and if the air and water pressures are correct.

Quarterly tests should ascertain if each water supply is in order and the test should bring into operation any automatic pump. The sprinkler heads and pipework must be inspected and special attention must be paid to signs of corrosion and to ensure that sprinkler heads have not been painted.

Dry and wet risers

Multi-storey buildings are difficult to evacuate and can be extremely hazardous in the event of an outbreak of fire, unless fixed fire-fighting equipment has been installed.

The type of fire-fighting equipment for multi-storey buildings can take the form of either a wet or dry riser, depending upon the height of the building and the local Fire Authority Regulations.

Dry riser (Fig. 11.22)

As the name implies, the riser does not normally contain water, but is charged with water by the fire brigade during an outbreak of fire. The fire brigade connect the suction side of their pumps to a water main via an underground fire hydrant, or hydrants (see Fig. 11.23). The outlet side of the pumps is connected to the dry-riser inlet, or inlets at ground level and the pumps force water from the main into the riser. An automatic air valve at the top of the riser opens to allow air in the pipe to escape, but closes when the pipe is full of water. The firemen can now enter the building and connect their hose reels to landing valves fitted to the riser (see Fig. 11.24).

A dry riser, therefore, is merely an extension of the fireman's hose and should only be installed where prompt attention can be relied upon from the local fire brigade, or from trained fire-fighting personnel on the premises. The riser should be sited inside a ventilated lobby of a lobby approach staircase, or in a staircase enclosure.

Size

In buildings which do not exceed 45 m in height and where only one 64 mm diameter landing valve is provided on any floor, the internal diameter of the riser should be 100 mm. In buildings between 45 m and 60 m in height, and in buildings less than 45 m in which two 64 mm diameter landing valves are provided on each floor from the riser, the internal diameter should be 150 mm.

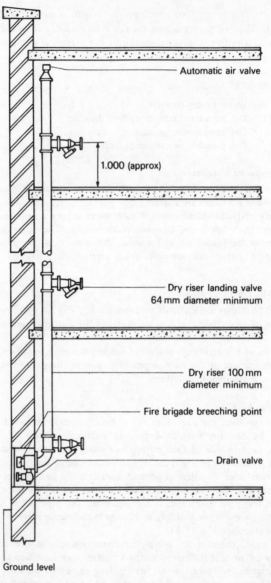

Labels on figure:
- Automatic air valve
- 1.000 (approx)
- Dry riser landing valve 64 mm diameter minimum
- Dry riser 100 mm diameter minimum
- Fire brigade breeching point
- Drain valve
- Ground level

Fig. 11.22 Dry riser

Note: Buildings above 60 m in height should be provided with a wet riser.

Inlets

The inlets to the riser should be sited on the external wall of the building at 760 mm above ground level and not more than 12 m from the riser. The inlets

290

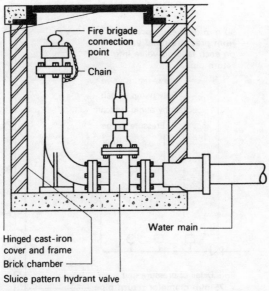

Fig. 11.23 Underground fire hydrant

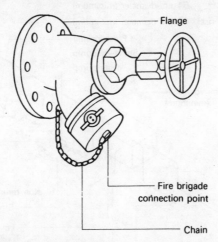

Fig. 11.24 Landing valve fire hydrant

should be within 18 m of an access road suitable for the fire brigade pumping appliance.

A 100 mm diameter riser should be fitted with two inlets, and a 150 mm riser with four inlets, each inlet consisting of a 64 mm instantaneous male coupling and a back-pressure valve. The inlets should be protected by a cap secured with a suitable length of chain and a 25 mm drain valve should be fitted at the lowest point of the riser.

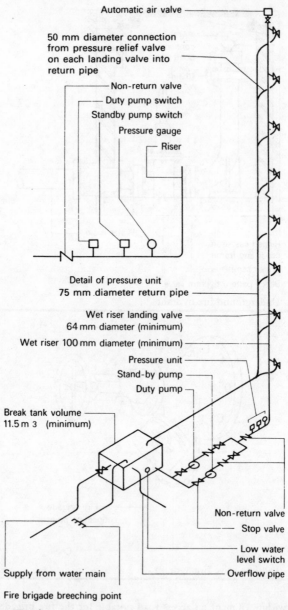

Automatic air valve

50 mm diameter connection
from pressure relief valve
on each landing valve into
return pipe

Non-return valve
Duty pump switch
Standby pump switch
Pressure gauge
Riser

Detail of pressure unit
75 mm diameter return pipe

Wet riser landing valve
64 mm diameter (minimum)

Wet riser 100 mm diameter (minimum)

Pressure unit
Stand-by pump
Duty pump

Break tank volume
11.5 m 3   (minimum)

Non-return valve
Stop valve
Low water
level switch
Overflow pipe

Supply from water main

Fire brigade breeching point

Fig. 11.25   Wet riser

The inlets should be fitted inside a metal box, the door of which should be glazed with wired glass and its position indicated by 'Dry Riser Inlet' painted on the inner face of the glass in 50 mm block letters. The door should be fastened

292

by a spring lock which can be opened from both outside or inside the building without the aid of a key, after the glass has been broken.

Construction of riser

The riser should be of galvanised steel piping, Class C, BS 1387 (red band) screwed and socketed. The fittings should be of steel or malleable iron galvanised and of steam quality. All changes in direction in the run of piping, should be made with standard bends and elbows must not be used.

Earthing

Dry risers should be electrically earthed.

Wet risers (Fig. 11.25)

Buildings exceeding twenty storeys or 60 m in height above ground level, whichever height is the least, should be provided with one or more wet rising mains to be used exclusively for fire-fighting purposes. As the name implies, the riser is always charged with water under pressure, fed by pumping sets from a break tank. Hydrants are connected to the riser on each floor and the pumps should be capable of providing a pressure of 410 kPa at the highest hydrant.

To protect the hosepipe connected to the riser, the hydrants on the lower floors of tall buildings should incorporate an orifice plate, so that when water is being discharged the outlet pressure is limited to 520 kPa.

A 75 mm diameter return pipe should be connected from the hydrants back to the supply source and the static water pressure with no flow of water should not exceed 690 kPa in the pipework.

The number of wet risers to be provided, the positions in which they are fitted, the outlets fitted to them and all similar details of construction and materials should conform to the same specifications as given for dry rising mains. The riser should only be installed in a heated building and should be electrically earthed.

Pumps

To provide an adequate supply of water to each riser at all times, duplicate pumps should be provided, one of which is for stand-by purposes. Each pump should be capable of delivering a minimum flow rate of 15 litre/s. The pumps should be connected in parallel, with their suctions permanently 'wet' when the tank is filled. The pumps may be run by electrical power, in which case a stand-by generator of sufficient capacity should be provided in case of mains failure. Alternatively, the stand-by pump may be driven by a petrol or a diesel engine. The pumps should be controlled to start automatically when a fall in pressure occurs in the riser exceeding 3 per cent of the normal static pressure, and to stop automatically when the normal pressure is re-established. The pumps may also be started by a flow of water when a fire brigade hose-reel is used, and therefore a pressure switch must be fitted in the pipeline on the delivery side of the pumps.

Water supply

The water supply to the riser should be either from a break tank of not less than 11.5 m^3 in volume, supplied from a water main at the rate of not less than 27 litre/s, or from a break tank of not less than 45.5 m^3 in volume, supplied from a water main at the rate of not less than 8 litre/s. In addition to the normal supply through the ball valve, the tank should be furnished with a 150 mm diameter fire brigade breeching inlet at street level. This inlet should have four 64 mm internal diameter instantaneous male couplings for connection to the fire brigade pumps.

The supply pipe should not be connected directly to the break tank, but should deliver water through a bend above it. An overflow pipe capable of

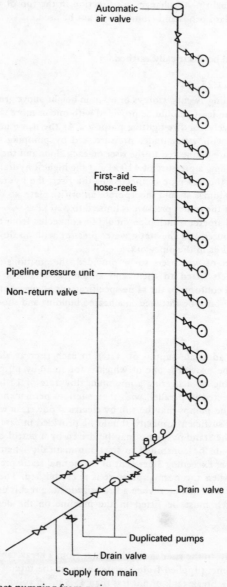

Fig. 11.26 Direct pumping from main

developing 375 litre/s to the open air should be connected to the break tank.

Note: During the construction of a building, fire risks can occur and wet risers should therefore be put into operation as construction work proceeds. To ensure a flow of water to the landing valves when the duty pump is in operation, all stop valves should be strapped and padlocked in an open position. The wet riser should be capable of withstanding a test pressure of twice the working pressure.

Where it is not possible to ensure that no part of the building is more than 61 m from the riser, an additional riser should be installed.

Hose-reel installations

These are for first-aid fire-fighting only, but it is often possible for a fire to be extinguished or contained by the occupants in its initial stage by the use of a jet of water from a hose-reel. It is not usual for portable fire extinguishers to be dispensed with when such a system is installed.

The hydraulic requirements for hose-reels is that they should be able to deliver 0.4 litre/s at a distance of 6 m from the nozzle, and that three should be capable of operating simultaneously. A pressure of 200 kPa is required at each nozzle, and if the water main cannot provide this at the highest reel pumping equipment must be installed.

Hose-reels should be provided at the rate of one reel for every 418 m^2 of floor area and the nozzle should reach to within 6 m of the furthest part of the building. They should be sited in an escape corridor, so that they may be used by people leaving the building, and if the hose has been used in a room full of smoke it can guide its user to safety.

Water supply

Some Water Authorities will permit direct pumping from the main, providing that a reasonable supply of water is available at the highest reel without the use of pumps (see Fig. 11.26).

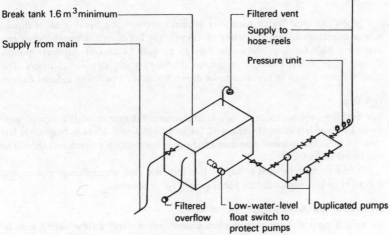

Fig. 11.27 Pumping from low-level break tank

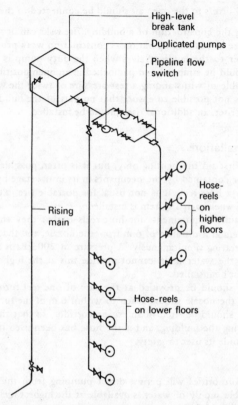

High-level
break tank

Duplicated pumps

Pipeline flow
switch

Hose-
reels
on
higher
floors

Rising
main

Hose-reels
on lower floors

Fig. 11.28 Pumping from high-level break tank

When the local Water Authority requires the use of a break tank, it should hold a minimum volume of water of 1.6 m³. The break cistern may be sited at a low or a high level, as shown in Figs 11.27 and 11.28 and duplicate pumps should be provided having a minimum discharging capacity of 2.3 litre/s. The stand-by pump may be required to be driven by either a petrol or a diesel engine.

Pipe sizes

For buildings up to 15 m in height the internal diameter of the supply pipe should be not less than 50 mm, and for buildings above 15 m in height not less than 64 mm. The internal diameter of the pipe connection to each reel should be not less than 25 mm.

The riser may be used to supply the domestic cold-water storage cistern, but it is safer to provide an independent supply for hose-reels.

Automatic control of pumps

To switch on the duty pump when a hose-reel is used, a flow switch may be inserted in the pipeline: water passing through the switch causes the electrical circuit to be completed and the pump will start and run for as long as the water flows. When the flow of water stops, the flow switch opens the electrical circuit and stops the pump.

Alternatively, a pipeline pressure unit may be used which switches off the pump when the maximum pressure produced by the pump has been reached, this pressure being retained by a non-return valve. When a hose-reel is used, the pressure in the pipeline falls and the first pressure switch will start the duty pump. If the duty pump fails to operate within 10 s, the second pressure switch will start the stand-by pump and this will operate while any hose-reel is in use.

Automatic pneumatic system (Fig. 11.29)

Two sources of water supply may be provided for the hose-reels by the installation of an automatic pneumatic cylinder in addition to a break cistern. The system incorporates automatic water supply and pressure at all floor levels by the stored water in the cylinder pressurised by air. Immediately a hose-reel is used on any floor, the air in the cylinder forces water through the pipework to the nozzle and pressure or flow switches are therefore not required on the pipeline. In an emergency, the duty pump is automatically brought into operation and water is pumped from the break tank.

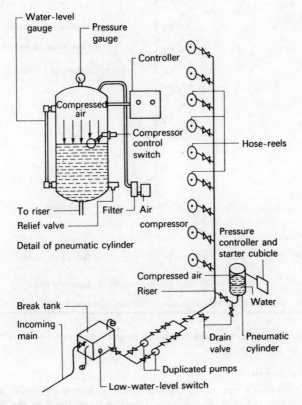

Fig. 11.29   Auto-pneumatic system

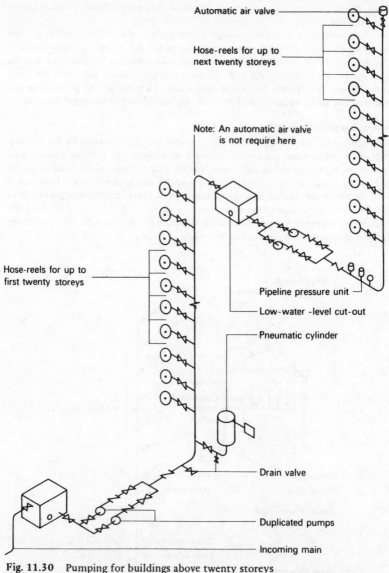

Automatic air valve

Hose-reels for up to
next twenty storeys

Note: An automatic air valve
is not require here

Hose-reels for up to
first twenty storeys

Pipeline pressure unit

Low-water-level cut-out

Pneumatic cylinder

Drain valve

Duplicated pumps

Incoming main

Fig. 11.30 Pumping for buildings above twenty storeys

For buildings above twenty storeys in height it becomes necessary to pump in stages (see Fig. 11.30).

Hydraulic hose-reels

These consist of 19 mm or 25 mm i.d. (internal diameter), non-kinking, reinforced rubber hosepipe wound on a metal reel and fixed to the wall at a suitable height. The lengths of the hose are shown in Table 11.6.

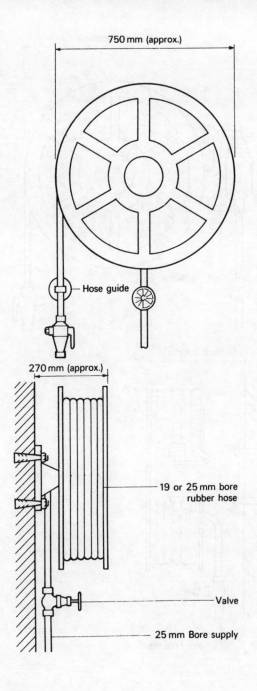

750 mm (approx.)

Hose guide

270 mm (approx.)

19 or 25 mm bore
rubber hose

Valve

25 mm Bore supply

Fig. 11.31   Fixed hose-reel

299

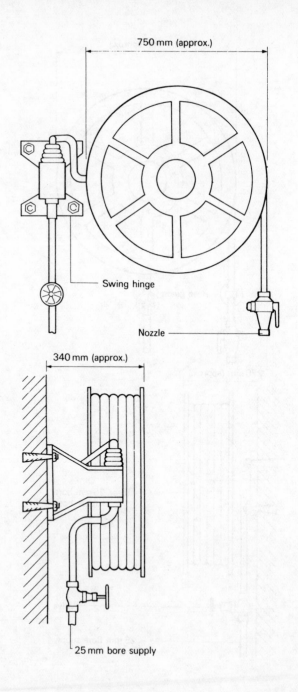

750 mm (approx.)

Swing hinge

Nozzle

340 mm (approx.)

25 mm bore supply

Fig. 11.32   Swinging-type hose-reel

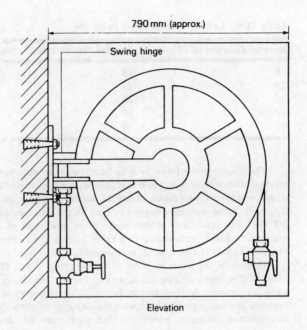

790 mm (approx.)

Swing hinge

Elevation

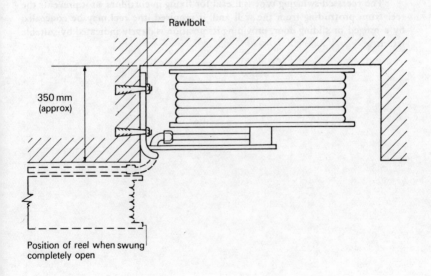

Rawlbolt

350 mm
(approx)

Position of reel when swung
completely open

Fig. 11.33 Swinging and recessed hose-reel

Table 11.6 Lenths of rubber hose in metres

Internal diameter in 19 mm	Internal diameter in 25 mm
18	18
23	23
30	24
37	30
46	37

The outlet end of the hose is fitted with an approved nozzle, having an internal diameter of 5 mm or 6 mm, and with a pressure of 200 kPa at this point it will produce a horizontal throw of water of approximately 8 m, and about 5 m high. Some reels are designed to turn on the water automatically by drawing off the first few turns of the hose. When this type of reel is installed it is essential to place the isolating stop valve inside a service duct close to the reel to prevent the valve being shut off accidentally.

Hose-reels are made in three different types: fixed (Fig. 11.31), swinging (Fig. 11.32), and swinging-recessed (Fig. 11.33). The choice of reel is dependent upon its position relative to the fire risk. The fixed type is the cheapest but requires the hosepipe to be drawn off sideways, unless a special roller device is incorporated through which the hosepipe may be drawn off in various directions.

The swinging type permits the reel to turn through an angle of 180° and gives more flexibility for drawing off the hosepipe than the fixed type.

The recessed-swinging type is useful for fixing in corridors, as it prevents the reel from protruding from the wall and, if required, the reel may be concealed by a hinged or sliding door, providing its position is clearly indicated by suitable lettering.

Appendix A

Definition

The unvented hot-water storage system may be defined as being a secondary circuit which is not provided with a vent pipe, permanently open to the atmosphere, and is fed with cold water either from the main or a storage cistern. See Figs. A.1 and A.2.

Building Regulations 1985

To meet the requirements of the Regulations two temperature-activated devices, operating in sequence are required, as follows:

1. A non re-setting thermal cut-out to BS 3955; *Electrical controls for domestic appliances:* Part 3: 1979.
2. A temperature relief valve to BS 6283, *Safety devices for use in hot water systems;* Part 2: 1982, *Specification for temperature relief valves for use at pressures up to and including 10 bar;* or Part 3: 1982 *Specification for combined temperature and pressure relief valves for pressures up to and including 10 bar.* The two devices are additional to any thermostatic control which is fitted to maintain the temperature of the stored water.

Systems

In a directly heated system, the thermal cut-out should be on the storage system. In an indirectly heated system, the heating coil should only be connected to an energy supply fitted with a temperature operated energy cut-out. In both directly and indirectly heated systems, the temperature relief valve, as specified in paragraph 2, should be located directly on the storage vessel, preferably within 150 mm of the top but in every case within the top 20 per cent of the volume of water in the vessel.

Installation

The unit or packaged system should be installed by an approved installer and include the installation of a discharge pipe from any safety device releasing hot water. The discharge pipe should be of suitable metal and its size should be the same as the discharge outlet size on the safety device. The discharge should be via an air break to a tun-dish and the pipe should be laid to a continuous fall and be no longer than 9 metres, unless the bore is increased.

The pipe should discharge in a visible but safe place such as a gully, where there is no risk of contact with the hot water by persons using the building.

Hot-water temperature

The design and installation of unvented hot-water storage systems should be such that the highest water temperature at any time should not exceed 100 °C.

Note: The system should be in the form of an approved proprietary unit or package.

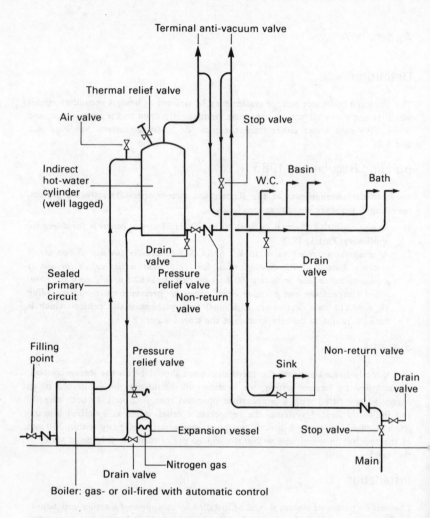

Fig. A.1 Mains-fed unvented hot-water storage system

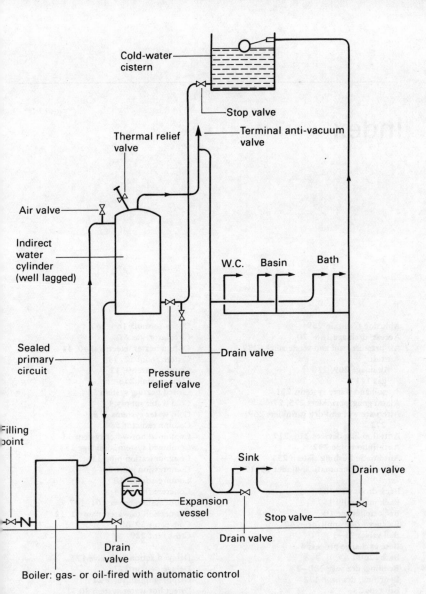

Fig. A.2 Cistern-fed unvented hot-water storage system

Cold-water cistern

Stop valve

Thermal relief valve

Terminal anti-vacuum valve

Air valve

Indirect water cylinder (well lagged)

Sealed primary circuit

Drain valve

Pressure relief valve

Filling point

W.C. Basin Bath

Sink

Drain valve

Expansion vessel

Stop valve

Drain valve

Drain valve

Boiler: gas- or oil-fired with automatic control

305

Index